PEARSON SCIENCE 1

TEACHER'S RESOURCE

Linda Aspen-Baxter
Tisdale Middle & Secondary School
North East School Division

Lynn Bryan
Professional Writer
British Columbia

Penny Mohar
Teacher
North East School Division
Saskatchewan

Connie Molnar
Teacher-Librarian
Lord Asquith School
Prairie Spirit School Division

Christine Treptau
Teacher
St. Gabriel School
Regina Catholic Schools

PEARSON

IN PARTNERSHIP WITH
Rubicon

ISBN 978-1-77058-883-7
9 781770 588837

ADVISORY BOARD

REVIEWERS

Lynn Bryan
Professional Writer
British Columbia

Lindsay Charabin
Learning Coordinator
Light of Christ Catholic School Division
Saskatchewan

Teresa Koop-Hunter
Teacher
Prairie Spirit School Division
Saskatchewan

Hyacinth Schaeffer
Hyxpectations Educational Consulting
Alberta

Kelsey Shields
Principal
Good Spirit School Division
Saskatchewan

Christine Treptau
Teacher
Regina Catholic Schools
Saskatchewan

EXPERT ADVISORS

Dr. Glen S. Aikenhead
Professor Emeritus
University of Saskatchewan

Dr. David Booth
Professor Emeritus
OISE, University of Toronto

Dr. William Brooks
Partner
eclecthink international

Wilfred Burton
Retired Educator
Saskatchewan

Dr. Herman Michell
Woodlands Cree
Vice President (Academics)
First Nations University of Canada

Ted View
Vice-principal
Greater Saskatoon Catholic Schools
Saskatchewan

FIRST NATIONS AND MÉTIS CONTENT ADVISORS

Elder Julie Pitzel
Métis Nation

Jeanne Auramenko
Knowledge Keeper
Clearwater River Dené First Nation

Judy Bear
Traditional Knowledge Keeper
Sweetgrass Cree First Nation

Delvin Kanewiyakiho
Traditional Knowledge Keeper
Cree First Nation
Little Pine Reserve

Mary Lee
Knowledge Advisor
Chitek Lake First Nation

Sandy Pitzel
Knowledge Keeper
Métis Nation

Darlene Speidel
Lakota Traditional Knowledge Keeper

PEARSON

Pearson Canada Inc.
26 Prince Andrew Place
Don Mills, ON M3C 2T8
Customer Service: 1-800-361-6128

Rubicon
www.rubiconpublishing.com

We acknowledge the financial support of the Government of Canada through the Canada Book Fund for our publishing activities.

Associate Publisher: Cheryl Turner
Managing Editor: Dawna McKinnon
Executive Editor: Barbara Booth
Editorial Assistant: Kim Therriault
Creative Director: Jennifer Drew

6 17

ISBN: 978-1-77058-883-7

TABLE OF CONTENTS

UNIT 1 NEEDS AND CHARACTERISTICS OF LIVING THINGS

Table of Contents

Unit Indicators Correlation Chart — Needs and Characteristics of Living Things*	
Indicator	**Assessment Opportunities**
By the end of grade 1, students will be able to:	
LT1.1 Differentiate between living things according to observable characteristics, including appearance and behaviour.	
a. Use a variety of sources of information and ideas (e.g., picture books including non-fiction texts, Elders, naturalists, videos, Internet sites, and personal observations) to learn about observable characteristics of living things.	Lesson 1: 2, 3, 4, 5 Lesson 3: 3, 8 Lesson 5: 3, 7 Lesson 6: 7
b. Make and record observations and measurements about the observable characteristics of plants and animals using written language, pictures, and charts.	Lesson 2: 5, 6 Lesson 3: 4, 7 Lesson 5: 3, 4, 6
c. Group representations (e.g., photos, videos, drawings, and oral descriptions) of plants and animals according to various student-developed criteria.	Lesson 3: 5 Lesson 4: 7
d. Engage in personal, scientific, and Indigenous ways of organizing understanding of living things.	Lesson 1: 5, 6, 7 Lesson 4: 8 Lesson 6: 5
e. Describe characteristics common to humans (e.g., eyes, ears, hair, and numbers of limbs and teeth) and identify variations (e.g., eye colour, hair colour, skin colour, height, and weight) that make each human unique.	Lesson 3: 1 Lesson 6: 5
f. Compare observable characteristics (e.g., leaf, root, stem, flower, fruit, and seed) of plants of various types and sizes that live in different habitats.	Lesson 5: 4
g. Record information, using written language, pictures, and tables, about the appearance and behaviour of familiar animals, such as classroom or personal pets, at regular intervals over a specific time interval.	Lesson 3: 7 Lesson 4: 5
h. Describe the appearance and behaviour (e.g., method of movement, social grouping, diet, body covering, habitat, and nocturnal vs. diurnal orientation) of familiar animals (e.g., bumblebee, worm, dog, cat, snake, owl, fish, ant, beaver, rabbit, and horse).	Lesson 3: 3, 6, 7 Lesson 4: 1, 3, 4, 7
i. Differentiate among animals according to their observable characteristics.	Lesson 3: 4, 5, 6 Lesson 4: 3, 4
j. Compare characteristics of plants and animals at different stages of their lives (e.g., compare an adult dog with a pup, compare a young tree with an older established tree, and compare a baby bird with a fully grown bird).	Lesson 5: 6 Lesson 6: 2, 4, 6
k. Communicate knowledge (e.g., share a story, describe an experience, or draw a picture) about the observable characteristics of a favourite plant or animal.	Lesson 3: 7 Lesson 4: 7 Lesson 6: 6

Indicator	Assessment Opportunities
l. Respond positively to others' questions and ideas about the observable characteristics of living things.	Lesson 1: 2, 8 Lesson 3: 1, 7 Lesson 4: 1, 2
m. Recognize that some information about living things may not be realistic (e.g., stories such as *The Three Little Pigs*, and talking movie animals).	Lesson 4: 6
LT1.2 Analyze different ways in which plants, animals, and humans interact with various natural and constructed environments to meet their basic needs.	
a. Identify the physical needs, (i.e., food, water, air, and shelter) that plants, animals, and humans require for survival)	Lesson 1: 5 Lesson 2: 1, 3, 5 Lesson 5: 5 Lesson 7: 1, 3, 6
b. Pose questions about ways in which plants interact with their environments to meet their basic needs (e.g., How long does it take a seed to start to grow? How does the growth of a plant change if the seed is planted in soil, sand, or rocks? How tall will a bean plant grow?).	Lesson 2: Explain 6 Lesson 5: 2, 5 Lesson 7: 2
c. Pose questions about ways in which animals interact with their environments to meet their basic needs (e.g., How does a bird move from one tree to another? Where do animals go at night or during the day? How do animals escape from predators?).	Lesson 2: 1, 2 Lesson 3: 2 Lesson 4: 1, 2, 7 Lesson 7: 2
d. Investigate, through field trips to natural habitats, nature videos, and community walks, homes and habitats of local plants and animals to determine how they meet their basic needs.	Lesson 1: 5 Lesson 3: 7 Lesson 4: 4
e. Compare ways in which plants and animals that live within the local environment, and plants and animals that live in other environments, meet their needs for food, water, and shelter.	Lesson 5: 4 Lesson 7: 4, 6
f. Compare the kinds of food that different animals eat, their methods of eating (e.g., cracking, tearing, strangling, chewing, or swallowing whole), and the structures that they have for eating.	Lesson 3: 7 Lesson 4: 4
g. Explore the challenges that plants, animals, and humans encounter when attempting to meet their basic needs in constructed environments (e.g., lawn, sports field, street, playground, and city).	Lesson 1: 5 Lesson 7: 4
h. Discuss the need for caution when dealing with plants and animals (e.g., students may be allergic to a plant or animal, an animal may bite, and many common household plants are poisonous if ingested).	Lesson 1: 5, 7 Lesson 2: 4
i. Compare basic human needs to the needs of plants, other animals, and non-living things.	Lesson 7: 3, 4
j. Predict and model how certain animals will move (e.g., fly, run, swim, slither, walk, and swing) to meet their needs for food, shelter, and protection in their environment, based on personal observations, pictures, or videos.	Lesson 3: 6, 7
k. Explore how people demonstrate respect for living things by caring for domestic plants and animals (e.g., growing a plant, hatching eggs, and keeping a pet).	Lesson 5: 6 Lesson 7: 5

* Indicators are met in multiple lessons, but this correlation only identifies lessons in which the indictors are focused on.

Unit Planning Chart — Needs and Characteristics of Living Things

Lesson and Time*	Activities	Program Resources	Materials and Equipment*
Unit Opener: Getting Started 2 hours	**Introduce the Unit:** 1. Set Up an Ongoing Bulletin Board **Introduce the Books:** 2. Motivate Using the Fiction Book *Moko's Adventures on Earth* 3. View the Non-fiction Book *Living Things* **Introduce the Learning Targets:** 4. Post the Student-friendly Learning Targets	PM 1: I Wonder ... PM 5: Make a T-chart LM 1: Word Splash LM 2: Learning Targets Fiction Book: *Moko's Adventures on Earth* Lap Book Non-fiction Book: *Living Things* Skills Poster: Observing and Recording Science Poster: Where do I live?	
1: Classifying Living and Non-Living Things 3–4 hours	**Engage:** 1. Activate and Build on Prior Knowledge 2. Elicit "I Wonder ..." Statements 3. Make Connections Using the Non-fiction Book *Living Things* **Explore:** 4. Engage in Aboriginal Ways of Observing 5. Go on a Nature Walk **Explain:** 6. Summarize the Nature Walk Discoveries 7. Explore Aboriginal Perspectives of Living Things 8. Reflect on Learning **Extend:** 9. Go on an Alternative Nature Walk 10. Develop a Photo Book or Slide Presentation 11. Respond to Talk Time	PM 1: I Wonder ... PM 5: Make a T-chart PM 13: Look What I've Learned LM 3: This Is What I Can Do Non-fiction Book: *Living Things* Lap Book Traditional Knowledge Poster: Ways of Observing Skills Poster: Observing and Recording Science Poster: Where do I live?	• Sesame Street skit "Ernie Dresses a Snowman" • clipboards • cards for headings • pictures: living and non-living things • camera • markers • *Brother Eagle, Sister Sky* by Susan Jeffers • poster paper
2: Basic Needs of Living Things 3–4 hours	**Engage:** 1. Activate and Build on Prior Knowledge 2. Elicit "I Wonder ..." Statements 3. Explore Students' Basic Needs **Explore:** 4. Develop Safety Signs 5. Investigate the Basic Needs of Living Things **Explain:** 6. Revisit Predictions for Plant Growth 7. Reflect on Learning **Extend:** 8. Investigate Online Resources 9. Create a "Living" Thing 10. Create a Basic Needs Rap 11. Make Literature Links 12. Explore Other "I Wonder ..." Statements	PM 1: I Wonder ... PM 5: Make a T-chart PM 13: Look What I've Learned LM 4: My Basic Needs LM 5: Plant Predictions LM 6: Plant Check-up LM 7: Living Things LM 8: Non-living Things LM 9: Basic Needs LM 10: Where Do I Live? LM 11: This is What I Can Do Non-fiction Book: *Living Things* Science Poster: Where do I live? Skills Poster: Communicating and Teamwork Skills Poster: Safety in Science Class	• images of plants and animals surviving in unique environments • magazines • glue • pictures: stop sign and yield sign • bean seeds or pea seeds • baggies • paper towels • jug/pail of water • camera • scissors • 2 L milk cartons • wooden dowels • string or twine • hole punch • birdseed • envelopes • 28 cm × 43 cm coloured construction paper • dry-erase markers
3: Characteristics of Humans and Animals 3 hours	**Engage:** 1. Activate and Build on Prior Knowledge 2. Elicit "I Wonder ..." Statements **Explore:** 3. Read and Respond to the Fiction Book *Moko's Adventures on Earth* 4. Make a Venn Diagram 5. Compare Animals Using Student Criteria 6. Move Like Animals **Explain** 7. Carry Out a Fish Investigation 8. Talk With an Elder About Plants and Animals 9. Reflect on Learning **Extend:** 10. Write Riddles 11. Observe a Pet 12. Create an Imaginary Pet 13. Respond to Talk Time 14. Explore Other "I Wonder ..." Statements	PM 1: I Wonder ... PM 6: A Venn Diagram PM 13: Look What I've Learned LM 7: Living Things LM 12: Fish Observations LM 13: This Is What I Can Do Non-fiction Book: *Living Things* Fiction Book: *Moko's Adventures on Earth* Lap Book Traditional Knowledge Poster: Ways of Observing Skills Poster: Observing and Recording	• bulletin board paper • scissors • markers • goldfish • water • fish bowl or clear container to hold fish • fish food • nature videos showing local animals

Lesson and Time*	Activities	Program Resources	Materials and Equipment*
4: Behaviours of Animals 3–4 hours	**Engage:** 1. Activate and Build on Prior Knowledge 2. Elicit "I Wonder ..." Statements **Explore:** 3. Sort Animal Behaviours 4. Match Bird Beaks to Food Samples 5. Observe Animal Behaviours **Explain:** 6. Read Fairy Tales 7. Make a Trading Card 8. Develop a Class Web 9. Reflect on Learning **Extend:** 10. Write and Illustrate Stories 11. Go on a Scavenger Hunt 12. Make a Poster 13. Explore Other "I Wonder ..." Statements	PM 1: I Wonder ... PM 8: Make a Web PM 13: Look What I've Learned LM 7: Living Things LM 14: Matching Bird Beaks LM 15: My Animal Trading Card LM 16: This is What I Can Do Non-fiction Book: *Living Things* Lap Book Skills Poster: Safety in Science Class	• sunflower seeds • pliers • orange juice • straws • mini marshmallows • scissors • gummy worms • sand or soil • chopsticks • grass • water strainer • coloured rice • foam blocks • scoop with holes • bowls • fairy tales (with animals) • sticky notes • nature videos showing local animals
5: Characteristics of Plants 3 hours	**Engage:** 1. Activate and Build on Prior Knowledge 2. Elicit "I Wonder ..." Statements **Explore:** 3. Focus on Plant Characteristics 4. Compare Plant Differences **Explain:** 5. Discover How Plants Meet Their Needs 6. Observe and Document Plant Growth 7. Reflect on Learning **Extend:** 8. Decide If a Plant Needs Soil 9. Reading About First Nations' Perspectives on Plants 10. Listen to Stories Online 11. Play an Online Game 12. Respond to Talk Time 13. Make Literature Links 14. Explore Other "I Wonder ..." Statements	PM 1: I Wonder ... PM 13: Look What I've Learned LM 5: Plant Predictions LM 6: Plant Check-Up LM 17: Plant Labels LM 18: Focus on Plants LM 19: This is What I Can Do Non-fiction Book: *Living Things* Skills Poster: Observing and Recording	• 28 cm × 43 cm paper • construction paper • scissors • glue • growing bean plants • rulers
6: How Living Things Grow and Change 3–4 hours	**Engage:** 1. Activate and Build on Prior Knowledge 2. Talk About Life Cycles 3. Elicit "I Wonder ..." Statements **Explore:** 4. Identify the Characteristics of Changes in Living Things 5. Investigate Changes in Humans **Explain:** 6. Research Animal Life Cycles 7. Reflect on Learning **Extend:** 8. Compare Different Stages of Life 9. Play an Animal Mix-up Game 10. Explore Other "I Wonder ..." Statements	PM 1: I Wonder ... PM 13: Look What I've Learned LM 20: This Is What I Can Do Fiction Book: *Moko's Adventures on Earth* Non-fiction Book: *Living Things* Lap Book Traditional Knowledge Poster: Ways of Observing	• *The Very Hungry Caterpillar* by Eric Carle • baby and recent photographs • paper plates • rulers • scissors • glue • non-fiction books: animal growth
7: Taking Care of Basic Needs 3–4 hours	**Engage:** 1. Activate and Build on Prior Knowledge 2. Elicit "I Wonder ..." Statements **Explore:** 3. Compare Basic Needs 4. Investigate Shelter in Constructed Environments **Explain:** 5. Help Living Things Meet Their Basic Needs 6. Make a Healthy Environment for an Animal 7. Reflect on Learning **Extend:** 8. Watch a Video 9. Observe a Classroom Pet 10. Respond to Talk Time 11. Explore Other "I Wonder ..." Statements	PM 1: I Wonder ... PM 13: Look What I've Learned LM 7: Living Things LM 9: Basic Needs LM 10: Where Do I Live? LM 21: Constructed Environments LM 22: This Is What I Can Do Non-fiction Book: *Living Things* Lap Book Science Poster: Where do I live?	• magazines and fiction books • letter size white paper • scissors • glue • pencil crayons
Unit Closer: Putting It All Together 2–3 hours	**Looking Back:** 1. Consider the Learning Targets 2. Reread the Fiction Book *Moko's Adventures on Earth* 3. Identify New Vocabulary 4. Consider "I Wonder ..." Statements 5. Finish Reading the Non-fiction Book *Living Things* **Going Further:** 6. Develop a Living Things Museum	PM 4: Finding Out PM 9: I Found Out LM 2: Learning Targets LM 5: Plant Predictions LM 6: Plant Check-Up LM 23: Rate Your Learning LM 24: Exhibit Inquiry Fiction Book: *Moko's Adventures on Earth* Non-fiction Book: *Living Things*/Lap Book	• videos and pictures of museum exhibits

* Time and materials lists are for Core Learning Opportunities only.

UNIT 1

Unit Opener: Getting Started

Time
2 hours

Program Resources
PM 1: I Wonder ...
PM 5: Make a T-chart
LM 1: Word Splash
LM 2: Learning Targets
Fiction Book: *Moko's Adventures on Earth*
Non-fiction Book: *Living Things*
Lap Book
Skills Poster: Observing and Recording
Science Poster: Where do I live?

In this unit, students will learn that scientists classify things as living or non-living, while First Nations and Métis Elders understand that everything is alive and has Spirit. From a scientific point of view, students will investigate the differences between things that are living and things that are not living. They will learn how scientists describe how living things grow and develop, and how living things interact with their environments to meet their basic needs of air, water, food, and shelter. They will look at the observable characteristics of plants, animals, and humans, both appearance and behaviours, that are similar and those that make them unique.

Students will have the chance to explore the physical characteristics, movement, and behavioural traits of what scientists call living things. They will also learn how Aboriginal peoples carefully observe the world around them and use the circle as a way of organizing their understanding. As a group, students will develop vital skills such as planning and conducting simple investigations, posing questions, making observations, and reflecting on their learning.

Introduce the Unit

Note
Send home **LM: 1 Parent/Guardian Letter** asking for photographs of children as babies, as well as a more recent photographs. These will be used in Lesson 6: Explore 5.

1. Set Up an Ongoing Bulletin Board

- Prepare a bulletin board with the heading "Living Things." Display the Science poster **Where do I live?** Ask students to look at the poster and predict what the new science unit will be about. Encourage them to identify the living things found on the poster. Ask them how some of the living things are different or the same.
- Post a large "I Wonder ..." bubble, using **PM 1: I Wonder ...** as a model. Say, "I wonder what we will learn in this unit." Invite students to brainstorm ideas. Use questions to guide them toward formulating statements that reflect the big ideas of the unit:
  - I wonder what plants, animals, and humans need to live.
  - I wonder how plants, animals, and humans get what they need to live from their environments.
  - I wonder how some plants are the same as other plants, or different from them.
  - I wonder how some animals are the same as other animals, or different from them.
  - Have students start a science journal for the unit and record an "I wonder ..." statement that they want to answer.
- Make a Word Wall for science vocabulary. Students could copy these words into their journals to make a vocabulary page or picture dictionary.
- Develop a T-chart like the one shown on **PM 5: Make a T-chart.** Label the columns: Living and Non-living. As you complete each lesson, you can refer back to the T-chart and add words/pictures under the appropriate column. Students could also make a similar chart in their books using **PM 5** as an example.

- When the T-chart is introduced, draw students' attention to the Skills poster **Observing and Recording** and explain that a T-chart is a way to record, sort, and compare observations. Ask students: What are we sorting and comparing by using this T-chart? Guide students to come up with the answer. Encourage them to bring picture samples of living and non-living things from home to post on the chart.

***Traditional* Knowledge**

- The element of Spirit is a key component of the worldview common to most First Nations and Métis peoples. Objects that are classified in this unit as non-living, such as rocks and fire, are in fact animate and are imbued with Spirit according to some belief systems. Students may benefit from understanding that the scientific dichotomy does not negate their beliefs.

Introduce the Books

Notes
- This is a brief introduction to the books and the unit. Key concepts will be explored in more depth throughout the unit.
- This initial look at the book(s) can take place as a whole group, using the Lap Book, with small groups, at a centre, or during the literacy block of time.

2. Motivate Using the Fiction Book *Moko's Adventures on Earth*

Before: Tell students the title of the book. Ask them to predict what might happen in the story. Then show them the cover of the book and ask them to add to their predictions. Record their predictions on chart paper so they can be revisited during and after reading.

During: Set a purpose for reading. Tell students that Moko is an alien learning about Earth and ask them to focus on what Moko is learning.

- Use a Shared Reading approach to read the Lap Book, stopping each time you come to the sentence: *Moko had a lot to learn about Earth.* Ask students what Moko learned.

After: At the end of the story, Moko's friends land on Earth and start investigating the planet. Ask students to be Moko and tell his friends all the new things he learned about Earth.

- Then ask them to think of other things that Moko and his friends will learn about plants, animals, and humans while they are on Earth.

3. View the Non-fiction Book *Living Things*

Before: Using the Lap Book, show the cover of the book and read the title. Ask students what they think might be in the book.

During: Distribute copies of the book.

Pages 2–3: Ask students to raise their hands if they see something on these pages that is living. Ask students to volunteer answers. Then ask students to raise their hands if they see something that is non-living.

- Take a few minutes to look at each spread of the book. Then ask students what they think they will learn about in this book.

After: Return to pages 2–3. Invite students to talk to classmates about living and non-living things they see when they look outside their window at home or at school. Then, ask them to name one thing outside their window that is living, and one that is non-living.

Introduce Learning Targets

Notes
- These Unit Learning Targets are developed from the Science outcomes for this unit. If they seem overwhelming, leave them for now or choose key points to discuss.
- Lesson-specific learning targets are provided for each lesson.

4. Post the Student-friendly Learning Targets

- Enlarge **LM 2: Learning Targets** and post it in the classroom. Read the learning targets with students, explaining what they are going to learn throughout this unit. For each statement, ask students what they already know about the topic. Refer to the Learning Targets from time to time to ask students to reflect on what they have learned.

1 Classifying Living and Non-Living Things

Time
3–4 hours

Vocabulary
living
non-living

Program Resources
PM 1: I Wonder ...
PM 5: Make a T-chart
PM 13: Look What I've Learned
LM 3: This Is What I Can Do
Non-fiction Book: *Living Things*
Lap Book
Traditional Knowledge Poster: Ways of Observing
Skills Poster: Observing and Recording

Materials and Equipment
- Online video: "Ernie Dresses a Snowman"
- clipboards
- cards for headings
- pictures: living and non-living things
- camera
- markers
- *Brother Eagle, Sister Sky* by Susan Jeffers
- poster paper

GOAL

Students will understand and classify things as living or non-living by determining characteristics that are specific to living things as defined by a Euro-Canadian scientific perspective. Students will also consider First Nations and Métis perspectives of living things.

ASSESSMENT CHART

Science Indicators	Assessment Opportunities
LT1.1 a. Use a variety of sources of information and ideas to learn about observable characteristics of living things.	Engage 1, 2, 3 Explore 4, 5
LT1.1 d. Engage in personal, scientific, and Indigenous ways of organizing understanding of living things.	Explore 5 Explain 6, 7
LT1.1 l. Respond positively to others' questions and ideas about the observable characteristics of living things.	Engage 2 Explain 8
LT1.2 a. Identify the physical needs, (i.e., food, water, air, and shelter) that plants, animals, and humans require for survival.	Explore 5
LT1.2 d. Investigate, through field trips to natural habitats, nature videos, and community walks, homes and habitats of local plants and animals to determine how they meet their basic needs.	Explore 5
LT1.2 g. Explore the challenges that plants, animals, and humans encounter when attempting to meet their basic needs in constructed environments.	Explore 5
LT1.2 h. Discuss the need for caution when dealing with plants and animals.	Explore 5
English Language Arts Indicators	**Assessment Opportunities**
CR1.1 a. View, listen to, read and respond to a variety of texts including First Nations and Métis resources that present different viewpoints and perspectives on issues related to identity, community, and social responsibility.	Explore 4 Explain 7
CC1.3 e. Participate in small-group work.	Explore 5

BACKGROUND INFORMATION

All living organisms need to *obtain energy* by taking and using nutrients through eating or absorption. Living organisms can *move* and *respond* to stimuli (even though in plants this may be harder to detect). Living organisms *grow* and *reproduce* as well as *excrete waste* and perform the chemical reaction of *respiration*. During respiration, which takes place in both plant and animal cells, cells take in oxygen and release carbon dioxide. This process produces energy which is used in cellular/chemical reactions. It is often called cellular respiration to differentiate it from breathing/respiration.

Some things that scientists would classify as non-living may exhibit some characteristics of living things. For example, fire grows, it needs oxygen, and it responds to the stimuli of water, but it does not satisfy all of the characteristics of living things.

***Traditional* Knowledge**

Note that these explanations are Euro-Canadian worldviews that are not shared by all cultures. For many First Nations and Métis people, many things that science classifies as non-living have Spirit and are considered living. For instance, fire, rock, air, and water have Spirit. Some Elders consider these elements—which can give life and take life—to be imbued with a living energy. Some students may share this worldview.

Observation is a skill that ensured the survival of many hunter–gatherer societies. Through careful observation, hunters understood the behaviours, tracks, and patterns of animals. For example, hunters could observe and understand the behaviour and patterns of wild geese to know when to collect eggs and when to hunt the geese to avoid depopulating a local flock. Gatherers knew when certain types of berries could be harvested.

ASSESSMENT FOR LEARNING

Look for Evidence of Learning	Student-friendly Learning Targets
Can the student: • discuss the differences between things that are living or non-living? • find examples of living and non-living things in the environment? • sort things as living or non-living? • identify the basic needs of animals? • logically consider where animals find shelter in the natural environment?	(self-assessment) • I know what makes something living or non-living. • I can find living things outside. • I can find non-living things outside. • I know the basic needs of animals. • I can find where animals find shelter.

DI DIFFERENTIATING INSTRUCTION

For EAL

Create a visual dictionary of some of the living and non-living things that students may find on the nature walk. Encourage students to add to the visual dictionary throughout the unit.

For Enrichment

After completing Explore 4, challenge students to interview adults (e.g., parents, neighbours, relatives, Elders) to find out what tasks they learned from older relatives and how these tasks are different from similar tasks the students do.

For Extra Support

When discussing and developing "I wonder ..." statements, focus on one statement that students understand and ask students to predict the answer by drawing a picture or finishing a sentence frame connected to the "I wonder ..." statement.

CURRICULUM CONNECTIONS

Students will have the opportunity to develop skills and concepts in the following area:

Social Studies

DR 1.3 Demonstrate awareness of humans' reliance on the cultural environment to meet needs, and how location affects families in meeting needs and wants.

RW 1.1 Describe the influence of physical, spiritual, emotional and intellectual needs and wants on personal well-being.

CORE LEARNING OPPORTUNITIES

Engage

1. Activate and Build on Prior Knowledge

- Show students the Sesame Street video "Ernie Dresses a Snowman." Online versions can be found by searching the title.
  Engage students in a discussion by asking them the following questions:
  - What are some things that made Ernie believe the snowman was alive?
  - What reasons did Bert give to Ernie to tell him the snowman was not alive?
- After they have talked about what Bert and Ernie said, ask students to vote on who they think was right. Choose a few students to explain their vote. When students have a clear understanding of why the snowman was non-living, ask them:
  - What do you think makes something living?
    Through this discussion, generate a list of answers and record them. Some First Nations or Métis students may have different worldviews on what makes things living or non-living, and all viewpoints should be respected. (See Background Information.)

***Traditional* Knowledge**

- As an alternative to the video, show students pictures of things that are living and non-living. Create cards that say Living and Non-Living and have students hold up the card that they think is correct for each picture. Discuss the reasons for their responses.

Literacy Check
Can the student:
- read the "I wonder ..." statements in the class list and identify "I wonder ..." statements for his or her personal lists?
- copy "I wonder ..." statements from the class list onto his or her personal list?

2. Elicit "I Wonder ..." Statements

- Create a large "I Wonder ..." bubble on the board. Use **PM 1: I Wonder ...** as a reference or enlarge **PM 1** for continuous use. Collect a few pictures or samples of living and non-living things like a stuffed bear, a leaf, or a pencil. Model an "I wonder ..." form of inquiry with statements such as: "I wonder what makes something living," or "I wonder how I can decide if something is living or non-living." Invite students to offer other "I wonder ..." statements. Record these on a chart or paper strips, and then read them together. Provide students with copies of **PM 1: I Wonder ...** to record statements that interest them. Some students may require individual or small group assistance to identify statements and record them.
- Students could take home an "I wonder ..." statement to research at home with their families. Each Science class could start with a different student answering an "I wonder ..." statement researched at home.

Literacy Check
Can the student:
- read and respond to grade-appropriate books?

3. Make Connections Using the Non-Fiction Book *Living Things*

Before: Review the list of what makes something living that was generated after watching the Bert and Ernie video. You may want to copy the list onto a T-chart for future reference.

During: Use a Shared Reading approach to read the non-fiction book *Living Things*.

Pages 2–3: Ask students to identify a living and a non-living thing in the book. First Nations or Métis students may have different perspectives. (See Background Information.)
  - Ask students: Why is ________ considered living and ________ considered non-living?

Continue to ask this question about a few examples students give. Ask students to answer the question on page 3.

After: Make sure students make the connection between their answers and the reasons Bert gave for the snowman being non-living. Explain to students that this is the scientific way of classifying things as living or non-living and that there are other perspectives.

- Students may confuse the idea of something being non-living and something being dead. Be sure to address that something dead once had living characteristics while something non-living never possessed the specific characteristics of living things.

Explore

Traditional **Knowledge**

Literacy Check
Can the student:
- read and respond to a variety of texts including First Nations and Métis resources that present different viewpoints and perspectives?

4. Engage in Aboriginal Ways of Observing

- Display the Traditional Knowledge poster **Ways of Observing**. Identify and talk about every section of the poster individually.
- Start with the infant. Read the sentence and talk about the infant observing the world. From a young age, babies are able to observe, smell, and hear the world around them. These senses are keenly developed and help support survival. Traditionally, First Nations women swaddled their babies and bundled them into moss bags. Babies in moss bags only have their heads exposed and they observe the world around them using their senses of sight, smell, and hearing.
- Next, discuss the image of the child who is learning by doing. Have a student describe what is happening in the picture (a child is learning about the traditional task of mending a net for fishing).
- The Inuit woman is using her skills of observation and learning gained over a lifetime to ice fish.
- The grandfather is passing on his knowledge of herbs that can be collected and used as food or medicine to a young boy.
- Ask students what they have learned from an older adult.
- Consider inviting an Elder or Traditional Knowledge Keeper to visit the class to talk about teachings that are passed on to young people. (See the Program Overview for the appropriate protocol.)

5. Go on a Nature Walk

- Tell the class that they are going to make observations about living and non-living things while going on a nature walk.
- Refer to the Skills poster **Observing and Recording** to clarify how to observe the natural world using our senses of sight and hearing, and sometimes touch. Stress to students that they need to be cautious when making their observations. Explain to students that they may come across something that they are allergic to, or is poisonous or dangerous. Elicit other reasons why students should be cautious.
- Give individual students or partners a clipboard with **PM 5: Make a T-chart** and tell the class that they will be using the T-chart to record their observations during the walk using pictures and words.
- Take students outside for a walk around the school property. Take a camera to photograph the things students observe.

Safety Check
- Ensure students are properly supervised during the nature walk. If possible, ask for volunteers to help supervise students.
- Be sure to tell students to avoid touching any objects on the walk unless they are given permission.

- Have students or pairs investigate, collect data, and explore on their own during the walk. Then gather students and have them identify what they observed as living or non-living. Ask students to identify how the organisms they identified on the walk meet their four basic needs of air, water, food, and shelter. (Plants take in air through their leaves and water and nutrients through their roots.)
- Next, take students to an area that is primarily non-living, such as a playground structure. Ask them to find something that is living. They may find a plant growing through a paved area or an ant crawling around. Talk about why it is more difficult for living things to grow in an area that is predominantly non-living (constructed environment). (This topic will be discussed further in Lesson 6.)

***Traditional* Knowledge**

- Remind students of the First Nations and Métis worldview that all things have Spirit and deserve respect. Remind them to be respectful when observing and handling living and non-living things on the walk.

Explain

Science Check
Can the student
- identify living and non-living things?
- transfer his or her knowledge into the classroom environment?

6. Summarize the Nature Walk Discoveries

- When you return to class, ask students to share what they wrote on their T-charts. Jot down a list of all of the objects that students saw on the walk.
- Then ask students to come up to the board one at a time. Instruct each student to identify one of the items on the list as living or non-living by circling the word with a marker. Use one colour for living things and another for non-living things.

***Traditional* Knowledge**

7. Explore Aboriginal Perspectives of Living Things

- Tell students they are going to hear a story about the worldview shared by many Aboriginal peoples. Introduce students to some of the key ideas that will be brought up by the author:
  - Everything is living and needs to be respected as a part of this world.
  - Everything has a history that needs to be honoured.
  - All living things are connected like a web and if one thing is removed, it can be a bad thing for other living things.
  - Our basic needs are met by many of the things we consider non-living, and they need to be valued.
  - All things have Spirit and are considered to be living.
- Read the story *Brother Eagle, Sister Sky* by Susan Jeffers. (If the book is not accessible, search online for an audio-book version of the story.)
- Go through the images of the story again and ask students which of the key ideas above they would use to give a title to each image. Then ask students to think of something from their lives that they would give the same title.
- Have students make a poster using one of the key ideas from the book as a title. Tell them to focus on aspects of their own lives and how the ideas can be shown in their own environment.

Literature Link
Brother Eagle, Sister Sky
by Susan Jeffers

Literacy Check
Can the student:
- make connections between the key ideas and the story images?
- show examples of the key ideas in their own lives?

8. Reflect on Learning

- Have students record evidence of their learning using assessment tools such as **PM 13: Look What I've Learned**. Encourage students to note at least two things they have learned about identifying living and non-living things and something they still wonder about.
- Hand out **LM 3: This Is What I Can Do** as a self-assessment. Read the learning targets with students and have them respond on their own. Some students may need assistance.

OTHER LEARNING OPPORTUNITIES

Extend: Activity Bank

At any time, choose from the following options to replace or supplement the Core Learning Opportunities to meet students' needs and/or interests.

9. Go on an Alternative Nature Walk

- Expand your community walk to include a local creek or prairie environment that will show a larger variety of living and non-living things. Tell students that they should try to find one living and one non-living thing that is different from what they found in Explore 5. Have a few older students join the class and help students take photos of what they find. You might also show students related videos.

10. Develop a Photo Book or Slide Presentation

- Students could also document their classroom nature walk by creating a photo book or slide presentation. Have them write short captions below each photo to identify the things that are living and the things that are non-living. Model an example of a caption for students before they begin the activity.

***Traditional* Knowledge**

11. Respond to Talk Time

- Explore activity and discussion questions 1, 2, or 3 in Talk Time on page 24 of the non-fiction book *Living Things*. Remind students of First Nations and Métis perspectives that everything has Spirit and is living.

2 Basic Needs of Living Things

Time
3–4 hours

Vocabulary
basic needs
air
water
food
shelter

Program Resources
PM 1: I Wonder ...
PM 5: Make a T-chart
PM 13: Look What I've Learned
LM 4: My Basic Needs
LM 5: Plant Predictions
LM 6: Plant Check-up
LM 7: Living Things
LM 8: Non-living Things
LM 9: Basic Needs
LM 10: Where Do I Live?
LM 11: This is What I Can Do
Non-fiction Book: *Living Things*
Science Poster: Where do I live?
Skills Poster: Communicating and Teamwork
Skills Poster: Safety in Science Class

Materials and Equipment
- images of plants and animals surviving in unique environments
- magazines
- glue
- pictures: stop sign and yield sign
- bean seeds or pea seeds
- baggies
- paper towels
- jug/pail of water
- camera
- scissors
- 2 L milk cartons
- wooden dowels
- string or twine
- hole punch
- birdseed
- envelopes
- 28 cm × 43 cm coloured construction paper
- dry-erase markers

GOAL

Students will gain an understanding of the basic needs of living things by making connections to their own basic needs.

ASSESSMENT CHART

Science Indicators	Assessment Opportunities
LT1.1 b. Make and record observations and measurements about the observable characteristics of plants and animals using written language, pictures, and charts.	Explore 5, 6
LT1.2 a. Identify the physical needs, (i.e., food, water, air, and shelter) that plants, animals, and humans require for survival.	Engage 1, 3 Explore 5
LT1.2 b. Pose questions about ways in which plants interact with their environments to meet their basic needs.	Engage 1, 2 Explain 6
LT1.2 c. Pose questions about ways in which animals interact with their environments to meet their basic needs.	Engage 1, 2
LT1.2 h. Discuss the need for caution when dealing with plants and animals.	Explore 4
LT1.2 k. Explore how people demonstrate respect for living things by caring for domestic plants and animals.	Explore 5
English Language Arts Indicators	**Assessment Opportunities**
CR1.3 h. Listen to and carry out directions with four to six simple steps.	Explore 5
CC1.2 a. Understand that making pictures, illustrations, and other representations clarify and extend understanding.	Engage 3 Explore 4, 6
CC1.3 e. Participate in small-group work.	Explore 5

BACKGROUND INFORMATION

All living things require food, water, air, and shelter in order to survive. Food gives living things energy, which is needed for bodily functions like breathing, moving, and developing cells. Plants are considered producers because they make their own food through the process of photosynthesis. Animals and humans are considered consumers because they consume other living things.

In animals, water is used to help regulate temperature and carry out chemical reactions that allow them to move and grow. Plants use water to grow, transport food, and in the process of photosynthesis.

Most living things use oxygen and carbon dioxide in many of the chemical reactions needed for life. Humans absorb oxygen through lungs, while some animals absorb it through gills or the skin. Even animals living in water can absorb oxygen from the water using gills. A by-product of humans and animals breathing in oxygen is releasing carbon dioxide. Plants take in carbon dioxide (which is also used in photosynthesis to make food) through their leaves and release oxygen as a by-product.

For most living things, shelter is considered a *space* for living in — this space provides protection, resources, territory, and comfort. Almost every animal claims a space for living, sometimes called a territory. Plants grow in many different environments and spaces such as soil, rock, sand, or water.

The terms living and non-living are used at this level as a simplification of the terms biotic and abiotic. Note that things that were once living like a leaf or an apple that have fallen from a tree are still considered biotic. It is not necessary for students to delve into the topic this deeply, but be prepared in case this point comes up in discussions of living and non-living.

ASSESSMENT FOR LEARNING

Look for Evidence of Learning	Student-friendly Learning Targets
Can the student: • recall the four basic needs? • make connections between their daily actions and how these actions meet their needs? • identify examples of how they care for the basic needs of other living things?	(self-assessment) • I know the four basic needs of living things. • I can give examples of how I care for the basic needs of living things.

DI DIFFERENTIATING INSTRUCTION

For EAL

Take photos of every step when making the bean plant centre and develop a picture reference to assist students in following the proper procedure.

For Enrichment

Have students document the growth of the bean plant by measuring its height weekly. At the end of the unit, use **PM 7: Make a Bar Graph** to compare the size of the bean plant at various stages of its growth.

For Extra Support

Have student leaders from a higher grade come into the classroom and become experts in one of the centres. During the centre work, these student leaders can help support the activities and answer any immediate questions students may have.

CORE LEARNING OPPORTUNITIES

Engage

1. Activate and Build on Prior Knowledge

- Display some of the images of plants and animals that were found on the Nature Walk. As you identify an image, ask students questions that model "I wonder ..." statements and focus on the basic needs of that living thing. For example:
  - I wonder how a bird finds food.
  - I wonder how grass gets air.
  - I wonder how a tree finds water.
  - I wonder where a squirrel finds shelter.
- Ask students to discuss and respond to these questions with partners or in small groups.
- Use library resources or the Internet to show students images of plants and animals that survive in environments that students are not familiar with. Some examples can include seaweed in the ocean, a cactus in the desert, a seal in the arctic, or a lizard in the jungle.
- Again, ask students questions about the basic needs:
  - I wonder how seaweed gets oxygen in the ocean.
  - I wonder how cactus finds water in the desert.
  - I wonder how a seal finds shelter in the Arctic.
  - I wonder how a lizard catches food in the jungle.

  Give students time to hypothesize and discuss these "I wonder ..." statements.
- Ask students to choose one of the questions discussed and research the answer at home. Set up a Science Show and Tell to display their findings.

Literacy Check
Can the student:
- read the "I wonder ..." statements in the class list and identify "I wonder ..." statements for his or her personal list?
- copy "I wonder ..." statements from the class list onto his or her personal list?

2. Elicit "I Wonder ..." Statements

- Model an "I wonder ..." form of inquiry with statements such as: "I wonder how different animals and plants meet their basic needs," and "I wonder how animals and plants survive in environments constructed by people."
- Invite students to offer other "I wonder ..." statements. Record these on a chart or paper strips, and then read them together. Provide students with copies of **PM 1: I Wonder ...** to record statements that interest them. Some students may require individual or small group assistance to identify statements and record them.

Science Check
Can the student:
- discuss and define the basic needs?
- connect visual images to the definitions?

3. Explore Students' Basic Needs

- Distribute copies of **LM 4: My Basic Needs**. Ask students to draw a picture of themselves in the middle circle.
- Ask students what their four basic needs are. Record them on the board as students identify them (air, water, food, shelter).

Literacy Check
Can the student:
- copy down the definitions properly?
- connect the written definition with the pictures?

- Focus on one need at a time and develop a class definition for each of the four basic needs. Refer to the Background Information about basic needs. Have students copy the definitions of the basic needs onto their copies of **LM 4**.
- In each of the sections on **LM 4**, ask students to use words, drawings, or images cut from magazines to identify how they meet their needs for air, water, food, and shelter.
- Students could also make a collage. Post student collages so students can reference them throughout the unit. The topic of basic needs will be discussed throughout this unit and specifically in Lesson 7.

Explore

Science Check
Can the student:
- identify examples of when to be cautious around living things?
- connect the safety suggestions to their actions in science class?

4. Develop Safety Signs

- Show students pictures of a stop sign and a yield sign. Ask students what each of these signs means and where they are used. Tell them that they are going to develop safety signs for the class to to help them be careful and respectful around other living things. The stop sign will be used when students need to stop their activities and the yield sign will be used when they need to slow down and be careful.
- Make a T-chart on the board. Draw a stop sign at the top of one column and and a yield sign at the top of the other column. You might also hand out copies of **PM 5: Make a T-chart** for students to record along with you.
- Ask students for examples of when people have to be cautious and careful around living things (e.g., students may be allergic to plants/animals, animals that are scared or aggressive might bite, some animals might sting, some plants are poisonous, students have to be respectful of plants and animals by not harming them or their environments, etc.).
- As students are suggesting examples, ask them if each example is something that should be put in the Stop or Yield column.
- When the class has finished listing examples, have each student choose one example from the T-chart or think of a different example, and make a Stop or Yield sign for that suggestion. For example, a Yield sign with the words "YIELD if a bee is buzzing around you," or "STOP! Do not touch a butterfly. You might break its wings."
- Post the signs on the wall and review them with students whenever they will be interacting with living things during the unit.

5. Investigate the Basic Needs of Living Things

- Prepare centres for students to investigate the following questions:
  Centre 1: Can We Grow and Take Care of Living Things?
  Centre 2: Can We Classify Things as Living or Non-living?
  Centre 3: Can We Help Animals Find Food?
  Centre 4: Can We Decide What Living Things Need to Survive?
  Centre 5: Can We Find Where Animals Live?
- You may want to invite parents or older students to assist at the centres.

- Follow the procedure below at each centre:
  - Make simple instruction cards for each centre.
  - Take students on a tour of each centre to explain the purpose and read the instructions for each activity.
  - Use the Skills poster **Communicating and Teamwork** to support working with partners or teams.
  - Use the Skills poster **Safety in Science Class** to discuss safety considerations for each activity.
  - Provide copies of appropriate line masters for each centre, but modify them to meet your students' needs.
  - The Extend Activity Bank for this lesson provides alternative activities for centres.

Tips

- Grow a few extra seeds in case students' plants don't grow.
- The bean/pea plant will grow in a baggie for about a month, but then should be transplanted into soil.
- If possible, tape the baggie to a window because this allows the seeds to grow in a warm environment so students are able to see the roots grow while leaving the plant unharmed.

Centre 1: Can We Grow and Take Care of a Living Thing?

- This activity sets up the investigation at the end of the non-fiction book *Living Things*. It is important to begin growing the plant of your choice now, so that students are able to collect data and monitor its growth. This activity will be revisited in Lesson 4 and Lesson 6.
- Refer to **LM 5: Plant Predictions**. Provide bean or pea seeds, baggies, paper towels, and a jug or pail of water. Students will investigate the growth process of a plant and will record its growth over one month.
- Have students wet two pieces of paper towel and wrap one seed in the paper towel. Ask students why they need to use a wet paper towel. Next have them place the seed and towel in a baggie. Provide an example of a seed already in paper towel in a bag for students to refer to as they work.
- Provide copies of **LM 5** for students to draw what they think the plant will look like in a day, a week, and a month.
- Provide copies of **LM 6: Plant Check-Up** and have students record their observations of the plant's growth in one day, one week, and one month.
- You may want to take a photograph of a seed at one day, one week, and one month, that can be used in later discussions.

Centre 2: Can We Classify Things as Living or Non-Living?

- Students will be reviewing previous knowledge by identifying and sorting living and non-living things. (See Background Information.)
- Copy **LM 7: Living Things** and **LM 8: Non-Living Things** and cut them out. Also, provide pieces of paper labelled: *Living* and *Non-living*.
- Mix the cards and lay them face down on the table. Have students take turns flipping over a card and then the group decides which category the card belongs in.
- When a group has finished, ask them to go through the images on the *Living* sheet of paper to identify and agree on the basic needs of each living thing.

Centre 3: Can We Help Animals Find Food?

- Students will make bird feeders. For each bird feeder, provide a 2 L milk carton, one thin wooden dowel, string or twine, and birdseed. Students will also need scissors and a hole punch.
  Ask parents to contribute clean milk cartons for this activity.
- Make a Bird Window: Pre-draw or pre-cut (according to student ability)

> **Safety Check**
> - Talk to the class about how to safely use scissors if you have them do the cutting.

window-shaped holes on opposite sides of the milk carton. The holes should be identical so use a template to draw them onto the carton. The placement of the windows will determine how much birdseed is needed in the feeder, because the seed should fill the bottom of the carton right up to the window.
- Make a Perch: Use the hole punch to make a hole under each bird window. Push a wooden dowel all the way through the milk carton and make another hole on the opposite side. Pull the dowel through so that equal parts of the stick are exposed on both sides of the carton. (You may want to have an adult present to help insert the dowels and to hot glue both holes so the perch is secure.)
- Make a Hanger: Use the hole punch to punch two holes about 4 cm apart on the top seam of the carton (where the carton width is twice as thick). Thread the string through the holes and tie the ends into a loop.
- Put birdseed in the feeder and hang it outside.

> **Tips**
> - To simplify this activity, you could pre-cut the flip cards.
> - Keep the flip cards to use again in Lesson 7, Explore 3.

Centre 4: Can We Decide What Living Things Need to Survive?
- Prepare an envelope for each of the five animals on **LM 9: Basic Needs**. Cut out the images on **LM 9** and place all of the needs of each animal in one of the envelopes, then print the animal's name on the envelope. Students will need construction paper, scissors, and glue.
- Have student create a flip card by folding a 28 cm × 43 cm piece of construction paper in half lengthwise. Students should then make four approximately equal "flaps" by cutting up to the folded edge on one side of the card. Have students label the four flaps: Air, Water, Food, Shelter. Provide a model for students to follow. Then have students choose one of the five different animal envelopes and print the name of the animal on the uncut/back side of the flip card. Students then decide which of the four basic needs the picture cards in the envelopes represent and glue those cards under the correct flap.
- Go over the correct answers for the animals using **LM 9** for reference. Talk about how plants and animals that live in water get oxygen from the water.

> **Safety Check**
> - Be aware and discuss student allergies to the seeds in the birdseed. Look online for alternative feed recipes that can be used for students with allergies.

Centre 5: Can We Find Where Living Things Live?
- For materials, you will need the Science poster **Where do I live?** Laminate the poster if possible and have students use dry-erase markers to connect the living things to possible shelters. Or, if the poster is not laminated, copy **LM 10: Where Do I Live?** and have students cut out the living things to place on the poster. Each group should work together to identify a possible shelter for each living thing. Students may have more than one idea for shelter for each living thing, so they may make more than one line. Discuss with students the need for the group to agree on the lines before they make their marks.
- Go over the poster as a class to determine the shelter that most students chose for each of the living things.
- Have students copy the class's answers onto **LM 10**.

Explain

Science Check
Can the student:
- identify the differences between living and non-living things?
- identify basic needs?
- understand that non-living things cannot change to living things?

6. Revisit Predictions for Plant Growth
- Ask students to recall and explain what they did in Centre 1: Can We Grow and Take Care of a Living Thing?
- Tell students they will be collecting data and observing changes in the plant throughout the unit. Ask students what questions they want to answer. Encourage questions that touch on plant growth and basic needs.
- As a class, develop one question that this investigation will answer. For example: How much will a seed grow in one month?
- Ask students to get out their copy of **LM 5: Plant Predictions** and share their predictions with a neighbour. As a group, discuss how the seed might change (e.g., roots will grow, a stem will grow up, leaves may form).
- Go over the pictures of the basic needs on **LM 5**. It is important that students understand that plants only have three basic needs, so have students correct, if necessary, this part of **LM 5** by identifying the sun, water, and soil as the items needed. (This will be discussed further in Lesson 5.)
- Ask students to look at their copies of **LM 6: Plant Check-up** and describe how the plant looked after "one day" and "one week." You might also show a few photographs that you took at these two points or draw a likeness on the board.
- Have students keep **LM 5** and **LM 6** together so they can continue to make observations to be used in the culminating activity.

7. Reflect on Learning
- Hold up the materials, poster, or card for each learning centre. Ask students to retell what they were trying to find out (purpose), what they did (procedure), and what they found out (conclusion) for each centre.
- Have students record evidence of their learning using assessment tools on **PM 13: Look What I've Learned.** Encourage students to note at least two things they learned about the characteristics and needs of living things and something they still wonder about.
- Hand out **LM 11: This is What I Can Do**. Read the learning targets with students and have them respond on their own. Some students may need assistance.

OTHER LEARNING OPPORTUNITIES

Extend: Activity Bank

At any time, choose from the following options to replace or supplement the Core Learning Opportunities to meet students' needs and/or interests.

8. Investigate Online Resources

- Explore websites such as National Geographic Kids for fun and interactive games and activities that students can explore on their own or at home.

9. Create a "Living" Thing

- Ask students to try to make a non-living thing living by adding physical characteristics to it. Students will take a rock and add features such as eyes, mouth, fur, wings, tail, and/or feet using tissue paper, pom-poms, felt, pipe cleaners, and glue.
- Ask students if the rock is now living. Review the classification as a class. Something living cannot be created out of a non-living thing, even if it has some of the characteristics of something living.

10. Create a Basic Needs Rap

- Use the non-fiction book *Rapping about Animal Homes* by Bobbie Kalman or *Rapping About What Animals Eat* by Bobbie Kalman to talk about one of the basic needs of animals. These books explain some basic needs of animals in an interesting and engaging way. Then they encourage students to develop their own raps about one of the animals introduced and their basic needs.

11. Make Literature Links

- Read or view one of the books listed in Literature Links or others. Encourage student to discuss how they can tell if something is living or non-living.

Literature Links

What is a Living Thing? by Bobbie Kalman

Is it a Living Thing? by Bobbie Kalman

Is it Living or Non-Living? by Rebecca Rissman

What's Alive? by Kathleen Weidner Zoehfeld

Living and Nonliving (My World of Science) by Angela Royston

Backyard by Donald Silver

12. Explore Other "I Wonder …" Statements

- Return to the "I wonder …" statements not yet answered and any new wonderings that have come up. With students, plan and set out centres where they can explore these wonderings. Encourage them to make and test predictions.
- Working in groups, students can rotate to all the centres or focus on one per group. They could share their findings in oral, written, or electronic presentations.

3 Characteristics of Humans and Animals

Time
3 hours

Vocabulary
animal
human
characteristics
similarities
differences
survive

Program Resources
PM 1: I Wonder ...
PM 6: A Venn Diagram
PM 13: Look What I've Learned
LM 7: Living Things
LM 10: Where Do I Live?
LM 12: Fish Observations
LM 13: This Is What I Can Do
Non-fiction Book: *Living Things*
Fiction Book: *Moko's Adventures on Earth*
Lap Book
Skills Poster: Observing and Recording
Traditional Knowledge Poster: Ways of Observing

Materials and Equipment
- bulletin board paper
- scissors
- markers
- goldfish
- water
- fish bowl or clear container to hold fish
- fish food

GOAL

Students will be able to identify the similarities and differences between different animals, including humans.

ASSESSMENT CHART

Science Indicators	Assessment Opportunities
LT1.1 a. Use a variety of sources of information and ideas to learn about observable characteristics of living things.	Explore 3 Explain 8
LT1.1 b. Make and record observations and measurements about the observable characteristics of plants and animals using written language, pictures, and charts.	Explore 4 Explain 7
LT1.1 c. Group representations of plants and animals according to various student-developed criteria.	Explore 5
LT1.1 e. Describe characteristics common to humans and identify variations that make each human unique.	Engage 1
LT1.1 g. Record information, using written language, pictures, and tables, about the appearance and behaviour of familiar animals, such as classroom or personal pets, at regular intervals over a specific time interval.	Explain 7
LT1.1 h. Describe the appearance and behaviour of familiar animals.	Explore 3 Explain 6, 7
LT1.1 i. Differentiate among animals according to their observable characteristics.	Explore 4, 5, 6
LT1.1 k. Communicate knowledge about the observable characteristics of a favourite plant or animal.	Explain 7
LT1.1 l. Respond positively to others' questions and ideas about the observable characteristics of living things.	Engage 1 Explain 7
LT1.2 c. Pose questions about ways in which animals interact with their environments to meet their basic needs.	Engage 2
LT1.2 d. Investigate, through field trips to natural habitats, nature videos, and community walks, homes and habitats of local plants and animals to determine how they meet their basic needs.	Explain 7
LT1.2 f. Compare the kinds of food that different animals eat, their methods of eating, and the structures that they have for eating.	Explain 7
LT1.2 j. Predict and model how certain animals will move to meet their needs for food, shelter, and protection in their environment, based on personal observations, pictures, or videos.	Explore 6, 7

English Language Arts Indicators	Assessment Opportunities
CR1.1 c. Relate aspects of stories and characters from various texts to personal feelings and experiences.	Explore 3
CC1.3 d. Share and talk about what is being learned, and stay on topic when speaking.	Explore 6

BACKGROUND INFORMATION

Note that the scientific terms are biotic and abiotic, but that living and non-living are more age-appropriate terms. Knowing this will help avoid any confusion that these terms separate things into categories of alive or dead.

Biotic things are related to or result from living things, directly. Abiotic things are not derived from living organisms. Thus, dead things remain biotic (in the class of living things). Confusion can arise when thinking beyond one stage of removal. A log (living) is turned into paper (non-living). A rock is made of things that were once living, as is oil; but those things would be classified as abiotic.

ASSESSMENT FOR LEARNING

Look for Evidence of Learning	Student-friendly Learning Targets
Can the student: • identify individual characteristics of themselves and compare it to others? • identify characteristics of plants and animals? • sort and compare characteristics of animals? • connect animal movements to specific animal characteristics?	(self-assessment) • I know what is different between my physical characteristics and those of my neighbours. • I can identify characteristics of plants and animals. • I can sort and compare characteristics of animals. • I can connect animal movements to specific animal characteristics.

DI DIFFERENTIATING INSTRUCTION

For EAL

Create pictures that correspond to the terms identified for human characteristics. During the fish observations, have photographs of each of the steps in sequence for students to reference and follow.

For Enrichment

Students could complete the sorting activities independently by choosing their own animals to use for the classification. Provide different types of fish for the fish activity, so that students can compare the similarities and differences of the characteristics of different fish.

For Extra Support

Use a line master of a human body shape rather than having students trace their bodies.
Pre-select animal movements for the charades game Explain 7 and find videos online that isolate that specific movement. These videos can be a reference for any students who can't decide how to move for a specific animal.

CURRICULUM CONNECTIONS

Students will have the opportunity to develop skills and concepts in the following areas:

Health

USC1.5 Explore the association between a healthy sense of "self" and one's positive connection with others and the environment.

Arts Education

CP1.1 Create movements and movement patterns in response to stimuli such as stories, poems, music, or objects as starting points.

CP1.7 Investigate a variety of formal and informal patterns in art work and the environment, and apply observations to own work.

CORE LEARNING OPPORTUNITIES

Engage

1. Activate and Build on Prior Knowledge

- Draw the outline of a human body on the board or chart paper. Ask students to name the main body parts that most people have. Add the parts they name to the drawing and label them. Tell students that the body parts we can describe are called characteristics.
- Have students work with partners and provide each pair with enough bulletin board or butcher paper to trace out their body shapes. Have each student lie down on the paper while the other student traces his or her body outline, and then switch. Then have students trade places and trace out the other partner's body shape. Afterwards, have students label the main parts of their body (e.g., head, ears, arms, etc.) using the class drawing.
- Have students colour their features to portray their unique characteristics (e.g., length and colour of hair, colour and shape of eyes, colour of skin).
- Tell students that just because we have characteristics that are the same doesn't mean that we all look the same. Then ask students to compare their coloured body shape with their partner's. Have them observe and talk about the differences between the two bodies. Tell students to find a new partner and compare the body shapes again to find the similarities and differences.
- Gather the class for a discussion. Ask students:
  - What kind of characteristics did you share with others?
  - Were there any characteristics that you did not share with anyone else in the class?
- As a follow-up, read pages 4–5 in the non-fiction book *Living Things*. Using the question at the bottom of page 5, have students generate a list of characteristics that are different or the same for different people. You might also discuss the characteristics that are the same or different for the animals on page 4.
- Have students take their outline home and share with a parent or guardian.

Science Check
Can the student:
- identify characteristics of humans and how they vary?
- compare characteristics of humans to those of other animals and plants?
- work cooperatively with a partner to accomplish the task?

2. Elicit "I Wonder ..." Statements

- Ask students to summarize what they did in Engage 1 and then think about what it would be like to compare the characteristics of a human to another living thing, such as a puppy or a tree.
- Add to the classroom "I Wonder ..." bubble. Model "I wonder ..." statements such as: "I wonder how characteristics of humans and animals are the same," or "I wonder how characteristics of humans and animals are different."
- Invite students to offer other "I wonder ..." statements. Record these on a chart or paper strips and then read them together. Provide students with copies of **PM 1: I Wonder ...** to record statements that interest them. Some students may require individual or small group assistance to identify statements and record them.

Literacy Check
Can the student:
- read the "I wonder ..." statements in the class list and identify "I wonder ..." statements for his or her personal list?
- copy "I wonder ..." statements from the class list onto his or her personal list?

Explore

✓ Literacy Check
Can the student:
- demonstrate comprehension of grade-appropriate books?
- understand and apply cues and make connections to construct meaning when reading?

3. Read and Respond to the Fiction Book *Moko's Adventures on Earth*

Before: Hold up the fiction book. Ask students to share what they remember about this story.

- Tell students to visualize what it would be like to visit a different world. Have students talk to a neighbour about the mistakes they might make if they were visiting another world for the first time.

During: Use a Shared Reading approach to read the Lap Book again. Ask students to put up their hands to signal every time they notice that Moko identifies an animal or plant incorrectly. Students' hands should go up when Moko makes the following mistakes: Rocks will talk (pg 4); a squirrel will talk (pg 7); a flower is an animal (pg 8); a flower can smell (pg 8); the bird is a plant (pg 9); the worm is a plant (pg 11).

After: Ask students why Moko had such a hard time deciding what was human, plant, or animal. What are some characteristics of the plants or animals that he could have identified correctly?

- Use the Lap Book to review each mistake that Moko made and talk about the characteristics that Moko needed to look for. (The rock isn't human because it has no eyes, nose or mouth, and it does not breathe or talk.)

4. Make a Venn Diagram

- Turn to pages 6–7 in the non-fiction book *Living Things*. Have students compare the similar and different characteristics of humans and birds.
- Choose another animal and make similar comparisons to humans. This time, model the use of a Venn diagram using **PM 6: A Venn Diagram**.
- Have students study the animals on page 7 and answer the questions at the bottom of the page. Have students talk to a neighbour about the similarities and differences they see in some of the animals.
- Hand out copies of **PM 6: A Venn Diagram**. Ask students to complete a Venn diagram using two animals of their choice.

✓ Science Check
Can the student:
- correctly sort and compare animal characteristics?
- make their own criteria for sorting animals?

5. Compare Animals Using Student Criteria

- Read the Sort It Out on pages 10–11 in the non-fiction book *Living Things*. Have pairs of students choose two animals to compare. Then share their answers to the questions with the class.
- Distribute copies of **LM 7: Living Things** to each student. (You could also use the animals on **LM 10: Where Do They Live?**) Have students cut out the Living Things cards. Individually or in partners, ask students to group the animals according to different characteristics. Have pages 10 and 11 of the non-fiction book available for reference. Start by asking students group the animals by whether or not their ears stick out from their heads.
- Ask students to volunteer ideas of how the pictures can be sorted, and have the class sort according to criteria that students offer. Create a list on the board of the different criteria that students have used.
- Have students sort their own piles according to their own criteria of characteristics. Have students switch piles after they have been sorted and see if they can guess how the other person sorted out their cards. Ask students to keep track of the different criteria they used for sorting. Make a class list after they guessed each other's criteria and discuss.

Science Check
Can the student:
- connect animal movements to specific animal characteristics?

6. Move Like Animals

- Ask students for some examples of how different animals move. (A fish swims by pushing the water with short fins and steering with the tail. Rabbits and frogs use their strong back legs to jump. A snake slithers and uses its muscles to push its way along the ground.)
- Have students play charades using the animals on **LM 7: Living Things**. (You could also use the animals on **LM 10: Where Do I Live?**) Separate students into groups and focus on the different features of the animals. They should move with no sounds while the rest of their group tries to guess the animal. After students have guessed the correct animal, ask students to explain why the animal moves that way and what basic need the animal is trying to meet with that movement. Afterward, show students videos of different animals and how they move.

***Traditional* Knowledge**

- You could show students videos of First Nations or Métis dances that mimic the movement of animals such as the Rabbit Dance.

Explain

7. Carry Out a Fish Investigation

- Conduct an investigation using **LM 12: Fish Observations**. Explain to students that they will be observing a goldfish, and recording their observations. Review the Skills poster **Observing and Recording** and ask which senses they will use to observe the goldfish.
- Depending on the size of your class, observe the fish as a class, or have students observe the fish in small groups.
- Ask students to predict what they will see the fish doing. Then, elicit observations from students, such as "the gills are moving," "the mouth is opening and closing," "the fish is coming up to the top of the water." Encourage students to make connections between their observations of the fish's behaviours and how they help the fish meet it's needs. Talk about how there is oxygen in the water that the fish gets through it's gills.
- After all students have had a chance to observe the fish and participate in the discussion, complete **LM 12: Fish Observations**. Depending on the needs and abilities of students, complete **LM 12** as a class or have groups complete it on their own.
- Ask students to compare the type of food a fish eats with what a dog or cat eats. How is the way they eat different? Show students videos of how different animals eat, drink, and meet their basic needs.

***Traditional* Knowledge**

8. Talk With an Elder About Plants and Animals

- Show students the Traditional Knowledge poster **Ways of Observing**. Draw their attention to the Inuit woman ice fishing. Remind them that the woman is catching fish by using her observation skills and things she has learned about how fish behave. Then look at the older man talking with the young boy. He is teaching the boy about how to recognize different plants and herbs that can be eaten and/or used as medicine.
- Invite an Elder or Traditional Knowledge Keeper to visit now or later in the unit to talk about traditional ways of using plants and/or animals and the behaviours of animals. (See the Program Overview for protocols.)

9. Reflect on Learning

- Have students record evidence of their learning on **PM 13: Look What I've Learned.** They can also record in their journal or with a video or audio recording on a small device or camera. Encourage them to note at least two things they learned about the characteristics of humans and animals
- Hand out **LM 13: This is What I Can Do** to use as a self-assessment. Read the learning targets with students and have them respond on their own. Some students may need assistance.

OTHER LEARNING OPPORTUNITIES

Extend: Activity Bank

At any time, choose from the following options to replace or supplement the Core Learning Opportunities to meet students' needs and/or interests.

10. Write Riddles

- Have students write riddles that describe the characteristics of their favourite animals. They could work in partners or in small groups. Teams can then guess the animal based on the characteristics.

11. Observe a Pet

- Modify **LM 4: My Basic Needs** as necessary for this activity. Make copies available for students to complete this activity. Have students record observations of a family pet or a classroom pet.

12. Create an Imaginary Pet

- Have students create an imaginary pet, or draw their favourite pet. Then have students identify the unique characteristics of their pet and describe why they have those special characteristics. Refer them to "EekoCreature" (http://pbskids.org/eekoworld/index.html?load=eekocreature).

13. Respond to Talk Time

- Explore activity and discussion questions 4, 5, 6, or 7 in Talk Time on page 24 of the non-fiction book *Living Things.*
- Explore activities and discussion questions from Talk Time on page 16 of the fiction book *Moko's Adventures on Earth.*

14. Explore Other "I Wonder ..." Statements

- Return to the "I wonder ..." statements not yet answered and new wonderings that have come up. With students, plan and set up centres where they can explore these wonderings. Encourage them to make and test predictions.
- Working in small groups, students can rotate to all the centres or focus on one per group. They could share their findings in oral, written, or electronic presentations.

4 Behaviours of Animals

Time
3 hours

Vocabulary
behaviour

Resources
PM 1: I Wonder ...
PM 8: Make a Web
PM 13: Look What I've Learned
LM 7: Living Things
LM 14: Matching Bird Beaks
LM 15: My Animal Trading Card
LM 16: This is What I Can Do
Non-fiction Book: *Living Things*
Lap Book
Skills Poster: Safety in Science Class

Materials and Equipment
- sunflower seeds
- pliers
- orange juice
- straws
- mini marshmallows
- scissors
- gummy worms
- sand or soil
- chopsticks
- grass
- water strainer
- coloured rice
- foam blocks
- scoop with holes
- bowls
- fairy tales (with animals)
- sticky notes

GOAL

Students will investigate animal behaviour and movement.

ASSESSMENT CHART

Science Indicators	Assessment Opportunities
LT1.1 c. Group representations of plants and animals according to various student-developed criteria.	Explain 7
LT1.1 d. Engage in personal, scientific, and Indigenous ways of organizing understanding of living things.	Explain 8
LT1.1 g. Record information, using written language, pictures, and tables, about the appearance and behaviour of familiar animals, such as classroom or personal pets, at regular intervals over a specific time interval.	Explore: 5
LT1.1 h. Describe the appearance and behaviour of familiar animals.	Engage 1 Explore 3, 4 Explain 7
LT1.1 i. Differentiate among animals according to their observable characteristics.	Explore 3, 4
LT1.1 k. Communicate knowledge about observable characteristics of a favourite plant or animal.	Explain 7
LT1.1 l. Respond positively to others' questions and ideas about the observable characteristics of living things.	Engage 1, 2
LT1.1 m. Recognize that some information about living things may not be realistic.	Explain 6
LT1.2 c. Pose questions about ways in which animals interact with their environments to meet their basic needs.	Engage 1, 2 Explain 6
LT1.2 d. Investigate, through field trips to natural habitats, nature videos, and community walks, homes and habitats of local plants and animals to determine how they meet their basic needs.	Explore 4
LT1.2 f. Compare the kinds of food that different animals eat, their methods of eating, and the structures that they have for eating.	Explore 4
English Language Arts Indicators	**Assessment Opportunities**
CR1.1 b. Make and share connections among texts, prior knowledge, and personal experiences.	Engage 2
CC1.3 e. Participate in small-group work.	Explore 4 Explain 6

BACKGROUND INFORMATION

Animal behaviour is another distinguishing characteristic that scientists use to classify animals, including humans. Usually animal behaviour can be linked to the basic needs of survival. An example of this is how animals obtain food: they behave differently according to what they eat. Carnivores get all or most of their nutrients from animal matter, and will stalk and hunt prey, while herbivores eat only plant material, and will forage and store food. An omnivore is an animal that eats both animal and plant matter. Most humans are omnivores.

An adaptation is a characteristic that helps an organism survive. For example, Arctic hares have thick, white fur in the winter which helps them blend in with their snowy habitat, but their fur changes colour in the spring/summer to blend in with the rocks and vegetation around them. It is important for students to understand that adaptations do not happen overnight; nor can an animal adapt on purpose. Adaptations happen over many generations. Another example of an adaptation is mimicry. One example of this is a non-poisonous animal closely resembles a poisonous animal, causing predators to avoid both of them. For example, a King snake has similar colouring to the poisonous Coral snake.

ASSESSMENT FOR LEARNING

Look for Evidence of Learning	Student-friendly Learning Targets
Can the student: • identify behaviours that help animals live, eat, or sleep? • make predictions and draw conclusions about how animals' characteristics and behaviours help them meet their basic needs? • identify unrealistic behaviours in stories?	(self-assessment) • I can decide if a specific animal behaviour helps them live, get food, or sleep. • I know that animals have different characteristics and behaviours that help them meet their basic needs. • I know that sometimes stories exaggerate and make up unrealistic animal behaviours.

DI DIFFERENTIATING INSTRUCTION

For EAL

Provide a buddy or a learning partner who can help support students' progress through various activities, particularly Explore 4. Explicit instructions may be needed to ensure students have the background knowledge of vocabulary needed prior to beginning this section of the unit.

For Enrichment

Have students research some unique animal adaptations that have not been covered in class. Invite them to share some interesting facts with other students.

For Extra Support

Providing visuals for vocabulary words will help students who require extra support as well as EAL students.

For Explore 4, place students who require extra support with students who are able to work independently.

CORE LEARNING OPPORTUNITIES

Engage

1. Activate and Build on Prior Knowledge

- Have students think about animals and their behaviours. Ask students questions such as:
  - How does a worm move around?
  - How does a bat see in the dark?
- As students share their thoughts, try to focus their answers by asking them to state a characteristic of the animal in their answers (worms move by wriggling.)
- Then ask what basic need each animal is trying to meet with this behaviour. (The worm is moving to find food or is trying to survive by escaping predators. A bat is also hunting for food.)
- Have students talk to their neighbour to ask similar questions and try to answer each other's questions.

Literacy Check
Can the student:
- read the "I wonder ..." statements in the class list and identify "I wonder ..." statements for his or her personal list?
- copy "I wonder ..." statements from the class list onto his or her personal list?

2. Elicit "I Wonder ..." Statements

- Add to the classroom "I Wonder ..." bubble. Model "I Wonder ..." statements such as: "I wonder what makes animals behave differently," or "I wonder how animal behaviours change the way an animal looks."
- Invite students to offer other "I wonder ..." statements. Record these on a chart or paper strips and then read them together.
- Ask students to copy the new statements generated onto **PM 1: I Wonder ...**
- Once you have determined students' background knowledge, use the Lap Book to read pages 8–9 of the non-fiction book *Living Things*. Focus on the different animal behaviours shown. Ask students:
  - What other animals live in groups or alone?
  - What other animals are awake during the day or night?
  Encourage students to think about how each behaviour helps the animals meet their basic needs.

Explore

Science Check
Can the student:
- connect the examples of animal behaviours to other animals that they know about?
- provide appropriate answers that include behaviours, characteristics, and basic needs?

3. Sort Animal Behaviours

- Hand out copies of **LM 7: Living Things** to every student or group of students. (You could also use the animals on **LM 10: Where Do I Live?**) As a class, ask students to identify what the animals eat and sort them into different groups (e.g., insects, seeds, fish, plants, or other animals). When all of the animals are in groups, ask the class to identify characteristics that help them find/process their food.
- Have students point out unique features of each animal and try to explain how that feature helps the animal survive.
- Tell students to make piles according to where the animal lives — in the ground, on top of the ground, in the water, or in the air. Have students discuss in groups the unique characteristics that enable an animal to live in a specific habitat/place. (Birds have wings that allow them to spend time in the air.)

Science Check
Can the student:
- correctly read and identify the concepts they know or need to work on using LM 14?

Safety Check
- Ensure safe handling of objects like scissors and pliers.
- Investigate ahead of time if any student has food allergies. Even if the foods are not being ingested, some students may be allergic to the smell or touch of certain foods.

4. Match Bird Beaks to Food Samples

- Before starting this activity, show students the Skills poster **Safety in Science Class** and talk about rules and expectations when doing science experiments.
- Separate students into groups of seven. Provide each group with samples of food and objects that look and function like the beaks of different birds: sunflower seeds (to represent seeds) and pliers; orange juice (to represent nectar) and a straw; mini marshmallows (to represent meat) and scissors; mini fish in water (to represent fish) and a scoop with holes; gummy worms in sand or soil (to represent worms) and chopsticks; grass in water (to represent weeds) and a strainer; and coloured rice embedded in a foam block (to represent insects) and tweezers. Do not hand them out in the correct pairs. Hand out the "food" in labelled containers telling what type of food each represents and go over this with students.
- Tell students their job is to use the different "beaks" to try to pick up each type of food. As a group, they should decide which tool/beak is best suited to each type of food. Have the groups provide reasoning for their choices and explain their selections to the class.
- Hand out copies of **LM 14: Matching Bird Beaks**. Show students photos of each of the different types of birds. Draw students' attention to each bird's beak and connect it to the image on LM 14. Have students compare these beaks. Ask them how the beaks are similar and how they are different from one another. Which tool is most like each beak? Why might they have these differences? Answers: the hummingbird uses a beak like the straw to eat the nectar; the sparrow uses a beak like the pliers to eat seeds; the robin uses a beak like chopsticks to eat worms; the woodpecker uses a beak like the tweezers to eat insects; the pelican uses a beak like the scoop to eat fish; the duck uses a beak like the strainer to eat weeds; the eagle uses a beak like scissors to eat meat.
- Reinforce the concept of adaptations throughout this lesson. Remind students that each bird's beak has changed over many generations making some foods easier to eat than others.
- Show students videos of local birds and/or other animals focusing on how they eat and meet their other basic needs within their habitats.

5. Observe Animal Behaviours

- Have students observe a classroom pet or their own pet or a friend's pet for two or three days. They should make three or four observations at the same time each day such as first thing in the morning, late morning, in the afternoon, and if possible, in the evening. Tell them to watch for how the animal gets water and food, what type of shelter it has, and how it behaves at different times of the day. Show them how to make a chart in their journals with the four different times they will make observations down the left side and space for them to draw and write their observations at each time.
- Make a large chart similar to the one student's used and record their observations about what the pets did at each time of the day, and how they met their needs for water, food, and shelter. If students observed different pets, you may want to make a chart for each type and talk about how the animals behaved differently or the same.

Explain

✔ Literacy Check
Can the student:
- read and understand the story?
- summarize the story using the sentence frame?
- identify the pictures and words that show examples of unrealistic animal behaviours?

6. Read Fairy Tales

Before: Choose several fairy tales that students can read independently or in small groups. Focus on books that have animals as the main characters, such as the stories of *Three Billy Goats Gruff, The Three Little Pigs,* and *Henny Penny.*

During: Have students do an initial reading of the book within their groups. Then have one student in each group retell the story to reinforce comprehension.

- Give each group 10 sticky notes. Ask students to go through the story again and put a sticky note on spots in the story when an animal character is behaving in a way that would not happen in real life.

After: Have students pair up with other students who have read a different book to talk about their stories and the behaviours of the characters. Then gather the class back together to talk as a group about the unrealistic behaviours of the animals. Ask students why they think the unrealistic behaviours were used in the story. How would the stories be different if the animals acted like real animals?

- Have students work with a partner to go back through one of their stories and talk about how real animals would behave differently at each point where they previously placed a sticky note.

7. Make a Trading Card

✔ Science Check
Can the student:
- tell about the unique characteristics of animals?

- Tell students that the purpose of a trading card is to show information about a person in a small amount of space. Show students examples of trading cards and ask them to identify the different types of information you can find on a card (e.g., full name, date of birth, accomplishments).
- Explain to students that they will make a trading card for an animal of their choice. The purpose is to tell about that animal's unique characteristics. Distribute copies of **LM 15: My Animal Trading Card** and discuss the different categories that they will be researching.
- Brainstorm animals that students could research.
- Have students use non-fiction library resources or Internet search tools to do their research and record their findings on **LM 15**.
- Have groups of students take turns sorting the completed Animal Trading Cards by the different characteristics of the animals.

8. Develop a Class Web

✔ Science Check
Can the student:
- identify some animals' behaviours and characteristics that help them meet their needs?

- Have students summarize the concepts and ideas that they have learned in this lesson. Distribute copies of **PM 8: Make a Web**. Draw a web on the board with the words Animals in the centre and bubbles around it with the headings Basic Needs, Characteristics, and Behaviours. Ask students to recall what they have learned. Encourage them to copy down some of the information onto their copy of **PM 8**.

9. Reflect on Learning

- Have students record evidence of their learning using **PM 13: Look What I've Learned.** They can also record in their journal or with a video or audio recording on a smart device or camera. Encourage students to note at least two things they learned about animal behaviours and something they still wonder about.
- Hand out **LM 16: This is What I Can Do** as a self-assessment. Read the learning targets with students and have them respond on their own. Some students may need assistance.

OTHER LEARNING OPPORTUNITIES

Literature Links
From Head to Toe by Eric Carle
Bear Snores by Karma Wilson
Bat Loves the Night by Nicola Davies

Extend: Activity Bank

At any time, choose from the following options to replace or supplement the Core Learning Opportunities to meet students' needs and/or interests.

10. Write and Illustrate Stories

- Have students write or illustrate stories about their favourite animals with realistic or unrealistic behaviours. Show students books such as those listed in Literature Links to give them ideas. Provide an opportunity for students to present their stories to the class.

11. Go on a Scavenger Hunt

- Collect non-fiction books from the library and ask students to look through the books for various animal characteristics or behaviours. Have them discuss with a partner how the characteristics or behaviours help the animals survive.

12. Make a Poster

- Provide the cards on **LM 7: Living Things**. Make a poster for each animal grouping: insect, amphibian, bird, fish, mammal, and reptile. Have students add more pictures to each poster using magazines and the Internet. Once there are a few animals on each poster, discuss the unique characteristics of the animals in each group.

13. Explore Other "I Wonder ..." Statements

- Return to the "I wonder ..." statements not yet answered and any new wonderings that have come up. With students, plan and set out centres where they can explore these wonderings. Encourage them to make and test predictions.
- Working in groups, students can rotate to all the centres or focus on one per group. They could share their findings in oral, written, or electronic presentations.

5 Characteristics of Plants

Time
3 hours

Vocabulary
flower
stem
leaf
roots
leaves
trunk
soil
seed

Program Resources
PM 1: I Wonder ...
PM 13: Look What I've Learned
LM 5: Plant Predictions
LM 6: Plant Check-Up
LM 17: Plant Labels
LM 18: Focus on Plants
LM 19: This is What I Can Do
Non-fiction Book: *Living Things*
Skills Poster: Observing and Recording

Materials and Equipment
- 28 cm × 43 cm paper
- construction paper
- scissors
- glue
- growing bean plants
- rulers

GOAL

Students will be able to observe and classify the characteristics of plants and their basic needs.

ASSESSMENT CHART

Science Indicators	Assessment Opportunities
LT1.1 a. Use a variety of sources of information and ideas to learn about observable characteristics of living things.	Explore 3 Explain 6
LT1.1 b. Make and record observations and measurements about the observable characteristics of plants and animals using written language, pictures, and charts.	Explore 3, 4 Explain 6
LT1.1 f. Compare observable characteristics of plants of various types and sizes that live in different habitats.	Explore 4
LT1.1 j. Compare characteristics of plants and animals at different stages of their lives.	Explain 6
LT1.2 a. Identify the physical needs (i.e., food, water, air, and shelter) that plants, animals, and humans require for survival.	Explain 5
LT1.2 b. Pose questions about ways in which plants interact with their environments to meet their basic needs.	Engage 2 Explain 5
LT1.2 e. Compare ways in which plants and animals that live within the local environment, and plants and animals that live in other environments, meet their needs for food, water, and shelter.	Explore 4
LT1.2 k. Explore how people demonstrate respect for living things by caring for domestic plants and animals.	Explain 6
English Language Arts Indicators	**Assessment Opportunities**
CR1.3 h. Listen to and carry out directions with four to six simple steps.	Explain 5
AR1.1 a. Reflect on viewing, listening, reading, speaking, writing, and other representing experiences in the context of teacher-led discussions.	Explain 7

BACKGROUND INFORMATION

There are some important differences between plants and animals, although they are both living things. Plants are typically rooted in the ground and can't move from place to place on their own, while animals can move freely. Animals are dependent on plants or other animals for food. While plants make their own food through the process of photosynthesis.

Plants are considered living things. They can reproduce sexually and asexually. Sexual reproduction takes place when a flower is pollinated, and a seed is produced. Asexual reproduction takes place when an offspring comes from a single parent plant. An example of this is using a cutting from a plant to start a new plant. Plants obtain food by absorbing water and nutrients through their roots and by photosynthesizing where they absorb carbon dioxide and water, then use sunlight to convert it to sugar. During photosynthesis, plants produce oxygen as a by-product. This process of photosynthesis allows plants to grow. Plants can move and respond to stimuli — seedlings and vines will grow towards light, and some plants have the ability to close their leaves when there is no light or when they are threatened. (e.g., when touched)

ASSESSMENT FOR LEARNING

Look for Evidence of Learning	Student-friendly Learning Targets
Can the student: • identify differences between animal and plant characteristics? • compare different plants according to their characteristics? • collect data and make new predictions about the growth of plants? • demonstrate respect and responsibility for a living plant?	(self-assessment) • I know the differences between the characteristics of plants and animals. • I can compare different plants by how they look. • I know the basic needs of a plant. • I can collect information about my plant and make predictions about how it will grow. • I can show respect and responsibility for a living plant.

DIFFERENTIATING INSTRUCTION

For EAL
Post a labelled plant diagram for student reference or collect pictures of real flowers and plants and label them. Students can refer to these diagrams throughout the lesson as they explore plant characteristics.

For Enrichment
Have students research unusual plant parts and how they help the plant. Then they could present their research to the class. For example, the hairs on a Venus flytrap, the spines or thorns on a cactus, and the exploding seed pods of the Touch-me-not (impatiens).

For Extra Support
Prepare large diagrams of plants that have the characteristics and plant functions covered by windows or flaps. Students can use these diagrams as a guessing game to identify the parts of the plant.

CURRICULUM CONNECTIONS

Students will have the opportunity to develop skills and concepts in the following areas:

Mathematics
SS1.1 Demonstrate an understanding of measurement as a process of comparing.

Arts Education
CP1.7 Investigate a variety of formal and informal patterns in art work and the environment, and apply observations to own work.

CORE LEARNING OPPORTUNITIES

Engage

1. Activate and Build on Prior Knowledge

- Hand out a blank piece of paper to each student and have them fold it in half along the width. On one half, ask students to draw and colour their favourite animal. Have students talk to their neighbours about the different characteristics of their animals. This is also a good time to remind students that characteristics are the way something looks and acts. Ask students to label three characteristics.
- On the other half, ask students to draw a flower. As a class, identify the parts of their flower. Students may have flowers with different colours or shapes, but they should be able to identify these parts of a flower: petals, leaves, a stem, and roots.
- When both pictures are complete, have students open their page to show both pictures at the same time. Ask volunteers to share some of the characteristics they have identified for their animal or plant.

Literacy Check
Can the student:
- read the "I wonder ..." statements in the class list and identify "I wonder ..." statements for his or her personal list?
- copy "I wonder ..." statements from the class list onto his or her personal list?

2. Elicit "I Wonder ..." Statements

- Model an "I wonder ..." form of inquiry with statements such as: "I wonder why different plants are different," or "I wonder how different plants are the same."
- Invite students to offer other "I wonder ..." statements. Record these on a chart or paper strips, and then read them together. Provide students with copies of **PM 1: I Wonder ...** to record statements that interest them. Some students may require individual or small group assistance to identify statements and record them.

Explore

Science Check
Can the student:
- label basic plant parts?
- describe how plants are the same or different?

3. Focus on Plant Characteristics

Before: Ask students for the largest and smallest plants they can think of.
During: Read page 12 of the non-fiction book *Living Things.*
Page 12: Have students identify the parts of the plants that are the same and describe how they are the same. Ask them to name some other plants that have some of the same characteristics as the two plants shown. Then ask how some plants are different from the plants shown.
After: Ask students to draw a flower like the dandelion shown on page 12 of the non-fiction book. The plant should have a stem, a leaf, roots, and a flower. Have students cut out the words from Section 1 of **LM 17: Plant Labels** and glue the words onto their pictures in the appropriate spots. (Save the rest of the labels to be used in Explain 5.)

Literacy Check
Can the student:
- create their own flower using the model in the book?
- independently use the book to label their created flowers properly?
- use the new vocabulary to complete the sentence frames?

4. Compare Plant Differences

Before: Show students pictures or videos of plants growing in different habitats. Options include plants that live and grow in water, such a lily pads, seaweed, or sea lettuce, plants that live in deserts such as cacti, or grasses that live in grasslands. Ask students what is the same about all of these plants such as leaves, roots, stems, flowers, fruits, and seeds. Then ask how these plants are different. Discuss the different characteristics of each habitat and how the plants' characteristics help them survive in their habitat. Focus on how they get water, food, and air. Talk about whether the plants need shelter.

During: Read page 13 of the non-fiction book *Living Things.*

Page 13: Choose two plants at a time to focus on (you may want to cover up the others) and have students identify the differences in the plants in how the plants look and also using the labels on the diagrams on page 12.

After: Distribute copies of **LM 18: Focus on Plants** and have students independently label the diagram of the tree and complete the sentence frames using the words from the word bank.

Explain

5. Discover How Plants Meet Their Needs

- Hand back the large flower diagrams started in Explore 3 and Section 2 of **LM 17: Plant Labels**. Ask students what their plant needs to survive, referring to the plant that they are growing. As students identify sun, water, and soil, ask them to add those to their flower diagram and then cut out and add the labels for each using Section 2 of **LM 17**.
- Then talk about the functions of the different parts of the flower. Ask students:
  - What do you think the leaves do for the plant?
  - Why does the plant have roots?
  - What does the flower do for the plant?
  - Why do you think the flower needs a stem?
- As a class, discuss the answer to each question. Refer students to Section 3 of **LM 17**. As a class, read every Plant Function statement and have students vote on which function belongs to which plant part. When all of the functions have been voted on, supply students with the answers and have them add those sentences to the right spots on their diagram.

Science Check

Can the student:

- label the real plant by relating it to the diagrams that were previously taught?
- update their predictions to reflect a new stage of growth?
- treat the plant with respect?

6. Observe and Document Plant Growth

- During this activity, use the Skills poster **Observing and Recording** when talking about making proper observations of the plant and developing their prediction diagrams.
- Separate students into groups of four or five. Hand out the baggies with the sprouting beans that you started earlier. Remove each bean carefully so that the group can make observations on its growth. Remind students that this plant is a living thing and needs to be handled as little as possible and with respect.
- Hand out **LM 5: Plant Predictions** and **LM 6: Plant Check-Up** that students worked on previously. Ask each group to talk about their predictions for the growth of the plant compared to the actual growth that they see. Then have them draw what the plant looks like now and make a new prediction to represent what the plant will look like in another month on Part 2 of **LM 6**.

- Call out the plant parts (roots, leaf, stem, seed) and ask students to identify the different parts of the plant by pointing to that part of the plant with their pencils. Ask for volunteers to describe each plant part. Talk about the basic needs of the plant by posing questions such as:
  - What makes the plant a living thing? (It grows; it obtains food; it takes in water; leaves take in air.)
  - How do you think the plant gets food? (From the seeds; when the seed is used up, the plant makes food from sun, water, soil, and air.)
  - How do you think the plant gets water? (It brings in water through the roots.)
- First, let students explore the answers and come to conclusions on their own, and then discuss the answers as a class.

7. Reflect on Learning

- Have students record evidence of their learning on **PM 13: Look What I've Learned**. They can also record in their journal or with a video or audio recording on a smart device or camera. Encourage them to note at least two things they learned about characteristics of plants and something they still wonder about.
- Use **LM 19: This Is What I Can Do** as a self-assessment. Read the learning targets with students and have them respond on their own. Some students may need assistance.

OTHER LEARNING OPPORTUNITIES

Extend: Activity Bank

At any time, choose from the following options to replace or supplement the Core Learning Opportunities to meet students' needs and/or interests.

8. Decide If a Plant Needs Soil

- Ask students what plants need. They will likely include soil in the list. Discuss how different plant grow in different environments such as tulips which grow in soil, beach grasses and cactus that grow in sand, kelp that grows in water. Pose the question, "Does a plant really need soil?" to the class. (Some mosses and orchids grown in air.) Have them hypothesize why or why not. Use the **PM 3: A Fair Test** for students to develop their own criteria for testing this question. Conduct an experiment using the student-made criteria and have students use the **PM 9: I Found Out** to record their conclusions.

***Traditional* Knowledge**

9. Reading About First Nations' Perspectives on Plants

- Make fiction and non-fiction books on the topics of the lesson available to students to extend their reading. One possibility is the book *Relatives With Roots* by Leah Marie Dorion.

Literature Links
Plants are Living Things
by Bobbie Kalman

From Seed to Plant
by Gail Gibbons

What Do Roots Do?
by Kathleen V. Kudlinski

A Seed is Sleepy
by Dianna Hutts Aston

10. Listen to Stories Online
- Listen and watch a story being read about the basic needs of a plant and how it grows. Examples include: "Sid the Seed,""Peep Plants a Seed," and "One Seed." Provide an opportunity for students to share ideas about stories that they have read.

11. Play an Online Game
- Introduce students to online games that focus on the topics of this lesson. Have students play the online game "Growing Plants" found on the BBC Schools website.

12. Respond to Talk Time
- Explore discussion question 8 in Talk Time on page 24 of the non-fiction book *Living Things.*

13. Make Literature Links
- Encourage students to look on the Internet or in books such as those listed in Literature Links to find out more about different plants and their parts. Students could present their research to the class.

14. Explore Other "I Wonder ..." Statements
- Return to the "I wonder ..." statements not yet answered and any new wonderings that have come up. With students, plan and set out centres where they can explore these wonderings. Encourage them to make and test predictions.
- Working in groups, students can rotate to all the centres or focus on one per group. They could share their findings in oral, written, or electronic presentations.

6 How Living Things Grow and Change

Time
3–4 hours

Vocabulary
life cycle

Program Resources
PM 1: I Wonder ...
PM 13: Look What I've Learned
LM 20: This Is What I Can Do
Fiction Book: *Moko's Adventures on Earth*
Non-fiction Book: *Living Things*
Lap Book
Traditional Knowledge
Poster: Ways of Observing

Materials and Equipment
- *The Very Hungry Caterpillar* by Eric Carle
- baby and recent photographs
- paper plates
- rulers
- scissors
- glue
- non-fiction books: animal growth

Tip
For Explore 4, students will need a baby photograph and a more recent photograph. Ensure that **LM 1: Parent/ Guardian Letter** has been sent home requesting photocopies, or emailed digital photographs, so they can be cut out.

GOAL

Students will learn about growth and change in animals and plants and will compare the characteristics of plants and animals at different stages of life.

ASSESSMENT CHART

Science Indicators	Assessment Opportunities
LT1.1 a. Use a variety of sources of information and ideas to learn about observable characteristics of living things.	Explain 6
LT1.1 d. Engage in personal, scientific, and Indigenous ways of organizing understanding of living things.	Explore 5
LT1.1 e. Describe characteristics common to humans and identify variations that make each human unique.	Explore 5
LT1.1 j. Compare characteristics of plants and animals at different stages of their lives.	Engage 2 Explore 4, 5 Explain 6
LT1.1 k. Communicate knowledge about the observable characteristics of a favourite plant or animal.	Explain 6
English Language Arts Indicators	**Assessment Opportunities**
CR1.1 b. Make and share connections among texts, prior knowledge, and personal experiences.	Engage 1, 2
CC1.1 e. Use inquiry to explore a question or topic of interest related to the themes and topics being studied.	Explain 6
CC1.2 a. Understand that making pictures, illustrations, and other representations clarify and extend understandings.	Explain 6
CC1.4 d. Write about familiar topics using the learned vocabulary to express ideas.	Explain 6

BACKGROUND INFORMATION

One of the indicators that something is living or "biotic" is its growth, also considered a *life cycle*. For some living things, such as a frog, a tree, or a butterfly, there are significant differences between the stages in their lives. Other living things, such as a human, a horse, or a cat, have similar characteristics throughout all of their life stages and primarily increase in size and ability. Students will not need to understand the specifics of the life cycles of living things, but they should be able to identify the differences and similarities between a living thing at the beginning stage and at maturity.

Traditional Knowledge

First Nations and Métis peoples have always known the importance of cycles in nature. Cycles are a way to understand the natural world. For example, the day is a cycle of sunrise, noon, sunset, and night. The year is a cycle of spring, summer, autumn, and winter. Cycles are very important to First Nations and Métis ways of thinking. By studying the seasonal changes to plant life and the behaviour of animals, First Nations and Métis peoples learn the natural laws of circular interaction. They adapt their lives to those cycles for survival.

The book *The Sacred Tree,* by Phil Lane Jr. et al., presents a First Nations perspective of the Circle of Life and how life cycles are connected to the natural world. This will help you support conversations and questions regarding First Nations' worldviews on life cycles.

ASSESSMENT FOR LEARNING

Look for Evidence of Learning	Student-friendly Learning Targets
Can the student: • identify characteristics of animals and plants at different stages of life? • make logical predictions about how they will look when they grow? • demonstrate understanding of life cycles?	(self-assessment) • I can tell how some animals and plants change during their lives. • I can predict how I will look when I am older. • I can show and explain the life cycle of an animal.

DI DIFFERENTIATING INSTRUCTION

For EAL

Have students work with partners to complete the research activity in Explain 6. This will provide an opportunity for them to discuss and share ideas and find information together. Provide graphic organizers to make it easier for students to record the information they gather.

For Enrichment

Students could research the life cycle of a plant as well as an animal for Explain 6, or add another research page to identify the basic needs of the animal.

For Extra Support

Create a reading centre with a collection of non-fiction books that will support the understanding of the theme of life cycles and stages of growth.

CURRICULUM CONNECTIONS

Students will have the opportunity to develop skills and concepts in the following area:

Arts Education

CP1.7 Investigate a variety of formal and informal patterns in art work and the environment, and apply observations to own work.

CORE LEARNING OPPORTUNITIES

Engage

1. Activate and Build on Prior Knowledge

- Using the Lap Book, direct students' attention to the fiction book *Moko's Adventures on Earth*. Ask students if they remember the different living things they learned about in the book (e.g., squirrels, flowers, robins, grass, and worms). Show them each of the living things.
- Ask students to pretend that they are Max and Molly. What would they tell Moko about how these living things change as they grow? Have students choose one living thing to discuss with a partner and then share their ideas with the class. Remind students that living things grow and change as they age. They go through something called a life cycle. Some living things change a lot as they go through their life cycle.

2. Talk About Life Cycles

- Read the story *The Very Hungry Caterpillar,* by Eric Carle. If the book is not available in your school, there are several versions online.
- Draw students attention to the changes that the caterpillar goes through throughout the story, and how different it looks at the end. Some guiding questions could include:
  - What characteristics have changed?
  - What did the caterpillar need to do to change?
  - Does every animal change like the caterpillar?
  - Does every animal grow and change?
  - How is a caterpillar's life cycle different from a human life cycle?

Note: This book has an incorrect reference to a butterfly emerging from a cocoon. A butterfly emerges from a chrysalis and a moth emerges from a cocoon. You may want to draw this to the attention of the children and discuss how a fiction book may not always have correct information.

Literature Link
The Very Hungry Caterpillar
by Eric Carle

✓ Science Check
Can the student:
- talk about animal life cycles?
- correctly identify the life cycle of an animal?
- correctly pick out characteristics that stay the same or are different during the different stages of growth?

3. Elicit "I Wonder …" Statements

- Model an "I wonder …" form of inquiry with statements such as: "I wonder how many ways humans are the same." or "I wonder if all animals change in the same ways as they grow."
- Invite students to offer other "I wonder …" statements. Record these on a chart or paper strips, and then read them together. Provide students with copies of **PM 1: I Wonder …** to record statements that interest them. Some students may require individual or small group assistance to identify statements and record them.

✓ Literacy Check
Can the student:
- read the "I wonder …" statements in the class list and identify "I wonder …" statements for his or her personal list?
- copy "I wonder …" statements from the class list onto his or her personal list?

Explore

4. Identify the Characteristics of Changes in *Living Things*

Before: Ask students to describe different kinds of trees.

During: Distribute copies of the non-fiction book *Living Things.*

Page 14: Look at the picture of the growing tree and answer the question at the bottom of the page as a class. (e.g., The tree grows taller. The tree grows more needles. The trunk grows wider.) Ask students for examples of how other plants change as they grow.
After: Assist students in responding to the questions on page 15 (e.g., A kitten is smaller; a chick has different feathers).

Science Check
Can the student:
- make logical predictions about how he or she will look at different stages of life?

5. Investigate Changes in Humans

- Show students the Traditional Knowledge poster **Ways of Observing**. Point out how the poster shows an infant, a child, an adult, and an elder. Explain to students that a circle is used by scientists and by many cultures, including Aboriginal peoples in Canada to show life cycles.
- Prior to this lesson, ask students to bring in a photocopy of one of their baby photographs, as well as a copy of a more recent photograph of themself. Hand out a paper plate to each student. Model how to use a ruler to separate the paper plate into four sections. Students then label each section: Baby, Child, Teen, Adult.
- Have students glue their two photos onto the plate and then discuss how they have changed from when they were babies. Ask students to predict how they will be different as teenagers and finally as adults, focusing on physical characteristics.
  - Will they be taller?
  - Will they have different hair?
  - Will their eye colour change?
- Have students draw on their plates to show how they will change.

Explain

Literacy Check
Can the student:
- use the non-fiction resources to search for the needed answers?
- transfer their knowledge onto their activity or written work?

6. Research Animal Life Cycles

- Prior to class, collect non-fiction books about different animals and how they grow so students can compare differences and similarities.
- Ask students to choose an animal to research. Include animals that have common life cycles such as a bear, a dog, or a wolf, and animals that have uncommon life cycles such as a fly, a frog, or a mosquito.
- Tell students they will be doing some research to help them write their own animal book. They will need to look for clues in the books about how this animal changes as it grows. They could also use the Internet to do further research.
- Have students make a picture of the animal they chose at three different stages of growth. Students need to identify the characteristics that are the same and different in each stage of growth.
- Use the following format for the research pages:
  - Page 1: Title page (Draw a picture and write the name of the animal.) The Life Cycle of a ______________.
  - Page 2: This is what a ______________ looks like when it is very young. It is called a ______________.
  - Page 3: This is what a ______________ looks like when it is growing up. It is called a ______________.

- Page 4: This is what a ______________ looks like when it is an adult. It is called a ______________.
- Page 5: Here are things that stay the same as a ________________ is growing.
- Page 6: Here are things that change as a __________ is growing.

- Assemble the pages and make them into a book.
- Have students work in small groups to read each other's books and compare the life cycles of the animals. Ensure that each group compares animals with both similar and different life cycles.

7. Reflect on Learning

- Have students record evidence of their learning on **PM 13: Look What I've Learned**. They can also record in their journal or with a video or audio recording on a smart device or camera. Encourage them to note at least two things they learned about how living things grow and change and something they still wonder about.
- Use **LM 20: This Is What I Can Do** as a self-assessment. Read the learning targets with students and have them respond on their own. Some students may need assistance.

OTHER LEARNING OPPORTUNITIES

Extend: Activity Bank

At any time, choose from the following options to replace or supplement the Core Learning Opportunities to meet students' needs and/or interests.

8. Compare Different Stages of Life

- Show students a video that shows the growth of a living organism. Have them use a Venn diagram to compare the beginning and mature stages of life. They could use **PM 6: A Venn Diagram**.

9. Play an Animal Mix-up Game

- Provide pictures of different animals at different stages of their lives. Mix up the pictures and then have students sort out the different stages of each animal and place them in the correct sequence.

10. Explore Other "I Wonder ..." Statements

- Return to the "I wonder ..." statements not yet answered and any new wonderings that have come up. With students, plan and set out centres where they can explore these wonderings. Encourage them to make and test predictions.
- Working in groups, students can rotate to all the centres or focus on one per group. They could share their findings in oral, written, or electronic presentations.

7 Taking Care of Basic Needs

Time
3–4 hours

Vocabulary
food
shelter
air
water
environment

Program Resources
PM 1: I Wonder ...
PM 13: Look What I've Learned
LM 9: Basic Needs
LM 10: Where Do I Live?
LM 21: Constructed Environments
LM 22: This Is What I Can Do
Non-fiction Book: *Living Things*
Lap Book
Science Poster: Where do I live?

Materials and Equipment
- magazines and fiction books
- letter size white paper
- scissors
- glue
- pencil crayons

GOAL

Students will identify and compare the basic needs and environments of different animals and then identify healthy environments that meet all the animals' basic needs.

ASSESSMENT CHART

Science Indicators	Assessment Opportunities
LT1.2 a. Identify the physical needs (i.e., food, water, air, and shelter) that plants, animals, and humans require for survival.	Engage 1 Explore 3 Explain 6
LT1.2 b. Pose questions about ways in which plants interact with their environments to meet their basic needs.	Engage 2
LT1.2 c. Pose questions about ways in which animals interact with their environments to meet their basic needs.	Engage 2
LT1.2 e. Compare ways in which plants and animals that live within the local environment, and plants and animals that live in other environments, meet their needs for food, water, and shelter.	Explore 4 Explain 6
LT1.2 g. Explore the challenges that plants, animals, and humans encounter when attempting to meet their basic needs in constructed environments.	Explore 4
LT1.2 i. Compare basic human needs to the needs of plants, other animals, and non-living things.	Explore 3, 4
LT1.2 k. Explore how people demonstrate respect for living things by caring for domestic plants and animals.	Explain 5
English Language Arts Indicators	**Assessment Opportunities**
CC1.2 a. Understand that making pictures, illustrations, and other representations clarify and extend understanding.	Explain 7

BACKGROUND INFORMATION

Animals need water, air, food, and shelter to survive. Plants require light, water, air, and nutrients. Plants create their food through the process of photosynthesis. They have a number of different parts that help them survive, reproduce, and grow: leaves, roots, stems, flowers, fruits, and seeds. Animals have many adaptations that help them survive including different body coverings, ability to hear and see, methods of eating, and whether they are nocturnal or diurnal. They also, have many different ways of moving such as crawling, swimming, walking, and flying.

Animals found in nature have to meet all of their basic needs for survival. Domesticated animals have the same needs, but these are satisfied by the people who care for them. The lives of some animals have been changed greatly by the built environment of humans. Many have found ways to survive alongside humans, but others are threatened by these changes.

ASSESSMENT FOR LEARNING

Look for Evidence of Learning	Student-friendly Learning Targets
Can the student: • recall the four basic needs of all living things? • make connections between their daily actions and how those actions meet their needs? • pick out similarities and differences between how different animals meet their basic needs? • make logical connections between constructed environments, the lack of shelter for animals, and the adaptations animals need to survive? • identify examples of how people care for the basic needs of other living things? • create a healthy environment for an animal and identify the basic needs found in the environment?	(self-assessment) • I can talk about the four basic needs of all living things. • I know how I meet my basic needs. • I know animals have different ways of meeting their basic needs. • I know that some environments make it hard for animals and plants to survive. • I know how people can help plants and animals meet their basic needs. • I know what a healthy environment for an animal looks like.

DI DIFFERENTIATING INSTRUCTION

For EAL

Develop picture reference cards of the four basic needs. These cards can be used as identifying symbols that students can place over the environments and habitats for the activities.

For Enrichment

Encourage students to research animals that have unique needs, such as a unique food. What can they learn about the animals from these needs?

For Extra Support

For extra practice, cut up **LM 9: Basic Needs** and have students sort out the needs of all five animals. When making the "Pop-Up Environments" in Explain 7, you may wish to provide students with reference pictures of their animals in the appropriate environment before they draw their own pictures.

CURRICULUM CONNECTIONS

Students will have the opportunity to develop skills and concepts in the following areas:

Social Studies

IN1.3 Assess ways in which relationships help to meet human needs.
DR1.3 Demonstrate awareness of human reliance on the natural environment to meet needs, and how location affects families in meeting needs and wants.

Health

USC1.5 Explore the association between a healthy sense of "self" and one's positive connection with others and the environment.

CORE LEARNING OPPORTUNITIES

Engage

1. Activate and Build on Prior Knowledge

Before: Ask students to recall the four basic needs that have been talked about during this unit. Have them talk to classmates to try to come up with the four needs: air, water, food, and shelter. Have students share their answers and write the correct four terms on the board as they are identified.
During: Read pages 16–20 in the non-fiction book *Living Things.*
Pages 16–17: Read the text and talk about the image. Ask students to answer the question.
Pages 18–19: Repeat the same questioning strategy for the robins and the dandelion on pages 18 and 19. Record students' answers on the board in a web.
Page 20: Turn to page 20 and ask the question: How do you meet your needs? Remind students that they need to answer this question by looking at all four basic needs. Provide a sample answer of how you meet your needs, for example, "I meet my need for water by having a water bottle on my desk."
After: Use a Think-Pair-Share strategy, with students first thinking about the answers for themselves, and then sharing with a partner before they share with the class.

Literacy Check
Can the student:
- read the "I wonder ..." statements in the class list and identify "I wonder ..." statements for his or her personal list?
- copy "I wonder ..." statements from the class list onto his or her personal list?

2. Elicit "I Wonder ..." Statements

- Model an "I wonder ..." form of inquiry with statements such as: "I wonder if humans have the same needs as other animals," or "I wonder how humans help animals meet their needs?"
- Invite students to offer other "I wonder ..." statements. Record these on a chart or paper strips, and then read them together. Provide students with copies of **PM 1: I Wonder ...** to record statements that interest them. Some students may require individual or small group assistance to identify statements and record them.

Explore

Science Check
Can the student:
- recall the four basic needs?
- apply their previous learning to the introduced pictures?

3. Compare Basic Needs

- Hand back the Basic Needs flip cards that were developed in Lesson 2. Each student was given one of five different animals and their needs that had to be sorted.
- Separate students into groups so that there is a student with a flip card for each animal in every group. Have students sit in a circle holding their flip card with the animal name facing outward and the flaps facing the student.
- Have students guess, one at a time, how each animal meets its four basic needs. The student who has that animal will then tell the rest of the group if the answers are correct.
- Ask students to open up all of the flip cards and lay them flat in the middle of the group. Have students suggest other animals that have similar needs to the ones on the flip cards. Use the following questions

to guide this discussion, about all of the animals listed:
- What similarities and differences in the basic needs of these animals do you see?
- Which animals eat the same kind of food or different kinds?
- Which animals have the same kind of water source?
- How do most of the animals get air?
- What are the differences in the shelter of the animals?
- How do these basic needs compare to those of non-living things?
- Have students discuss these answers as a group and then share their ideas with the class. Then ask students how a flip card showing *their* basic needs would look different from the ones they made for the animals. What pictures would show how they meet their needs?

Science Check
Can the student:
- recall the living spaces of the animals on the poster?
- make plausible predictions regarding where the animals could live in the constructed environments?
- understand that not all animals will be able to have their needs met in the constructed environments?

4. Investigate Shelter in Constructed Environments
- Distribute copies of **LM 10: Where Do I Live?** and have students cut out the pictures.
- Display the Science poster **Where do I live?** Ask students for suggestions of where the different cut-out animals could live. Lead them to understand that most of the animals on the poster live in nature, rather than in the house.
- Distribute copies of **LM 21: Constructed Environments**. (You may want to cut or fold **LM 21** in half so students focus on only one environment at a time.)
- Ask students to identify the new environment on the line master, and ask them how the environment on the line master is different from the environment on the poster. Lead students to understand that the difference is that the playground is not natural. It is a constructed environment made by people, and it was not always there. Note that not all photos on the poster are natural environments. Some living things, including the child, will be matched to the house.
- Ask students to try to place the animals in the playground on **LM 21** by finding shelters for the animals. Tell students that not all the animals will find shelter in this new environment.
- When all students have placed their animals, ask them to share where they placed each animal. Ask students questions such as:
  - Would a mouse really live under a slide? Why?
  - What animals cannot find shelter in this new environment?
  - What happens to those animals?
- Repeat this process with the picture of the town on **LM 21**.
- Discuss with students some challenges that trees or plants may have in meeting their needs in the middle of a town. (trees may not have enough room to grow or enough water)
- Ask students what living things live in the playground around the school. What would make it difficult for living things to live in the playground?
  - Do humans have problems meeting their needs in a town?
  - Where do humans get food and water in a town?
  - Where does food in stores come from?
  - What kind of shelter do they live in?
  - Where do they get air?

Explain

Science Check
Can the student:
- identify examples of how they care for the basic needs of other living things?

5. Help Living Things Meet Their Basic Needs

Before: Ask students where animals living in nature get food and water. Then ask them where pets get food and water.
During: Show students page 21 in the non-fiction book *Living Things*. Focus on one photo at a time and ask students to identify what the human in the photo is doing. What basic need is that action helping a living thing meet?
After: Ask students for other ways that they can help living things meet their basic needs. Generate a list on the board of the different ways people can help animals and plants. Have students choose one item from the board, draw a picture of themselves doing that task, and add the following sentence frame to complete.
"I can help __________ meet their need for ________ by __________."

Science Check
Can the student:
- create a realistic environment for an animal?
- identify how the animal meets its basic needs?
- provide examples of how the environment meets the needs of the animal?

6. Make a Healthy Environment for an Animal

- Ask students to choose a picture of one animal that they have learned about in this unit. This picture should be about 6–8 cm high. Provide a list of animals for them to choose from ensuring that half of the animals are local and half of the animals are not. Encourage students to each choose a different animal so that they can compare how different animals meet their needs for food, water, and shelter.
- When all students have chosen one animal, ask them to think about what a healthy environment looks like for that animal. Students may need to research using the resource centre or the Internet to get a good visual of an environment. Be sure students can identify how each animal meets its needs for survival.
- Have students make a "Pop-up Environment" by first folding a piece of letter-size paper widthwise.
- On the inside top half of the folded paper, ask students to draw and colour the healthy environment for their animal that shows the ways their animal meets its four basic needs. The bottom of the picture should be at the crease of the fold.
- After the environment is coloured, demonstrate how to refold the page so the picture is on the inside and cut two 4 cm tabs into the crease toward the middle of the piece of paper. These tabs should be about 3 cm apart from each other.
- Open the paper up again and push the cut tab into the folded piece of paper so that it folds out on top of the drawn environment.
- Have students glue their animal onto the tab so it sticks out from the background. Add a piece of construction paper or cardstock to the back of the paper for stability.
- On the bottom of the piece of paper have students write about their animal's environment using the following sentence frame:
  This is a healthy environment for a __________________.
  It needs ____________________ to survive.
- Provide time for students to share their pop-up environments with classmates and compare how the different animals meet their need for food, water, and shelter in different ways.

7. Reflect on Learning

- Have students record evidence of their learning on **PM 13: Look What I've Learned**. They can also record in their journal or with a video or audio recording on a smart device or camera. Encourage them to note at least two things they learned about taking care of basic needs and something they still wonder about.
- Use **LM 22: This Is What I Can Do** as a self-assessment. Read the learning targets with students and have them respond on their own. Some students may need assistance.

OTHER LEARNING OPPORTUNITIES

Literature Links
The Lorax by Dr. Seuss
Memoirs of a Goldfish by Devin Scillian
Franklin Wants a Pet by Paulette Bourgeois
Diary of a Worm by Doreen Cronin
Children Make Terrible Pets by Peter Brown

Extend: Activity Bank

At any time, choose from the following options to replace or supplement the Core Learning Opportunities to meet students' needs and/or interests.

8. Watch a Video

- Select a video about how an endangered species has lost its environment and how that has affected its ability to meet its basic needs. Provide an opportunity for students to share ideas about the video after viewing it.

9. Observe a Classroom Pet

- Read one or two of the books from the Literature Links, such as *Memoirs of a Goldfish.* Discuss the needs of different types of pets, and which animals would make good classroom pets.
- Students can make observations about how their pets at home meet their basic needs and report their findings back to the class.

10. Respond to Talk Time

- Choose activities and discussion questions from Talk Time on page 24 of the non-fiction book *Living Things* or page 16 of the fiction book *Moko's Adventures on Earth* that students have not engaged in or responded to throughout the unit.

11. Explore Other "I Wonder ..." Statements

- Return to the "I wonder ..." statements not yet answered and any new wonderings that have come up. With students, plan and set out centres where they can explore these wonderings. Encourage them to make and test predictions.
- Working in groups, students can rotate to all the centres or focus on one per group. They could share their findings in oral, written, or electronic presentations.

UNIT 1

Unit Closer: Putting It All Together

Time
2–3 hours

Program Resources
PM 4 Finding Out
LM 2: Learning Targets
LM 5: Plant Predictions
LM 6: Plant Check-Up
LM 23: Rate Your Learning
LM 24: Exhibit Inquiry
Fiction Book: *Moko's Adventures on Earth*
Non-fiction Book: *Living Things*
Lap Books
PM 9: I Found Out

Materials and Equipment
- videos and pictures of museum exhibits

Looking Back

1. Consider the Learning Targets

- Display the learning targets that were introduced in the Unit Opener on a chart or screen. Explain that these are the big ideas about the needs and characteristics of living things.
- Read the learning targets aloud. Stop after each one to ask students to provide explanations and examples to illustrate the learning target.
- Ask students to think about how well they can do the things on the list. Use a Think Aloud strategy and a copy of **LM 23: Rate Your Learning** to model how students should rate themselves.
- Distribute copies of **LM 23** for students to complete as you read each of the learning targets. Some students may be able to read and complete it on their own.

2. Reread the Fiction Book *Moko's Adventures on Earth*

Before: Ask students to summarize some of the new things that Moko learned about Earth. Would they make the same mistakes as Moko? Why or why not?
During: Separate students into groups and distribute copies of the book. Have students read the book as a group for enjoyment. You may want to have the groups read the book as a reader's theatre and assign character and narrator roles to students.
After: Have students share some of the new things they have learned throughout this unit that they could teach Moko. Students could make cartoon strips that show Moko making a classification mistake and then the student correcting the mistake for Moko.

Literacy Check
Can the student:
- recall and define vocabulary words that were used throughout the unit?
- reflect on his or her "I wonder ..." statements and give answers that show understanding of the outcomes?
- critically reflect on his or her learning by rating their knowledge?

3. Identify New Vocabulary

- First, make a list of the unit vocabulary words on the board and ask students to privately rate, on paper, how well they know each word. They could rate the words on a four-point scale such as the following:
  (1) I don't know the word;
  (2) I remember the word from a lesson;
  (3) I can tell you what the word means;
  (4) I can teach what that word means to another student.
- Make a class word collage of all the new vocabulary words. Before you do this, compile the student votes to find out how the majority rated each vocabulary word, and then use that rating to decide how big the word will be presented on the collage (size 1, 2, 3 or 4 with the words rated 1 being the biggest).
- If possible use the website http://www.wordle.net/ to make a wordle for the class using the same rating criteria as above to determine the size of the words.
- Review the smallest words, to help students build understanding.

4. Consider "I Wonder ..." Statements

- Ask students to think back to the things they have wondered about throughout the unit. Review students' copies of "I wonder ..." statements. Have them pick one important wondering that has been answered and tell a partner about it.
- Students can record their statement and what they learned about it on **PM 9: I Found Out**.
- Ask students to think about other "I wonder ..." statements that they would ask now that they know more about the characteristics of living things. Record their questions, and, if time permits, review the Skills poster **Finding Out** and, with students, plan an exploration that follows the inquiry steps. Set up the inquiry for students to experience in small groups at a centre. Provide copies of **PM 4: Finding Out** for students to complete as a group while following the steps.

5. Reread the Non-fiction Book *Living Things*

Before: Show students the non-fiction book Living Things. Ask them whether they like reading fiction books or non-fiction books. What are non-fiction books good for? What are fiction books good for?

During: Hand out copies of Living Things to small groups and have them read through the book together.

After: Do the activity on pages 22-23.

Pages 22–23: In this activity, students will transplant the plant to a pot of soil. If the class did not start the growth process at the beginning of the unit, then have students plant the seeds as directed in the book and complete **LM 5: Plant Predictions** at this time.

- If students are starting this project from previously grown plants, have them refer back to **LM 6: Plant Check-Up**.
- Ask students to describe how their plant looks now compared to their predictions made in Lesson 5. Review with students the four basic needs of the plant and have them identify the characteristics of the plant that help it meet its basic needs.
- Have students gently take the plant out of the baggie and lay it on a piece of paper. Remind them that the plant is a living thing that should be respected.
- Using the directions on page 23 of *Living Things*, have students transplant their plant into the soil. Ask students to continue to collect data on their plant when they take it home by drawing a weekly picture of the plant's characteristics.

Tip
When transplanting the plant, start with a half cup of soil and have students make a larger hole in the soil to compensate for the roots. Add soil to bury the roots instead of pushing the roots into the soil to prevent damage to the roots.

Science Check
Can the student:
- listen and read the directions on how to properly transplant their plant?
- assess and modify their predictions about how the plant grew?
- identify the basic needs of the plant?
- measure the plant growth and transfer that data onto a bar graph?
- maintain a journal of the plants progress at home?

Going Further

6. Develop a Living Things Museum

Introduction

- Tell students that they will be developing group exhibits for a museum. Look at videos and pictures of museum exhibits, or go on a class trip to a museum to show students what an exhibit is and how it is used to explain an idea. In general, an exhibit explains an overall concept using pictures, models, words, and usually some kind of hands-on activity.

Tip
The exhibit suggestions on LM 24 have been written for teacher or adult use. If these examples are going to be given to students, consider editing them for the appropriate reading level.

Literacy Check
Can the student:
- use resources to find the answers to their inquiry statement?
- read and comprehend the guiding questions on PM 3 and PM 4?
- express their knowledge in oral, written, and picture formats for their exhibit presentation?

Preparation

- Ask students to look at their "I wonder ..." statements from the unit and circle some of the statements that they want to learn more about. You can group students with partners according to which statements they are interested in learning more about, or you may want to select statements that will suit the needs of students according to ability and resources.
- The "I wonder ..." statements that are chosen for the exhibit should be broad enough for a demonstration or activity and address a specific indicator from the unit. Consider using the sample statements listed in **LM 24: Exhibit Inquiry** for students who may need extra support.
- Tell students that they will need four different parts in their exhibit, including coloured pictures, a 3-D model or diagram, a write-up of their inquiry, and a hands-on experiment or demonstration that answers their exhibit's inquiry statement. Use **PM 4: Finding Out** as a jumping off point for the inquiry. Ensure that students have an understanding of their "I wonder ..." statement, a prediction, and a plan for finding out the answer. Provide additional support to students as needed.
- Students will need sufficient time to do research using online resources, the library, and the materials and information from this unit.
- The experiments will likely have to be done at home and brought to school as a completed experiment.
- Have students develop a script for presenting their exhibit and rehearse before the presentation.

Science Check
Can the student:
- successfully articulate their inquiry project?
- recall and discuss their research?
- provide unprepared answers to questions about their inquiry project?

Presentation

- Invite parents and other classes to visit your "museum." Consider developing guiding questions for the visitors that reflect students' learning and having students develop handouts that clearly explain their exhibits. Direct students to give the handouts to people viewing the exhibits. Tell students to be prepared to answer questions from visitors.

Evaluation

- Have students develop a collaborative classroom evaluation to be used to evaluate their exhibits as a class. Focus their attention on what they think the important parts of their exhibits are and what a good exhibit or presentation would look like. Collect their ideas to make a rubric for evaluation. Ask an older class/buddy class to participate in peer evaluation by using the rubric as they go through the exhibits and listen to the student presentations.

UNIT 1 NEEDS AND CHARACTERISTICS OF LIVING THINGS

Table of Contents

Name:______________________________________

Parent/Guardian Letter

Date: ______________________________

Dear Parent/Guardian:

During the Science unit Needs and Characteristics of Living Things, we will be examining the characteristics of plants and animals; how they grow and change; and how they meet their needs for air, food, water, and shelter.

During one of the activities, the children will be exploring how they have personally grown and changed from the time they were babies. They will also predict how they might change in the future.

To help us with these activities, please send in a baby photograph and a more recent photograph of your child that can be cut up. You can send photocopies or printed copies, or email digital photographs. If none of these options is possible, and you would like the photos returned, please let us know so that we can copy them and return the original. If you do not have a baby photograph, we can use two photographs taken one or two years apart.

Thank you for helping your child make concrete connections to his or her learning.

Please send photographs by ____________________________________.

Teacher's Name: ______________________________

Name:____________________________________

Learning Targets

Put a check mark to show what you can do.

☐	I can identify if something is living or non-living.
☐	I can group living things by characteristics I can see.
☐	I can describe some ways that plants, animals, and humans are the same and different.
☐	I know the basic needs that all living things need to survive.
☐	I can describe how animals look and act differently because of their needs.
☐	I can tell how some plants and animals survive in different environments.
☐	I can help a living plant grow.

Name:______________________________

This Is What I Can Do

Put a check mark to show what you can do.

☐	I can identify whether something is living or non-living.
☐	I know that in the worldview of some First Nations and Métis peoples, everything has Spirit and is living.
☐	I can find information in different places and organize it.
☐	I know the basic needs that animals and plants need to survive.
☐	I can be careful around animals and plants to protect them and myself.

Put a  beside what you do best.

Put a blue  beside the one you need to practise.

Name:______________________________

My Basic Needs

I need ______________________. This means I need ______________.	I need ______________________. This means I need ______________.
I need ______________________. This means I need ______________.	I need ______________________. This means I need ______________.

Name:____________________________________

Plant Predictions

What do you think the seed will look like in one day, one week, and one month? Draw a picture or write a sentence to record your predictions.

one day	one week	one month

Circle what the seed  will need to survive:

Name:____

Plant Check-up

Part 1: Describe the plant. Use words or pictures.

in one day	in one week	in one month

Colour one watering can every time the plant gets water. How many times did you water it?

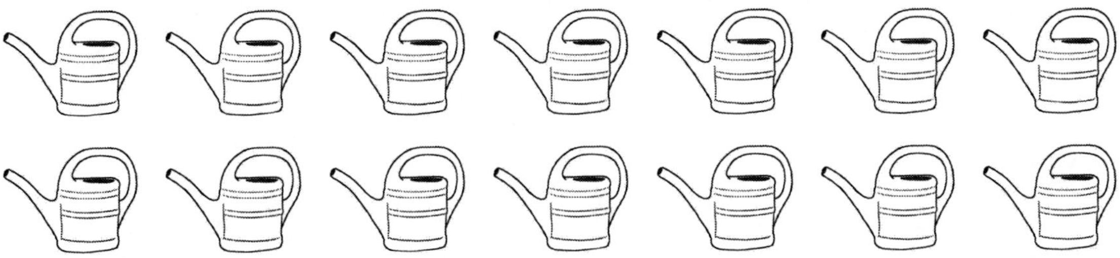

Part 2:

What does the plant look like now?	What do you think the plant will look like in one month?

Name:______________________________________

Living Things

Cut out the pictures and make cards with them.

pig

salmon

gopher

tree

mosquito

frog

rabbit

cardinal

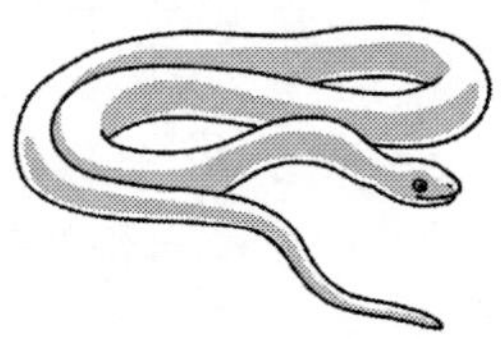

snake

sunflower

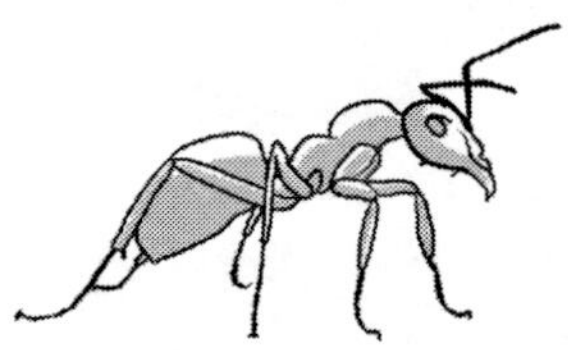

ant

dragonfly

Name:______________________________

Non-Living Things

Cut out the pictures and make cards with them.

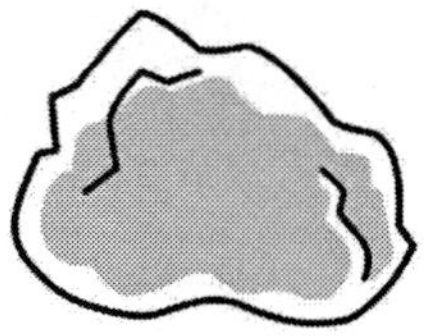
rock

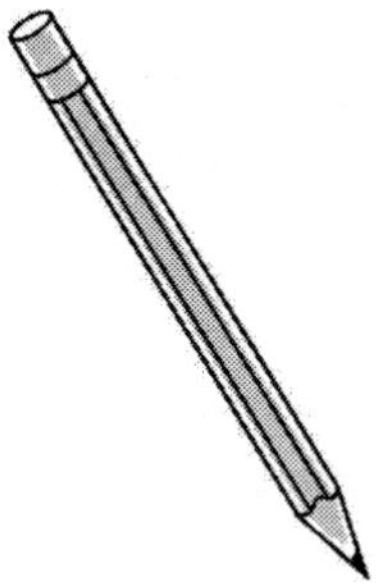
pencil

water

sunglasses

rubber duck

baseball

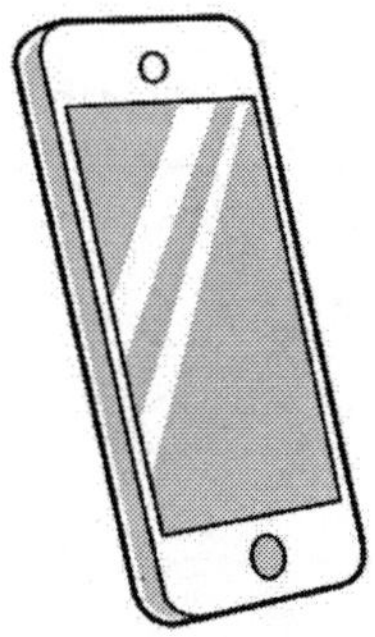
cell phone

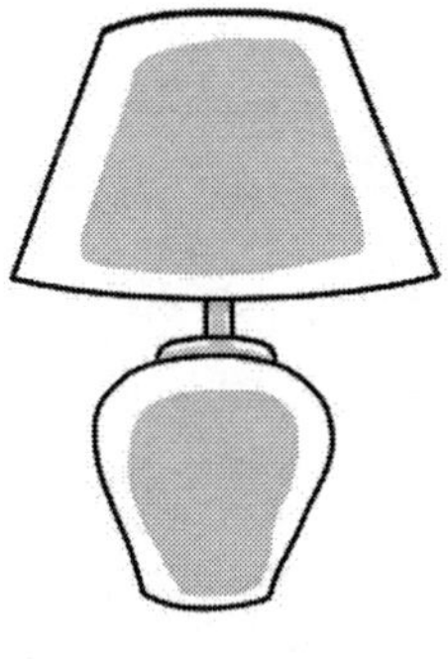
lamp

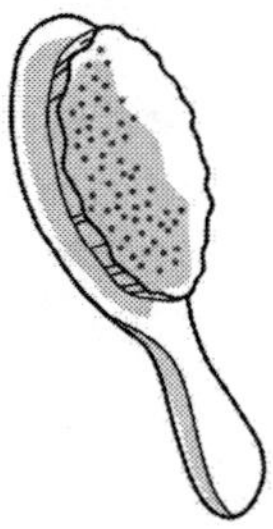
hairbrush

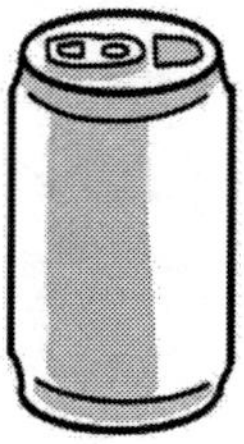
drink can

house

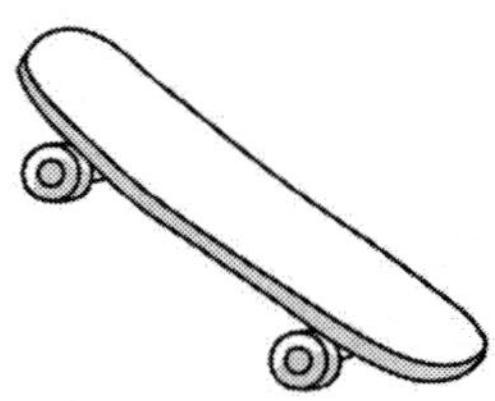
skateboard

Name:________________________________

Basic Needs

Shelter	Water	Food	Air
Robin			
		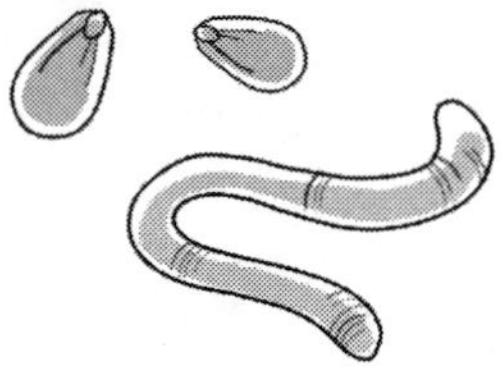	
Rabbit			
	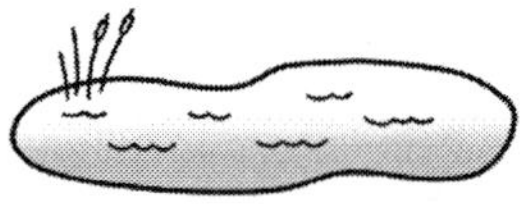		
Frog			
		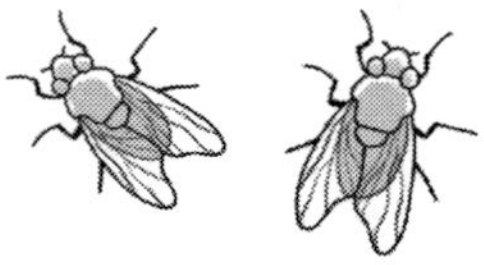	
Fish			
	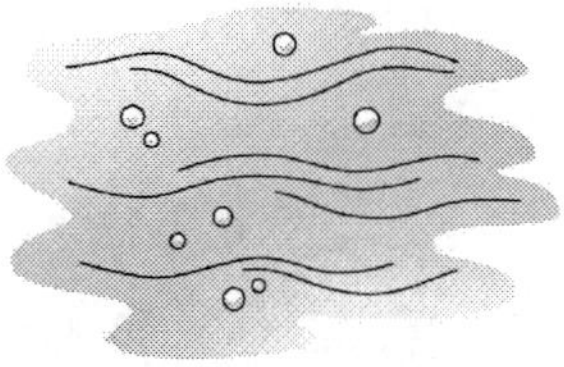	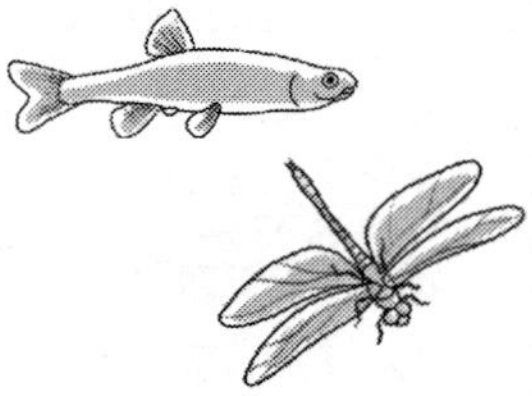	
Bee			
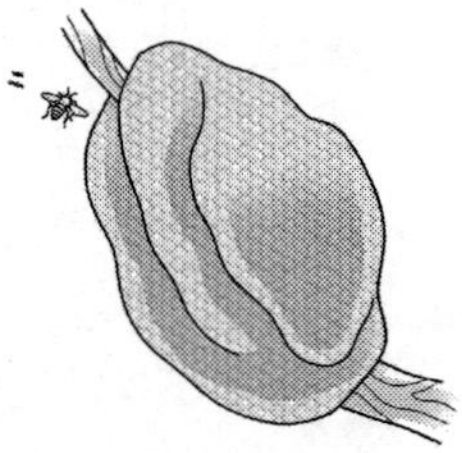			

Name:____

Where Do I Live?

Place the living things on their shelters on the Science poster: Where do I live?

black-eyed Susan

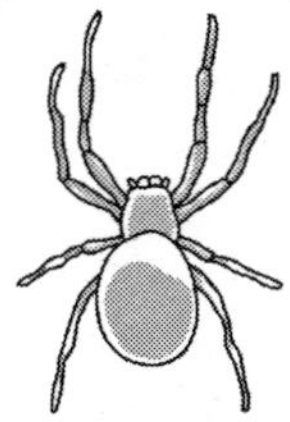

spider

human

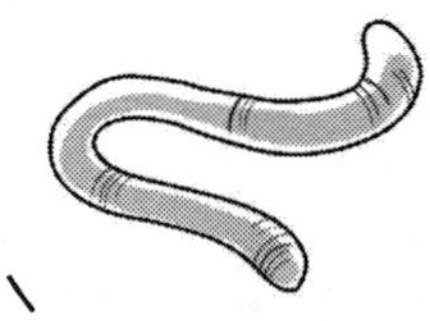

earthworm

budgie

frog

deer

snake

mouse

cat

violet

fox

hawk

rabbit

Name:______________________________

This Is What I Can Do

Put a check mark to show what you can do.

☐	I can describe how some plants and animals meet their basic needs.
☐	I can describe how I meet my basic needs.
☐	I can be careful around animals and plants to protect them.
☐	I can predict, observe, and record the growth of a plant.
☐	I can sort things into the groups of Living and Non-Living.
☐	I can describe where some animals find shelter.

Put a ☺ beside what you do best.

Put a blue ? beside the one you need to practise.

Name:______________________________

Fish Observations

A. Watch the fish for a few minutes.

Draw the fish. Label the body parts: eye, mouth, fin, tail, and gill.

B. Look at the fish's eyes.

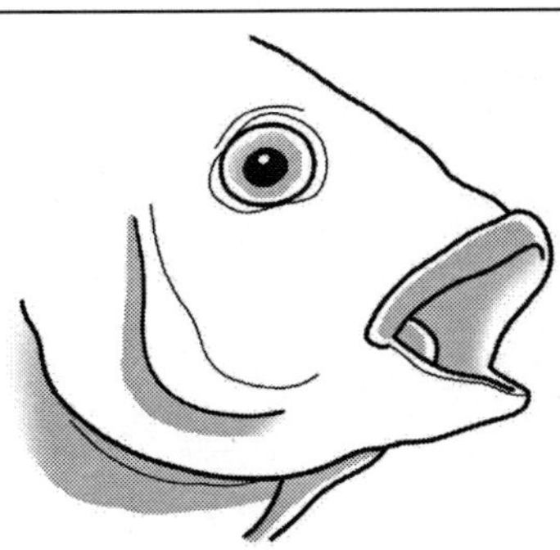

How are the fish's eyes the same as your eyes?
How are they different?

____

____

____

C. Look at how the fish moves.

<table>
<tr><td>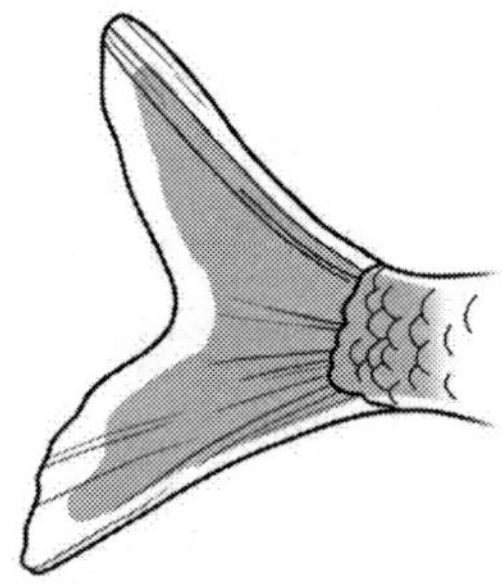</td><td>What body parts does the fish use to move?
____
____
______________________________</td></tr>
</table>

D. Draw a picture of how the fish eats.

What kind of food do you think a fish in a lake eats?

____

Name:__________________________________

This Is What I Can Do

Put a check mark to show what you can do.

☐	I can observe characteristics of animals and plants.
☐	I can observe characteristics of humans that are different.
☐	I can sort animals based on different characteristics.
☐	I can identify some characteristics of fish.
☐	I can carefully observe living animals so I do not hurt them.
☐	I can describe how different animals move because of their characteristics.

Put a  beside what you do best.

Put a blue  beside the one you need to practise.

Name:________________________________

Matching Bird Beaks

Tools

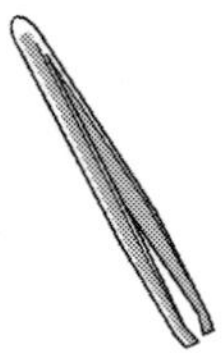				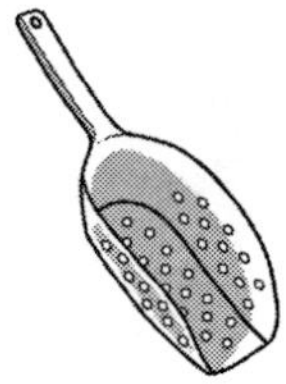	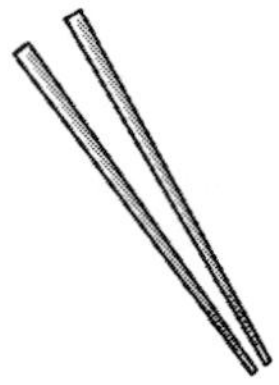	
tweezers	pliers	strainer	straw	scoop	chopsticks	scissors

Bird Beaks

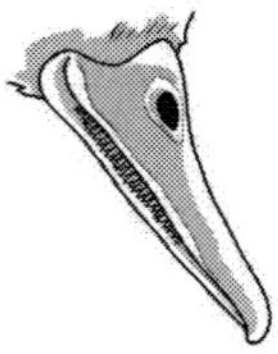	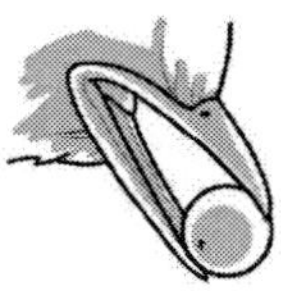	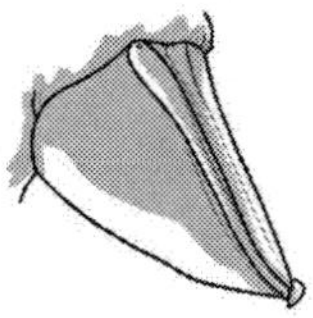	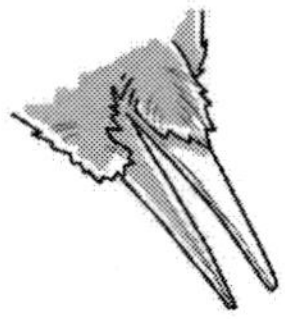			
duck	robin	pelican	woodpecker	sparrow	eagle	hummingbird

Finish the sentences. Circle the tool that is like the bird's beak.
What kind of food do you think each bird eats? Write your idea in the blank.

A hummingbird has a beak like (**a straw, tweezers**). Food? __________________

A sparrow has a beak like (**a scoop, pliers**). Food? __________________

A robin has a beak like (**a strainer, chopsticks**). Food? __________________

A woodpecker has a beak like (**tweezers, pliers**). Food? __________________

A pelican has a beak like (**scissors, a scoop**). Food? __________________

A duck has a beak like (**a strainer, a straw**). Food? __________________

An eagle has a beak like (**scissors, chopsticks**). Food? __________________

Name:____________________________________

My Animal Trading Card

My animal is: ____

It lives in ______________________________

____

It looks like ____________________________

____

____

It eats _________________________________

____

____

____

Something interesting about my animal is that it ____________________________________

____

This is special because it helps my animal survive by ________________________________

____

____

____

Name:____________________________________

This Is What I Can Do

Put a check mark to show what you can do.

☐	I can identify the four basic needs of animals.
☐	I can describe how some animals look and act.
☐	I can describe how the way some animals look helps them get their needs.
☐	I can describe how some animals act in ways that help them get their needs.
☐	I can identify when books have animals that have characteristics that animals really don't have.

Put a ☺ beside what you do best.

Put a blue ? beside the one you need to practise.

Name:____________________________________

Plant Labels

Cut out the words from each section and use them as labels.

Section 1: Plant Parts

stem	leaf	root	flower

Section 2: Plant Needs

sun	water	air

Section 3: Plant Functions

Collects sunlight

Gets water from the soil

Moves water and food up and down the plant

Makes pollen

Name:____________________________________

Focus on Plants

A. Label the diagram of the tree.

Parts of the Tree
leaves
roots
stem

B. Use the pictures on page 13 of *Living Things* to finish each sentence. Use the word bank.

Word Bank
stems
leaves
flowers
roots

A sunflower and a fern have similar __________________.

A birch tree and a spruce tree have similar __________________.

A __________________ and a __________________ have similar __________________.

A tulip and a dogwood have different __________________.

A cactus and a birch tree have different __________________.

A __________________ and a __________________ have different __________________.

Name:______________________________________

This Is What I Can Do

Put a check mark to show what you can do.

☐	I can describe the different characteristics of plants and animals.
☐	I can compare different plants by how they look.
☐	I can tell how some plants get their basic needs to help them to survive.
☐	I can make a diagram of a plant at different times in its life.
☐	I can make predictions about how a plant will grow. I record what I see using pictures, words, and charts.
☐	I can show respect for a plant by taking care of it.
☐	I can get information about living things from books, videos, and the Internet.

Put a  beside what you do best.

Put a blue  beside the one you need to practise.

Name:____

This Is What I Can Do

Put a check mark to show what you can do.

☐	I can tell how animals look different or the same at different times in their life cycles.
☐	I can tell how plants look different or the same at different times in their life cycles.
☐	I can predict how I will look at different times in my life cycle.
☐	I can find information in different places.
☐	I can describe the life cycle of an animal that I researched.

Put a  beside what you do best.

Put a blue  beside the one you need to practise.

Name:______________________________

Constructed Environments

People built these environments.

Where can plants and animals live in these environments?

Name:____________________________________

This Is What I Can Do

Put a check mark to show what you can do.

☐	I can identify the four basic needs of living things.
☐	I can describe how some animals get their basic needs.
☐	I can describe how some plants get their basic needs.
☐	I can tell how plants and animals live in places built by people.
☐	I can describe how humans can help animals and plants get their basic needs.
☐	I can make a healthy environment for an animal.

Put a  beside what you do best.

Put a blue  beside the one you need to practise.

Name:________________________________

Rate Your Learning

Circle the number that tells about you.

1 means I can do it very well.

2 means I can do it, but I need some practice.

3 means I need a lot more practice.

1	2	3	I can tell if something is living or non-living.
1	2	3	I can group living things by how they look.
1	2	3	I can describe some ways that plants, animals, and humans are the same and different.
1	2	3	I know the basic needs that all living things need to survive.
1	2	3	I can describe how animals look and act differently because of their needs.
1	2	3	I can tell how some plants and animals survive in different environments.
1	2	3	I can help a living plant grow.

Name:________________________________

Exhibit Inquiry

These cue cards have been written for teacher or adult reference. They provide some exhibit ideas, but you or your students may have other ideas.

I wonder what happens if a plant does not get air, water, or sunlight.

Research: Find out what happens to a plant if it does not get air, water, or sunlight.

Picture: Draw a diagram of the plant. Label the parts of the plant and their functions.

Activity: Grow a plant without air or water or sunlight for one week only.

Air – put a clear plastic bag over the plant
Water – do not water the plant for one week
Sunlight – put the plant in a box so that it does not get light

I wonder how the environment changes how animals live.

Research: How is the environment of a local animal changing? How does the changing environment change how the animal lives?

Pictures: Draw a picture of a healthy environment for the animal and a picture of an unhealthy environment for the animal.

Activity: Make a 3-D model of a healthy environment for the animal.

I wonder how plants get water.

Research: How plants get water.

Pictures: Draw a picture to show how a plant gets water.

Activity: Show that plants take in water using coloured water and a lettuce leaf or white carnation.

I wonder how animals change as they grow.

Research: The life cycle of a butterfly, a frog, or a bird

Pictures: Draw pictures of the life cycle of a butterfly, bird, or frog

Activity: Research how the animal changes at different times in its life cycle and how it gets its basic needs: air, water, food, shelter. Make a poster or a model showing the life cycle and how the animal gets its needs at the different times.

UNIT 2 USING OBJECTS AND MATERIALS

Table of Contents

Unit Indicators Correlation Chart — Using Objects and Materials*	
Indicator	**Assessment Opportunities**
By the end of grade 1, students will be able to:	
OM1.1 Investigate observable characteristics and uses of natural and constructed objects and materials in their environment	
a. Pose questions about characteristics and uses of common materials.	Lesson 1: 2 Lesson 3: 4, 6
b. Distinguish between objects and materials found in nature and those constructed by humans.	Lesson 2: 1, 3
c. Observe natural and constructed objects and materials in their environment in a safe and respectful manner using all their senses as well as technologies, such as hand lenses, cameras, and microphones, which enhance the senses.	Lesson 2: 3, 4
d. Record relevant observations about common objects and materials using written language, pictures, and tables.	Lesson 1: 4, 5, 7
e. Compare the properties (e.g., texture, colour, smell, hardness, and lustre) of materials that appear in familiar natural (e.g., tree, lawn, rock, and creek) and constructed (e.g., clothing, toys, electronics, furniture, and buildings) objects.	Lesson 2: 4
f. Distinguish between the materials used to construct an object and the object itself.	Lesson 2: 6, 7 Lesson 3: 1, 3, 5, 6
g. Predict the characteristics (e.g., hardness, insulating ability, water resistance, absorbency, and flexibility) of common materials and carry out a procedure to test those predictions.	Lesson 3: 4, 5, 6 Lesson 4: 3
h. Explain why the characteristics of materials help to determine their usefulness within different objects.	Lesson 2: 7 Lesson 3: 1, 6
i. Evaluate the suitability of materials for a specific function.	Lesson 2: 7 Lesson 3: 6 Lesson 4: 1, 4
j. Sequence or group materials and objects according to one or more properties such as texture, colour, smell, hardness, and lustre.	Lesson 3: 3, 5
k. Analyze how common objects and materials are depicted in texts, pictures, and videos.	Lesson 1: 1, 5
l. Suggest alternative uses for common objects and materials.	Lesson 1: 3, 5
m. Generate conclusions about the properties and uses of materials based on personal observations and investigations.	Lesson 1: 4 Lesson 3: 6

Indicator	Assessment Opportunities
OM1.2 Examine methods of altering and combining materials to create objects that meet student- and/or teacher-specified criteria	
a. Select and use materials to carry out explorations of altering materials to change their appearance, texture, sound, smell, or taste (e.g., sanding, painting, or waxing a piece of wood, mixing two or more paints to obtain a particular shade or colour, popping popcorn, shaping clay, drying meat, tuning an instrument, and cooking food at different temperatures) to change the way they are used.	Lesson 4: 3, 7, 8
b. Assess how altering the smell, taste, appearance, texture, or sound of materials may change the way they may be used.	Lesson 4: 7, 8
c. Examine methods (e.g., gluing, stapling, taping, and buttoning) of joining materials of the same and different types.	Lesson 5: 1, 5
d. Use appropriate tools (e.g., glue, scissors, and stapler) correctly and safely for manipulating and observing materials and when constructing useful objects.	Lesson 4: 6, 7 Lesson 5: 5
e. Follow a simple procedure to make a useful object from recyclable materials (e.g., picture frame from old puzzles, holiday ornament from juice can lid, and musical instrument from tissue rolls).	Lesson 4: 6, 7 Lesson 5: 5
f. Design and construct a useful object that meets a student specified function by selecting, combining, joining, and/or altering materials.	Lesson 5: 5 Unit Closer: 6
g. Evaluate, using student-identified criteria, personally constructed objects with respect to their suitability for a particular function.	Lesson 4: 8 Lesson 5: 5
h. Communicate procedures and results of their design and construction process using drawings, demonstrations, and written and oral descriptions.	Lesson 5: 5, 6
i. Describe and demonstrate ways to use materials appropriately and efficiently to the benefit of themselves, others, and the environment (e.g., select the amount and kind of materials that are appropriate to a given task, recognize and demonstrate appropriate reuse of materials in daily activities).	Lesson 4: 1, 3, 6

* Indicators are met in multiple lessons, but this correlation only identifies lessons in which the indictors are focused on.

Unit Planning Chart — Using Objects and Materials

Lesson and Time*	Activities	Program Resources	Materials and Equipment*
Unit Opener: Getting Started 1 hour	**Introduce the Unit:** 1. Set Up an Ongoing Bulletin Board Display **Introduce the Books:** 2. Motivate Using the Fiction Book *A-Maze!* 3. View the Non-fiction Book *Objects Everywhere* 4. Introduce the Science Poster: How is it being changed? **Introduce the Learning Targets:** 5. Post the Student-friendly Learning Targets	PM 1: I Wonder ... LM 1: Learning Targets Fiction Book: *A-Maze!* Non-fiction Book: *Objects Everywhere* Lap Book Science Poster: How is it being changed?	• 10–20 common objects with an easily identified purpose, such as scissors, pencils, staples, paper clips, buttons, tape, etc.
1: Objects and Their Use 2–3 hours	**Engage:** 1. Activate and Build on Prior Knowledge 2. Elicit "I Wonder ..." Statements **Explore:** 3. Determine Purposes for Objects 4. Go on a Scavenger Hunt **Explain:** 5. Read and Respond to the Non-fiction Book *Objects Everywhere* 6. Discuss Which Objects to Use and Why 7. Make A Venn Diagram 8. Invite an Elder to Show Traditional Materials and Their Uses 9. Reflect on Learning **Extend:** 10. Think of Creative Uses for Objects 11. Create an Ad to Sell an Object	PM 1: I Wonder ... PM 5: Make a T-chart PM 6: A Venn Diagram PM 13: Look What I've Learned LM 2: This Is What I Can Do LM 3: Scavenger Hunt Non-fiction Book: *Objects Everywhere* Lap Book Science Poster: How is it being changed? Skills Poster: Communicating and Teamwork	• 10–20 small classroom objects (e.g., a pencil, scissors, paper clips) • 2 hula hoops • objects used for writing
2: Similarities and Differences 2–3 hours	**Engage:** 1. Activate and Build on Prior Knowledge 2. Elicit "I Wonder ..." Statements **Explore:** 3. Sort Natural and Constructed Objects 4. Inspect and Compare Materials 5. Continue to Explore the Fiction Book *A-Maze!* **Explain:** 6. Read and Respond to the Non-fiction Book *Objects Everywhere* 7. Explore Materials 8. Reflect on Learning **Extend:** 9. Respond to the Book *Pinocchio* 10. Match Objects and Materials 11. Explore Other "I Wonder ... " Statements 12. Conduct an Interview	PM 1: I Wonder ... PM 5: Make a T-chart PM 7: Make a Bar Graph PM 13: Look What I've Learned LM 4: This Is What I Can Do LM 5: Same and Different LM 6: Objects and Materials Fiction Book: *A-Maze!* Non-fiction Book: *Objects Everywhere* Lap Book Science Poster: How is it being changed? Traditional Knowledge Poster: How are they made? Skills Poster: Observing and Recording	• 10–20 familiar objects with a variety of uses and materials • containers with natural and constructed objects (e.g., chalk, pencil, leaf) • samples of materials (wood, cloth, plastic, metal, glass) • objects used at school (e.g., scissors, pencils, staples, building blocks)
3: Compare and Contrast Objects and Materials 2–3 hours	**Engage:** 1. Activate and Build on Prior Knowledge 2. Elicit "I Wonder ..." Statements **Explore:** 3. Sort Materials 4. Use Scientific Inquiry **Explain:** 5. Read and Respond to the Non-fiction Book *Objects Everywhere* 6. Return to "Use Scientific Inquiry" 7. Reflect on Learning **Extend:** 8. Make a Literature Link 9. Play I Spy 10. Make A Venn Diagram 11. Make an Ice Cube's Jacket 12. Explore Other "I Wonder ..." Statements 13. Respond to Talk Time	PM 1: I Wonder ... PM 2: Let's Predict PM 13: Look What I've Learned LM 6: Objects and Materials LM 7: This Is What I Can Do LM 8: Objects and Materials Hunt Non-fiction Book: *Objects Everywhere* Lap Book Science Poster: How is it being changed? Skills Poster: Finding Out	• pictures of different types of chairs • 10–20 classroom objects that can be sorted by material type • 4 materials to test for absorbency • container

Lesson and Time*	Activities	Program Resources	Materials and Equipment*
4: Wise Use of Materials 2–3 hours	**Engage:** 1. Activate and Build on Prior Knowledge 2. Elicit "I Wonder ..." Statements **Explore:** 3. Plan a Fair Test for Absorbency 4. Think About Footwear **Explain:** 5. Read and Respond to the Non-fiction Book *Objects Everywhere* 6. Use Materials Wisely 7. Make Plans for Reusing Materials 8. Changing Objects to Reuse Them 9. Reflect on Learning **Extend:** 10. Make "We Care" Posters 11. Explore Other "I Wonder ..." Statements 12. Use Your Imagination 13. Respond to Talk Time	PM 1: I Wonder ... PM 2: Let's Predict PM 3: A Fair Test PM 5: Make a T-chart PM 6: A Venn Diagram PM 13: Look What I've Learned LM 9: This Is What I Can Do Non-fiction Book: *Objects Everywhere* Traditional Knowledge Poster: How are they made?	• piece of wood, water, glitter, paper, paper towel • different materials to test for absorbency, such as tinfoil, waxed paper, sponges, fabric, cardboard, newspaper • different kinds of sponges, paper towel, facial tissue paper, dishcloth/washcloth • 3 pairs of shoes of different material, such as leather runners, rubber boots, foam flip-flops • reused or recycled materials • old and broken crayon bits • mini muffin baking tray
5: Combine, Join, and Create 2–3 hours	**Engage:** 1. Activate and Build on Prior Knowledge 2. Elicit "I Wonder ..." Statements **Explore:** 3. Sort Joining Materials 4. Continue to Explore the Fiction Book *A-Maze!* **Explain:** 5. Read and Respond to the Non-fiction Book *Objects Everywhere* 6. Compare Joining Methods 7. Reflect on Learning **Extend:** 8. Create Unusual Structures 9. Explore Other "I Wonder ..." Statements 10. Make a Hat for a Parade 11. Make a Plan 12. Respond to Talk Time	PM 1: I Wonder ... PM 13: Look What I've Learned LM 10: This Is What I Can Do LM 11: My Fasteners LM 12: Make a Paper Tube Puppet LM 13: Which One? Fiction Book: *A-Maze!* Non-fiction Book: *Objects Everywhere*	• fasteners of many types, such as buttons, zippers, snaps, shoelaces • paper tube for each student • decorating materials such as feathers, glitter, tissue paper • container of materials for joining, such as paper, fabric, plastic lids, • cardboard • container of fasteners, such as staples, nails, screws, string, ribbon
Unit Closer: Putting It All Together 1–2 hours	**Looking Back:** 1. Consider the Learning Targets 2. Reread the Fiction Book *A-Maze!* 3. Consider "I Wonder ..." Statements 4. Use Reading Task Cards for *Objects Everywhere* 5. Finish Reading the Non-fiction book *Objects Everywhere* **Going Further:** 6. Hold an "Invention Convention"	PM 4: Finding Out PM 9: I Found Out LM 14: Rate Your Learning LM 15: Not Like the Rest LM 16: Read and Find LM 17: Coming Soon! LM 18: Present Your Invention Fiction Book: *A-Maze!* Non-fiction Book: *Objects Everywhere* Lap Book Skills Poster: Finding Out Skills Poster: Safety in Science Class	

* Time and materials lists are for Core Learning Opportunities only.

UNIT 2 Unit Opener: Getting Started

Time
1 hour

Program Resources
PM 1: I Wonder ...
LM 1: Learning Targets
Fiction Book: *A-Maze!*
Non-fiction Book: *Objects Everywhere*
Lap Book
Science Poster: How is it being changed?

In this unit, students will explore the properties of objects and materials that surround them in their everyday lives. Using the fiction and non-fiction books, posters, and activities in the teacher's guide, students will learn how to identify the objects they use and the purpose for which they are used. They will learn to observe objects and describe their similarities and differences. Students will also learn to compare and contrast the properties of objects and materials.

Through guided inquiry and discussion, students will follow simple procedures and explore and describe ways to create useful objects by combining or joining components and materials. The skills students will explore throughout the unit include making and recording relevant observations, selecting and using materials to carry out explorations, making predictions, communicating questions and ideas, and proposing answers.

***Traditional* Knowledge**

Traditionally, First Nations and Métis peoples have used the objects and materials around them in order to survive. Animal hides, fur, and seal skin were used to make clothing so they could stay warm during the long, cold winters. Today, moccasins, mukluks, jackets, and powwow regalia are still made from animal hides, as well as duck down. Trees, logs, stones, moss, and even ice and snow were used to make traditional shelters. Elm and cedar trees were used to build longhouses, where several families lived together. Bear hide was sometimes used in ceremonies.

Introduce the Unit

1. Set Up an Ongoing Bulletin Board Display

- Create a bulletin board with the heading "Objects and Materials." Read it to students.
- Post a large "I wonder ..." bubble like that on **PM 1: I Wonder ...** and say, "I wonder what we will learn in this unit." Invite students to brainstorm, using the title to help them predict what they think might be included. Model some "I Wonder" statements for students such as:
  - I wonder what the difference is between an object and a material.
  - I wonder what types of objects and materials we use on a daily basis.
- Record their ideas on a chart or paper strips to post on the bulletin board.
- Add vocabulary words, students' work, photos of objects and materials, and other items as the unit progresses. Note that vocabulary should be added as the unit progresses, all within the context of student learning.
- Use questions to guide them toward formulating "I wonder ..." statements that reflect the big ideas of the unit:
  - I wonder what different types of materials and objects there are around us.
  - I wonder how those materials and objects can be used.
  - I wonder how materials and objects can be changed so they can be used in different ways.

Notes

- This is a brief introduction to the book and unit. An in-depth look at key concepts can be found in the activities.
- This initial look at the fiction and non-fiction books can take place as a whole group, using the Lap Book, within small groups, at a teaching centre, or during the literacy block of time.

Introduce the Books

2. Motivate Using the Fiction Book *A-Maze!*

Before: Tell students that you have a book for them to read that is about a maze filled with riddles and challenges.

- In small groups, have students talk about their experiences with mazes. What do they know about mazes? Be prepared to explain what mazes are to students who are unfamiliar with them. You may wish to draw a maze or set up the class as a maze to help students understand the concept.
- Gather students together. Show the book and read the title, *A-Maze!* Ask students to use clues from the front cover and title to predict what this book will be about.

During: Distribute copies of the book.

Pages 2–11: Use a Picture Walk to give students a preview of the book. Stop at each two-page spread and ask:

- What do you see here?
- What do the pictures tell you about the characters?
- What do you think is happening?
- What might happen next? In a discussion, elicit that the children in the book are at a birthday party and are solving riddles and challenges in order to find their way through a maze.

After: Stop after page 11 in order not to reveal the ending. Tell students that they will have other opportunities to read the book and find out more about the party and the maze. Invite students to talk about their experiences with birthday parties. Have they ever seen a maze at a birthday party? This may be a good time to complete Talk Time 1, 2 and 3 on page 16 of *A-Maze!*

3. View the Non-fiction Book *Objects Everywhere*

Before: Using the Lap Book, show the cover of the book, read the title aloud, and invite students to talk about the cover picture. Explain that both this book and *A-Maze!* are part of the science unit they will be starting.

During: Distribute copies of *Objects Everywhere.* Start students on a Picture Walk through pages 2–7. Stop at each two-page spread to briefly discuss what students think they are going to learn about on these pages.

- Provide a few minutes for students to sit in small groups and browse through the pages, talking briefly about what catches their attention on each spread.

After: Gather students together and ask:

- What do you think you will learn from this book?
- What do you already know about objects?
- What is the main difference between this book and *A-Maze!* (*A-Maze!* tells a story; *Objects Everywhere* presents information through text and illustrations.) You may wish to introduce the terms *fiction* and *non-fiction* to students and encourage them to apply the terms to other books they read.

- Tell students that they will begin reading this book within the next few days.

4. Introduce the Science Poster: How is it being changed?

- Begin by displaying the poster **How is it being changed?** Ask students what other objects could have been included on the poster.
- Work with students to come up with a list of broad inquiry questions about the properties of objects and materials that you can revisit as you explore each lesson (e.g., What does that material feel like?). Record the questions. This will assist you in activating students' prior knowledge before beginning the unit.

Notes

- These Unit Learning Targets are taken from the outcomes for this unit. If they seem overwhelming at this point, leave them for now or pick out key words.
- Lesson-specific learning targets are provided with each lesson.

Introduce the Learning Targets

5. Post the Student-friendly Learning Targets

- Make and post a chart of the learning targets from **LM 1: Learning Targets**. Read them with students and go back to them from time to time so that students can check on what they have learned.

1 Objects and Their Use

Time
2–3 hours

Vocabulary
object
purpose

Program Resources
PM 1: I Wonder ...
PM 5: Make a T-chart
PM 6: A Venn Diagram
PM 13: Look What I've Learned
LM 2: This Is What I Can Do
LM 3: Scavenger Hunt
Non-fiction Book: *Objects Everywhere*
Lap Book
Science Poster: How is it being changed?
Skills Poster: Communicating and Teamwork

Materials and Equipment
- 10–20 small classroom objects (e.g., a pencil, scissors, paper clips)
- 2 hula hoops
- objects used for writing

Note
Though taste is a property of objects and materials, remind students that it is not safe to taste anything in a classroom setting when performing a science activity. For this reason, taste has not been included in the non-fiction book as a way to identify properties.

GOAL

Students will identify objects used at home and at school and the purposes for which they are used.

ASSESSMENT CHART

Science Indicators	Assessment Opportunities
OM1.1 a. Pose questions about characteristics and uses of common materials.	Engage 2
OM1.1 d. Record relevant observations about common objects and materials using written language, pictures, and tables.	Explore 4 Explain 5, 7
OM1.1 k. Analyze how common objects and materials are depicted in texts, pictures, and videos.	Engage 1 Explain 5
OM1.1 l. Suggest alternative uses for common objects and materials.	Explore 3 Explain 5
OM1.1 m. Generate conclusions about the properties and uses of materials based on personal observations and investigations.	Explore 4
English Language Arts Indicators	**Assessment Opportunities**
CR1.2 a. Identify and locate the key information in pictures, charts, and other visual forms (e.g., photographs, physical movement, icons) including traditional and contemporary First Nations and Métis resources and performances.	Explore 3

BACKGROUND INFORMATION

Objects are material things that can be seen and touched. They are made of different materials. What they are made of depends on what they are used for. The attributes, qualities, and characteristics of an object are its properties — things we can see, touch, hear, smell, or taste.

Objects have many different uses, although most include helping humans meet needs or solve problems. The objects that surround us often depend on our environment and how we use them. For example, a toothbrush is usually found in a bathroom, and textbooks are often found in a school. While some objects serve only one purpose, others serve two or more purposes (e.g., construction paper).

ASSESSMENT FOR LEARNING

Look for Evidence of Learning	Student-friendly Learning Targets
Can the student: • ask questions about materials, as well as their properties and their uses? • suggest other uses for common objects and materials? • record observations about common materials and objects using words, pictures, and charts? • use the pictures in the non-fiction book to understand the text?	(self-assessment) • I can ask questions about materials and their uses. • I can tell or show different ways to use objects and materials. • I can show what I know about objects and materials with words, pictures, and charts. • I can look at the pictures in the book to help me understand.

DI DIFFERENTIATING INSTRUCTION

For EAL

Have images on hand of the objects discussed in the books and activities. Students can use these images when examining how objects are used and how they help meet needs and solve problems. Students can also use the images when discussing the properties of objects and materials.

For Enrichment

Invite students to bring in a unique object they have at home (with permission) that they wish to share with the whole group. Have them share why the object is unique and how it is used.

For Extra Support

Provide access to a variety of materials that target different learning preferences and reading abilities. Having many books around the classroom about materials and objects will generate interest.

CURRICULUM CONNECTIONS

Students will have the opportunity to develop skills and concepts in the following area:

Mathematics

Patterns and Relations

SS1.2 b. Sort a set of familiar 3-D objects using a single attribute determined by the student and explain how the objects were sorted.

CORE LEARNING OPPORTUNITIES

Engage

1. Activate and Build on Prior Knowledge

- Gather students into a circle. Place 10 to 15 small objects from around the classroom in the centre of the circle.
- Explain to students that objects all have different uses and we use objects to solve problems or meet a need. Ask them to look closely at the objects in the circle.
- Pick up one object and ask:
  - What is this object called?
  - What is it used for? (What is its purpose?)
  - Does it help solve a problem or meet a need? How does it do that?
  - Which objects can be used for a similar purpose? (Ask a student to move those objects together.) Which one would be best to use? Why? Repeat with one or two more objects.
- Show the Science poster **How is it being changed?** and invite students to point out which objects are used at home, at school, or in both places. Discuss some of the objects using the questions above.
- Make word cards for *object* and *purpose*. With students, write a definition for each word. Add these to a word wall or chart, and have students write them in their word book or electronic dictionaries.

***Traditional* Knowledge**

- Ask students whether their family has ever changed an object into something new. For example, they may have used pine cones to make a bird feeder. This may be a good time to talk about some ways that First Nations and Métis peoples changed many objects and materials around them into useful tools and innovations.

Literacy Check

Can the student:

- read the "I wonder ..." statements in the class list and identify "I wonder ..." statements for his or her personal list?
- copy "I wonder ..." statements from the class list onto his or her personal list?

2. Elicit "I Wonder ..." Statements

- Model an "I wonder ..." form of inquiry. Say to students, "I wonder what objects I have in my desk drawer and how I use them." Take out a few objects and use a Think Aloud strategy to consider:
  - their use and purpose.
  - whether you need them in your desk.
  - whether there are better objects you could use instead for a particular purpose.
- In pairs or small groups, students could do the same with a few objects in their backpacks, desks, or bins.
- Invite students to offer other "I wonder ..." statements. Record these on a chart or paper strips, and read them together. Choose some statements to discuss and explore. Students can discuss their statements with a partner and perhaps write them on **PM 1: I Wonder ...**
- Invite students to check with family members to identify an object they use (at work or at home) and what purposes the object serves.

Explore

Science Check
Can the student:
- suggest other uses for common objects?
- recognize that some objects can be used for more than one purpose?

3. Determine Purposes for Objects

- Give each pair or group a small container with objects used for writing (e.g., chalk, pencil, marker, stylus pen, crayon). Include two to three unexpected objects (e.g., craft stick, straw, stick, nail). Allow groups time to observe, sort, and discuss the objects.
- Then, work with the objects in two ways. First, hold up a common writing tool (e.g., chalk) and an uncommon one (e.g., stick). Ask students to predict how each object can be used as a writing tool. Invite volunteers to test the predictions. Then, have students pick out and discuss objects that can be used for more than one purpose (e.g., craft stick: for a bookmark, in a craft, to stir, etc.).
- In a discussion, elicit the conclusion that different objects can be used for the same purpose, and that some can be used for more than one purpose.

Science Check
Can the student:
- sort objects according to given criterion?
- record observations correctly on the T-chart?

4. Go on a Scavenger Hunt

- You may choose to use the Skills poster **Communicating and Teamwork** before this activity to review for students the roles they will have and the etiquette of teamwork so that in the excitement of the activity, no one feels left out and no one does all of the activity on his or her own.
- Explain to students that they will go on a scavenger hunt to search for objects that are used for specific purposes. Have students use **LM 3: Scavenger Hunt** to guide their search. Read the captions aloud.
- Provide students with copies of **PM 5: Make a T-chart** to list objects that are hidden around the classroom (either by the teacher or other students).
- At the end of the hunt, gather the groups together to talk about their findings. Use a Shared Writing strategy to create a T-chart such as the one below.

Objects to Count With	Objects to Fix Things With
toothpicks, buttons ...	glue, pins, tape ...

- As an alternative follow-up activity, record the scavenger hunt discoveries on flash cards with words on the front and drawings or photos on the back. Some students could add a short description of the purpose of each object. Students can use the illustrations and/or the words to sort the objects according to use.

Explain

Literacy Check
Can the student:
- follow along and participate in viewing the illustrations and reading the text?
- gather information from the illustrations?
- respond to questions based on information from the text and illustrations, and by using background knowledge?

5. Read and Respond to the Non-fiction Book *Objects Everywhere*

Before: Using the Lap Book, show students the cover of *Objects Everywhere,* the non-fiction book. Remind them of their Picture Walk through the book when the unit was introduced.

During: Work as a whole group or in small groups based on students' reading level and needs, using a Shared Reading approach.

Page 2: Have students look at the picture and talk with a partner about what they see. Have them find objects that provide clues about the type of room it is and whose room it might be. Read the text. Students can answer the question in pairs by naming five objects in the classroom.

Page 3: Read the two sentences with students. Review the meaning of *purpose*. Discuss one object at a time. Ask: What is the purpose of this object? Note that some objects have more than one purpose.

Page 4: Read the sentence and view the objects. Together, read the question. Students can respond using a Think-Pair-Share strategy.

Page 5: Have students view the pictures and suggest what they have in common (e.g., they are all interesting, they are all pretty). In a discussion, elicit the term *decoration*. Read the text. Discuss the decorative aspect of the objects and ways in which the lower three meet needs as well. Ask: Does a lamp have to be decorative to be useful? Why or why not? Repeat for the clock and chair.

Page 6: Read the text. For objects shown (such as the stepstool) on page 6 and the top of page 7, ask: What is the object? What problem is it helping to solve?

Page 7: Invite a student to read the question. In pairs, have students name the objects and tell how they help solve problems.

After: Read the question on page 7, and assign a home connection response. The following day, have students draw their object and write or dictate a sentence telling how their object helps solve a problem. Compile these into a "Problem Solvers" booklet.

- Have students look around their house or yard and find an object used to help solve a problem. Encourage them to look for something others may not think of.

6. Discuss Which Objects to Use and Why

- Review the names of writing objects. Ask students which object(s) would best meet their needs in the following situations:
  - recording their science observations
  - printing on a tablet/computer screen
  - creating a birthday card
- Suggest a few activities such as playing soccer, going out in the rain, or participating in a drum circle. In a Think-Pair-Share, have students talk about an activity of their choice. They can discuss what objects are important parts of the activity, how they are used, and how they meet a need or solve a problem.

Science Check
Can the student:
- match objects to their use?
- determine which object best suits their needs?
- sort objects into more than one category and give reasons for their sorting?

7. Make A Venn Diagram

- Gather students in a circle around a collection of objects used at home, at school, and in both places. Set out two large hoops, intersected to form a Venn diagram. Add the labels Home, School, and Both.
- Invite volunteers to select an object, place it in the appropriate spot, and explain why they placed it there.
- Display the Science poster **How is it being changed?** Ask volunteers to name one of the objects and jump into the part of the hoop where it is used.
- Provide students with copies of **PM 6: A Venn Diagram**. With a partner, have students sort a few objects into the above categories and record the names of the objects. Have students talk about reasons that some objects are used in both places.

***Traditional* Knowledge**

8. Invite an Elder to Show Traditional Materials and Their Uses

- Invite an Elder to the classroom to share with students how First Nations and Métis peoples from the area use traditional objects and materials to meet a need or solve a problem.

9. Reflect on Learning

- Meet as a class to revisit the "I wonder ..." bulletin board or chart, and the students own "I wonder ..." LM pages.
- Invite students to share their learnings around their past "I wonder ..." statements, and record any new wonders that they may now have.
- Have students record evidence of their learning on **PM 13: Look What I've Learned,** in their journal, or in an audio recording. Encourage students to note at least two things they learned about the purpose of objects and something they still wonder about.
- Use **LM 2: This Is What I Can Do** as a self-assessment. Read the learning targets to students and have them respond orally or in writing (dictated or independently). Some students will be able to read and respond on their own.

OTHER LEARNING OPPORTUNITIES

Extend: Activity Bank

At any time, choose from the following options to replace or supplement the Core Learning Opportunities to meet students' needs and/or interests.

10. Think of Creative Uses for Objects

- Set out several objects and discuss ways in which they are commonly used (e.g., duct tape, water bottle, spoon). Challenge students to think creatively and brainstorm alternative and/or unique uses.
- In small groups, students can collaborate and select an object for which they will brainstorm creative uses. An example of a creative use for an object might be using a pretty jar to hold flowers. Have students make an illustrated web with captions to show their ideas. Volunteers can add labels to the web.

11. Create an Ad to Sell an Object

- Review with students several advertisements for common household objects. Have students identify all the words and images used to tell about the object's properties. Ask students how these words and images are used to enhance the viewer's opinion of the object's usefulness.
- Have students create an advertisement for an object they wish to sell. Remind students to include a description, a picture, the cost, and a contact person. Also remind students that a good description of the object's materials, use(s), and properties will help sell it.

2 Similarities and Differences

Time
2–3 hours

Vocabulary
material(s)
similar/similarities
different/differences

Program Resources
PM 1: I Wonder ...
PM 5: Make a T-chart
PM 7: Make a Bar Graph
PM 13: Look What I've Learned
LM 4: This Is What I Can Do
LM 5: Same and Different
LM 6: Objects and Materials
Fiction Book: *A-Maze!*
Non-fiction Book: *Objects Everywhere*
Lap Book
Science Poster: How is it being changed?
Traditional Knowledge Poster: How are they made?
Skills Poster: Observing and Recording

Materials and Equipment
- 10–20 familiar objects with a variety of uses and materials
- containers with natural and constructed objects (e.g., chalk, pencil, leaf)
- samples of materials (wood, cloth, plastic, metal, glass)
- objects used at school (e.g., scissors, pencils, staples, building blocks)

GOAL

Students will observe objects and materials in the natural and constructed world around them and describe the objects' similarities and differences.

ASSESSMENT CHART

Science Indicators	Assessment Opportunities
OM1.1 b. Distinguish between objects and materials found in nature and those constructed by humans.	Engage 1 Explore 3
OM1.1 c. Observe natural and constructed objects and materials in their environment in a safe and respectful manner using all their senses as well as technologies, such as hand lenses, cameras, and microphones, which enhance the senses.	Explore 3, 4
OM1.1 e. Compare the properties (e.g., texture, colour, smell, hardness, and lustre) of materials that appear in familiar natural (e.g., tree, lawn, rock, and creek) and constructed (e.g., clothing, toys, electronics, furniture, and buildings) objects.	Explore 4
OM1.1 f. Distinguish between the materials used to construct an object and the object itself.	Explain 6, 7
OM1.1 h. Explain why the characteristics of materials help to determine their usefulness within different objects.	Explain 7
OM1.1 i. Evaluate the suitability of materials for a specific function.	Explain 7
English Language Arts Indicators	**Assessment Opportunities**
CR1.4 e. Read aloud with fluency, expression, and comprehension any text that is already familiar and is at an independent reading level.	Explain 6

BACKGROUND INFORMATION

Materials are substances used to construct an object. Objects are made from one or more materials. Objects should be compared only to objects, and materials should be compared only to materials. To find out the similarities and differences between objects, we need to compare and contrast. We can use all our senses to make observations that help us define and distinguish between different objects.

***Traditional* Knowledge**

First Nations peoples, who have lived in Saskatchewan longer than any other cultural group, are known for using the materials they had at hand to fulfill all their needs. Many First Nations and Métis people consider items from nature in a very reverential light, as they were life-sustaining for their people for thousands of years and imbued with the Spirit that is in all matter.

On the Traditional Knowledge poster in this unit, there are several items that would have traditionally been made from natural plant or animal materials such as birchbark, corn husks, animal hides, and sinew.

ASSESSMENT FOR LEARNING

Look for Evidence of Learning	Student-friendly Learning Targets
Can the student: • tell the difference between natural and human-made objects? • compare the properties of natural materials and the properties of human-made materials? • explain what property the material has that makes it more or less useful for a certain object? • read fluently when following a familiar pattern in the text?	(self-assessment) • I can tell the difference between natural or human-made objects. • I can compare the properties of natural objects and materials. • I can compare the properties of human-made objects and materials. • I can say what properties a material has that makes it a good choice.

DI DIFFERENTIATING INSTRUCTION

For EAL

Whenever possible, provide students with physical objects that they can pick up or touch when discussing similarities and differences in objects and materials. If physical objects and materials are not available, provide photos of objects for students.

For Enrichment

Invite students to design a unique object made up of many different materials. Students can create the object, or they can draw a design of the object, explaining its use and properties as well as the different materials it includes.

For Extra Support

Establish stations for inquiry-based, independent learning activities. Add a station to continue the sorting of materials by whether they are natural or human-made or by attributes of students' choice.

CURRICULUM CONNECTIONS

Students will have the opportunity to develop skills and concepts in the following area:

Mathematics

Patterns and Relations

SS1.2 b. Sort a set of familiar 3-D objects using a single attribute determined by the student and explain how the objects were sorted.

CORE LEARNING OPPORTUNITIES

Engage

1. Activate and Build on Prior Knowledge

- Gather the class in a circle with 10 to 15 familiar objects with a variety of uses and materials in the centre. Invite volunteers to match objects that are similar in some way, and ask them to explain why they put the objects together (e.g., same size, colour, shape, use). Introduce the terms *similar/similarities*. Select a few objects and ask volunteers to find an object of a different size, colour, etc. Introduce the terms *different/differences*.
- Pick up a few of the objects and ask students what they think the objects are made of. Introduce the term *material*, saying that objects can be made of different materials. Use a Think Aloud strategy as you begin to sort the objects by their material.
- Put students into small groups, giving each group an object made of a different material. Have students go around the classroom and find two other objects made of a similar material. Bring the groups together to share their findings.
- Make word cards for *similar/similarities, different/differences,* and *materials.* Together, write definitions on each for a word wall or chart. Have students write the words in their word books or electronic dictionaries.

Safety Check
Remind students of the following:
- Do not touch sharp or hot objects.
- Do not taste foods without permission.

Literacy Check
Can the student:
- read the "I wonder ..." statements in the class list and identify "I wonder ..." statements for his or her personal list?
- copy "I wonder ..." statements from the class list onto his or her personal list?

2. Elicit "I Wonder ..." Statements

- Tell students that scientists use their senses to describe objects and materials. Discuss what "use their senses" means. Remind students that it is unsafe to taste anything in the classroom without an adult's permission.
- Point to an object and model an "I wonder ..." form of inquiry, such as "I wonder what this object feels like." Touch the object and use a Think Aloud strategy as you consider whether it is soft, hard, cold, bumpy, and so on. In pairs, have students move around the classroom and do the same with a few objects.
- Invite students to pose other "I wonder ..." statements. Record these on a chart or strips to add to your bulletin board. Choose some statements to discuss and explore. Students can talk about their "I wonder ..." statements with a partner and record them on **PM 1: I Wonder ...**
- Invite students to use their five senses to describe objects and materials at home. Remind them that safety always comes first.

Explore

3. Sort Natural and Constructed Objects

- Give each group a container with an equal number of objects that are natural and objects that are constructed (e.g., chalk, marker, pencil, crayon, leaf, stick, pine cone, rock).
- Have groups observe and sort, first according to material or shape and then other categories they can think of.

- Challenge students to sort the objects into two equal groups, figuring out that half are things found in nature and the other half are human-made.
- In a Shared Writing activity, record the results on **PM 5: Make a T-chart.**
- You may want to introduce the Traditional Knowledge poster **How are they made?** at the end of this activity to discuss how people from different cultures, including First Nations and Métis peoples, used items from nature to meet their needs.

Traditional **Knowledge**

- Allow students to share the knowledge they may already have about canoes, drums, moccasins, and dolls before explaining the materials used for each. (The canoe would have been made from the bark of a birch tree, and the Elder in the poster is holding a piece of bark. The doll would have been made from the husk of a corncob. The moccasins and drum would have both been made with the hide and sinew of an animal.)
- Having some bark or corn husk or even a piece of leather for students to touch and examine would help make the learning more concrete and meaningful. The idea of natural versus human-made is difficult for some students, especially if they have lived all of their lives in an urban setting.

Science Check

Can the student:

- effectively use senses and other tools to observe?
- make relevant and accurate observations?
- select and use materials to carry out his or her own explorations?
- listen to and share ideas?

4. Inspect and Compare Materials

- You may choose to use the Skills poster **Observing and Recording** before beginning this activity to review with students the rules for safely sorting their materials using all of their senses.
- Set up a display of objects made of materials with the properties below for discussion. Model how to make careful observations by asking the following questions:
  - What does it look like? Feel like? Sound like?
  - Can I see through it?
  - Will it bend? Break? Stretch? Squish?
  - Is it hard? Soft? Heavy? Light?
  - Is it natural or constructed?
  - What can it be used for?
- Have students compare different objects.
- Set up centres for students to explore various objects with these questions in mind.
- In a class discussion, elicit the names of materials that various objects are made of and write down the material names on word cards. Put students in groups and provide each group with a card, and ask them to find three objects made of that material.
- Come back together to talk about what students found. Play a game of Which Ones? by holding up three of the objects at a time and asking: Which ones are the same? Why? or Which one is different? Why? Students can then make up their own Which Ones? game for a partner to solve.

Literacy Check

Can the student:

- use picture and word clues to predict?
- read the riddle fluently in his or her presentation?
- read a patterned sentence?

5. Continue to Explore the Fiction Book *A-Maze!*

Before: Distribute copies of *A-Maze!* and let students look at pages 2–7 again. Review the characters and actions students identified during their Picture Walk.

During: Use a Read Aloud or Shared Reading approach for the following:

Pages 8–11: Read the riddle a few times, inviting students to join in. Together, read the characters' thoughts. Ask students which button they would push and why. The teacher should note that the riddle has multiple solutions, so more than one answer could be correct, for example there are two blocks, but only one of the other items. Ask students for other ways the items are the same or different.

After: In pairs, students can set up a three-object test to go with the story rhyme. Provide time for students to read the rhyme and present their test to other pairs.

Explain

6. Read and Respond to the Non-fiction Book *Objects Everywhere*

Before: Review the term *materials*. Hold up a rubber eraser, a plastic ruler, and a metal key. Ask students to name each object and tell what materials they are made of.

During: Work as a whole group or in small groups based on students' reading levels and needs. With the Lap Book, use a Shared Reading or Read Aloud approach for the following:

Page 8: Read the text. Talk about the materials in the pictures. Check whether the names of these materials are on the word wall and/or practise reading them on word cards that you can make now or during Explore.

Page 9 (top): Read the sentences. Have students identify the materials in each object pictured. Then, ask students to sort the objects according to similarities and differences. Write about the similarities using the following model:

These two objects are the same. 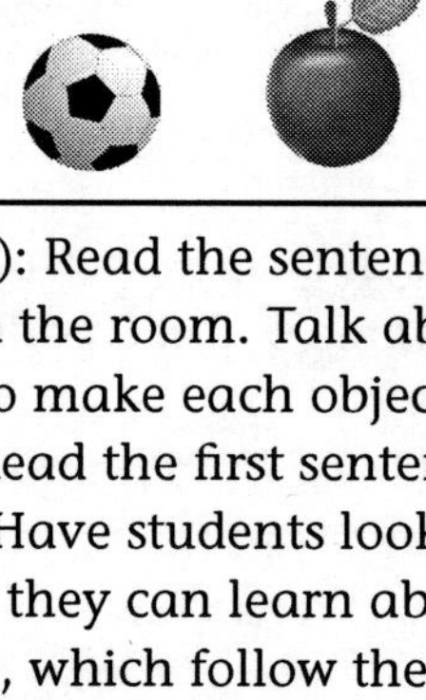	They are both round.

Page 9 (bottom): Read the sentence. Have students identify the materials in each object in the room. Talk about the importance of each of the materials used to make each object.

Pages 10–11: Read the first sentence on page 10, noting the highlighted word *properties*. Have students look at the images on pages 10 and 11 to find out ways they can learn about properties. Invite students to read pages 10 and 11, which follow the pattern of "We can ____ properties." After each sentence, stop and ask students to describe the properties of the pictured object. Brainstorm other objects with the same properties. In a discussion, elicit the understanding that our senses tell us about the properties of materials — what they look, sound, feel, taste, and smell

like. This helps determine similarities and differences.
After: Have students work on their own or in pairs to complete **LM 5: Same and Different**. Some students will be able to draw the objects only; others will be able to label them as well.

Science Check
Can the student:
- observe and sort objects and materials?
- observe and describe similarities and differences?
- record accurate observations on a bar graph?
- make and record relevant observations using written language and pictures?

7. Explore Materials

- Prepare to make a three-dimensional bar graph by giving each student a different object used at school. Have them explore and determine the material(s) in it. Then, set out flash cards with the names of materials beside a pile of large, coloured building blocks.
- Have students come, a few at a time, to set a building block above the flash card naming the material of the object they have been given. Note that some objects will be made of more than one material, so some students may set down multiple building blocks to indicate the different materials their object is made of. When this comes up, discuss the similarities and differences between the different types of materials.
- In a discussion, compare the towers of building blocks and draw a conclusion about which type of material is most commonly used and why.
- With students, choose two materials that are used the most and one material that is used the least. Record the numbers on **PM 7: Make a Bar Graph**.
- Read the question at the bottom of the bar graph, and ask students to respond to it. Talk about possible reasons for a particular material to be more prominent in the classroom.
- Ask students to explain in a sentence or two why they think certain materials on their graph are more useful for certain objects. To encourage students, you might give the example that plastic is a good material for lunch containers because it won't leak, and metal is better for pots because it can go on the stove.
- Students can work in pairs or small groups to find the objects, record their findings, and draw a conclusion.

8. Reflect on Learning

- Ask students to comment on how their explorations have helped answer the following questions:
  - How can I best describe objects and/or materials?
  - How can I sort objects and materials?
- Return to "I wonder ..." statements. Discuss what answers students have discovered, what they are still wondering about, and what new questions that have come up during explorations. Have students record evidence of their learning using self-assessment tools such as **PM 13: Look What I've Learned**, along with their journals or audio recordings. Encourage students to note at least two things they learned about observing objects and materials and something they still wonder about.
- Use **LM 4: This Is What I Can Do** as a tool for self-assessment. Read aloud the learning targets for students to respond to and discuss with you.

OTHER LEARNING OPPORTUNITIES

Extend: Activity Bank

At any time, choose from the following options to replace or supplement the Core Learning Opportunities to meet students' needs and/or interests.

Literature Link
Pinocchio

9. Respond to the Book *Pinocchio*
- Show the book cover, and ask students to look at the picture to predict the types of materials that might be in the book.
- Read aloud to students or do a Shared Reading of a big book if available. Talk about the story. Then, compare students' predictions to what actually was in the book. Make a materials list on a chart or whiteboard.

10. Match Objects and Materials
- Show the Science poster **How is it being changed?** along with the materials flash cards made earlier in the lesson. Ask students to point out objects depicted in the poster that are made of each material. Talk about
  - objects that are made of more than one material.
  - differences in the materials.
- Together, make a reference chart with material names and an object made of that material. Consider using the pictures on **LM 6: Objects and Materials**. Have students complete the line master in pairs and talk about the different properties of the various materials. Ask students to share the properties that the materials have that make them a good choice for that object. For example, a baseball bat is made of wood, which is strong and long lasting.

11. Explore Other "I Wonder ..." Statements
- Return to the "I wonder ..." statements not yet answered and any new wonderings that have come up. With students, plan and set up centres where they can explore these wonderings. Encourage them to make and test predictions.
- Working in small groups, students can rotate to all the centres or focus on one per group. They could share their findings in an oral, written, or electronic presentation.

12. Conduct an Interview
- Have students interview an older family member, such as a grandparent, to identify the toys he or she played with as a child and the materials those toys were made from.
- Students can compare and contrast their toys to those of their family members. They can share their results in an oral presentation or as a recording.

3 Compare and Contrast Objects and Materials

Time
2–3 hours

Program Resources
PM 1: I Wonder ...
PM 2: Let's Predict
PM 13: Look What I've Learned
LM 6: Objects and Materials
LM 7: This Is What I Can Do
LM 8: Objects and Materials Hunt
Non-fiction Book: *Objects Everywhere*
Lap Book
Science Poster: How is it being changed?
Skills Poster: Finding Out

Materials and Equipment
- pictures of different types of chairs
- 10–20 classroom objects that can be sorted by material type
- 4 materials to test for absorbency
- container

GOAL

Students will compare and contrast objects and materials and use scientific inquiry to answer questions about materials.

ASSESSMENT CHART

Science Indicators	Assessment Opportunities
OM1.1 a. Pose questions about characteristics and uses of common materials.	Explore 4 Explain 6
OM1.1 f. Distinguish between the materials used to construct an object and the object itself.	Engage 1 Explore 3 Explain 5, 6
OM1.1 g. Predict the characteristics (e.g., hardness, insulating ability, water resistance, absorbency, and flexibility) of common materials and carry out a procedure to test those predictions.	Explore 4 Explain 5, 6
OM1.1 h. Explain why the characteristics of materials help to determine their usefulness within different objects.	Engage 1 Explain 6
OM1.1 i. Evaluate the suitability of materials for a specific function.	Explain 6
OM1.1 j. Sequence or group materials and objects according to one or more properties such as texture, colour, smell, hardness, and lustre.	Explore 3 Explain 5
OM1.1 m. Generate conclusions about the properties and uses of materials based on personal observations and investigations.	Explain 6
English Language Arts Indicators	**Assessment Opportunities**
CR1.4 c. Use applicable pragmatic, textual, syntactic, semantic/lexical/morphological, graphophonic, and other communication cues and conventions to construct and communicate meaning when reading.	Explain 6
CC1.1 e. Use inquiry to explore a question or topic of interest related to the themes and topics being studied. Use the language of inquiry (e.g., "I want to find out if ...," "I know ...").	Explore 4

BACKGROUND INFORMATION

Sometimes, it can be difficult for a student to understand the difference between an object and a material. If something is used in the creation of an object, then it is considered a material. If you used a piece of paper to wrap a gift, for example, it would be considered an object. However, if it was used to create a papier mâché puppet or a paper hat, then that piece of paper is considered a material.

When students are asked to compare and contrast something, ensure that they fully understand what each word means. When you look at something carefully to see what similarities they have, you are *comparing* them. *Contrasting* is when you are noticing the differences between two or more objects. Ensure that students understand not to compare an object with a material, but instead, compare an object with an object, and a material with a material.

ASSESSMENT FOR LEARNING

Look for Evidence of Learning	Student-friendly Learning Targets
Can the student: • compare properties of natural materials and compare properties of human-made materials? • use picture cues and initial sound cues to understand what the text says? • engage in the inquiry process, asking and recording questions, researching and sharing information?	(self-assessment) • I can compare the properties of human-made objects and materials. • I can compare the properties of natural objects and materials. • I can look at pictures and the first sound of a word to help me read. • I can be a scientist: I can ask questions, find answers, and share ideas.

DI DIFFERENTIATING INSTRUCTION

For EAL

Use a Think Aloud strategy at centres when assisting students who are completing a line master or difficult activity. As a follow-up, providing students with additional exploratory activities with concrete objects and/or pictures will allow for additional support.

For Enrichment

When completing the "Sort It Out" activities in the non-fiction book *Objects Everywhere,* invite students to add objects from around the classroom to their groupings of the objects on the page based on the criteria they are using to sort.

For Extra Support

Create activities that vary in the degree of abstract thinking required. Add complexity or more structure to activities dependent on student needs, especially in the inquiry portion of the activity.

CURRICULUM CONNECTIONS

Students will have the opportunity to develop skills and concepts in the following area:

Mathematics

SS1.2 b. Sort a set of familiar 3-D objects using a single attribute determined by the student and explain how the objects were sorted.

CORE LEARNING OPPORTUNITIES

Engage

✔ Science Check
Can the student:
- use scientific vocabulary when comparing and contrasting objects or materials?
- recall and apply strategies learned in earlier lessons, such as asking questions and using his or her senses?

1. Activate and Build on Prior Knowledge

- Show students a collection of different chairs, including a lawn chair, folding chair, swivel chair, high chair, stool, or beanbag.
- Ask students what they can use to observe and compare these objects and the materials they are made of (e.g., their senses and other tools like magnifying lenses, etc.).
- Discuss the following questions with students:
  - In what way(s) would the use or purpose of these objects be the same? Different?
  - What materials were used to make each object?
  - How are the legs similar? Different? Which legs might be stronger than the others? Explain.
  - How are the backs similar? Different? Which back might be smoother than the others? Explain.
  - How are the seats similar? Different? Which seat might be softer than the others? Explain.
- If time permits, compare and contrast other objects or materials (e.g., adult/student scissors, glue stick/white liquid glue, raincoat/winter coat, wooden/mechanical pencil).
- Begin an ongoing list of words describing properties of materials and objects. Add these to a word wall or chart and/or make word cards to use in the upcoming activities.

✔ Literacy Check
Can the student:
- read the "I wonder ..." statements in the class list and identify "I wonder ..." statements for their personal list?
- copy "I wonder ..." statements from the class list onto their personal list?

2. Elicit "I Wonder ..." Statements

- Model an "I wonder ..." statement, such as "I wonder which objects or materials in this classroom are bumpy."
- Model for students how to answer the question like a scientist might, such as feeling different items in the room and describing their properties. For example, a scientist might say, "This eraser isn't bumpy, it is smooth." Have students check for bumpy objects in their backpacks, desks, or bins.
- Invite students to pose other "I Wonder ..." statements. Record these on a chart or strips to add to your bulletin board. Students can discuss their statements with a partner and write them on **PM 1: I Wonder ...**
- Have students compare two objects in their home. They can present their discoveries orally to small groups, perhaps with drawings or photos.

Explore

Science Check

Can the student:

- use scientific vocabulary when comparing and contrasting objects or materials?
- recall and apply strategies learned in earlier activities, such as asking questions and using his or her senses?

3. Sort Materials

- Gather in a sharing circle. Display the Science poster **How is it being changed?** Point to each picture and ask: "What is this? What material is it made of? How is it being changed?" Repeat with each picture until students have talked about objects made of glass, clay, and wood.
- Review the flash cards made in an earlier lesson for material names. Distribute the cards to volunteers and have them bring two or three objects made of the material back to the group. Students should recognize that some objects are made of more than one material. Discuss the function of each material.
- Pass the objects out to pairs of students. Have them use their senses to determine the look and feel of the material used to make their object. You may wish to make a few copies of **LM 6: Objects and Materials** and cut the cards out. These can be placed by objects with that property.
- Sort the objects into groups, such as shiny or dull, light or dark, squishy or hard, asking students to deduce your sorting rule (opposites). Have volunteers find more opposites (e.g., big/little, black/white).
- Ask students how else they can use their senses to group objects by their properties (e.g., texture, colour, smell, hardness, and lustre).
- In small groups, have students play a guessing game in which they take turns choosing three objects — two of the same material and one different. Students will then pick out the one object that is different.

4. Use Scientific Inquiry

- Use the Skills poster **Finding Out** to introduce the steps scientists take to find something out or to test something. Pose an "I wonder ..." statement. Say: I wonder which materials are waterproof. Think aloud as you follow the inquiry steps, briefly telling what each stage involves. Focus on planning and predicting.
- With students, make plans to inquire into materials that are waterproof. As a group, students will choose four materials to test, discuss how to carry out the test, and predict the results.
- Display a copy of **PM 2: Let's Predict** and, together, answer the first three questions.
- Set up and carry out the test. Talk about the results and what they indicate. Discuss and record answers to the last two questions.

CORE LEARNING OPPORTUNITIES

Explain

Literacy Check
Can the student:
- recall information from an earlier reading?
- predict words using initial sounds and picture cues?
- recognize words that have been presented?

5. Read and Respond to the Non-fiction Book *Objects Everywhere*
Before: As a review, ask students how our senses help us find out about properties of objects. Distribute copies of *Objects Everywhere* and have students turn to pages 10 and 11. Have students reread the pages with a partner, and discuss the question on page 11.
During: Work as a whole group or in small groups, based on students' reading level and needs.
Pages 12–13: Look at the illustrations on pages 12 and 13 one at a time. Have students name the picture and use what they know about beginning letters and the object to predict the word for each property.
- Ask students to identify opposites shown on the page. Start a "Property Words" chart with these properties as headings. Brainstorm a list of objects with these properties, and add to it from time to time.
- Read the other property words to students and discuss their meaning. Consider simplifying some (e.g., rigid: hard; absorbent: holds water).
- For each property, have volunteers find objects in the classroom that match that property. Add these property words to the chart, along with a list of objects with these properties.

Pages 14–15: Read the first four lines of text on page 14 to students, emphasizing the properties, purposes, and materials of the objects.
- Guide students in some initial sorting by asking them to find the objects in a certain category (e.g., objects to play with, objects made of plastic, objects commonly found at school). Then, have students continue in pairs. Observe students to make sure they are using an appropriate criterion for sorting.

After: In small groups or pairs, students can go on a scavenger hunt to find objects that match each property on **LM 8: Objects and Materials Hunt.**

Science Check
Can the student:
- make predictions based on an observed pattern?
- compare and contrast properties?
- record observations in words, pictures, and charts?

6. Return to "Use Scientific Inquiry"
- Draw attention to the Skills poster **Finding Out** to review the steps of scientific inquiry. Tell students this is the process they will follow to inquire into materials that are waterproof.
- Suggest additional questions about materials that students could investigate. Ask: Which materials are most flexible? Most absorbent? Strongest? Summarize the steps of inquiry. Remind students that the inquiry process does not go in order. Scientists are always going back to ask questions, etc., throughout an exploration.
- Set up a centre at which students can investigate one of the steps in the "finding out" process. Alternatively, have students work in small groups to investigate one of these or an "I wonder ..." statement of their own.
- For their investigations, students can gather materials to test and make plans and predictions. Provide copies of **PM 2: Let's Predict** for students to use in recording their questions, plans, predictions, results, and conclusions.
- Gather the groups together to talk about their inquiries.

- Ask students to explain which of the materials they tested would be good to use in their test. Give students an example (e.g., a soft material might be good for a blanket or stuffed toy). Ask them to draw and label an object that they predict could be made out of their material on the back of the **PM 2: Let's Predict**.

7. Reflect on Learning

- Ask students to comment on how their explorations have helped answer the following questions:
  - How can I use my senses, science vocabulary, and other tools to compare objects or materials?
  - How can I make good predictions using what I already know about a material?
- Return to "I wonder ..." statements. Discuss what answers students have discovered, what they are still wondering about, and what new questions may have come up during their explorations.
- Have students record evidence of their learning using self-assessment tools such as **PM 13: Look What I've Learned,** as well as their journals and/or audio recordings. Encourage students to note at least two things they learned about the purpose of objects and something they still wonder about.
- Use **LM 7: This Is What I Can Do** as a self-assessment. Read the learning targets to students and have them respond orally or in writing. Some students will be able to read and respond on their own.

OTHER LEARNING OPPORTUNITIES

Extend: Activity Bank

At any time, choose from the following options to replace or supplement the Core Learning Opportunities to meet students' needs and/or interests.

Literature Links
Three Little Pigs
Three Billy Goats Gruff
London Bridge Is Falling Down

8. Make a Literature Link

- Read aloud one or more of the stories found in the Literature Links. Have students describe the properties of the materials that appear in the selection and extend their thinking by asking questions about the effectiveness of the materials (e.g., What was used to build the little pigs' houses? Which material was weaker and which was stronger?).

9. Play I Spy

- Students can play I Spy by describing properties of objects or materials around the classroom (e.g., I spy something shiny, red, and rough).
- To make the game a challenge, encourage students to try to make their initial clues fit more than one object or material, and then provide further clues to narrow down the choices.

10. Make A Venn Diagram

- Students can compare and contrast two materials or objects using drawings or words on a Venn diagram using **PM 6: A Venn Diagram**.

11. Make an Ice Cube's Jacket

- Students can use materials found at home and experiment to see which materials are best to keep an ice cube from melting and report back to the whole group.
- As an alternative, set this up in activity centres around the classroom, each with a different material.

12. Explore Other "I Wonder ..." Statements

- Return to the "I wonder ..." statements not yet answered and any new wonderings that have come up. With students, plan and set up centres where they can explore these wonderings. Encourage them to make and test predictions.
- Working in small groups, students can rotate to all the centres or focus on one per group. They could share their findings in an oral, written, or electronic presentation.

13. Respond to Talk Time

- Complete Talk Time 1–5 on page 24 of *Objects Everywhere*.

4 Wise Use of Materials

Time
2–3 hours

Vocabulary
responsible /responsibly
reduce
reuse
recycle

Program Resources
PM 1: I Wonder ...
PM 2: Let's Predict
PM 3: A Fair Test
PM 5: Make a T-chart
PM 6: A Venn Diagram
PM 13: Look What I've Learned
LM 9: This Is What I Can Do
Non-fiction Book: *Objects Everywhere*
Traditional Knowledge Poster: How are they made?

Materials and Equipment
- piece of wood, water, glitter, paper, paper towel
- different materials to test for absorbency, such as tinfoil, waxed paper, sponges, fabric, cardboard, newspaper
- different kinds of sponges, paper towel, facial tissue paper, dishcloth/washcloth
- 3 pairs of shoes of different material, such as leather runners, rubber boots, foam flip-flops
- reused or recycled materials
- old and broken crayon bits
- mini muffin baking tray

GOAL

Students will compare and contrast objects and materials and use scientific inquiry to answer questions about materials. Students will also sort and change materials to make them useful again.

ASSESSMENT CHART

Science Indicators	Assessment Opportunities
OM1.1 g. Predict the characteristics (e.g., hardness, insulating ability, water resistance, absorbency, and flexibility) of common materials and carry out a procedure to test those predictions.	Explore 3
OM1.1 i. Evaluate the suitability of materials for a specific function.	Engage 1 Explore 4
OM1.2 a. Select and use materials to carry out explorations of altering materials to change their appearance, texture, sound, smell, or taste (e.g., sanding, painting, or waxing a piece of wood, mixing two or more paints to obtain a particular shade or colour, popping popcorn, shaping clay, drying meat, tuning an instrument, and cooking food at different temperatures) to change the way they are used.	Explore 3 Explain 7, 8
OM1.2 b. Assess how altering the smell, taste, appearance, texture, and/or sound of materials may change the way they may be used.	Explain 7, 8
OM1.2 d. Use appropriate tools (e.g., glue, scissors, and stapler) correctly and safely for manipulating and observing materials and when constructing useful objects.	Explain 6, 7
OM1.2 e. Follow a simple procedure to make a useful object from recyclable materials (e.g., picture frame from old puzzles, holiday ornament from juice can lid, and musical instrument from tissue rolls).	Explain 6, 7
OM1.2 g. Evaluate, using student-identified criteria, personally-constructed objects with respect to their suitability for a particular function.	Explain 8
OM1.2 i. Describe and demonstrate ways to use materials appropriately and efficiently to the benefit of themselves, others, and the environment (e.g., select the amount and kind of materials that are appropriate to a given task; recognize and demonstrate appropriate reuse of materials in daily activities).	Engage 1 Explore 3 Explain 6
English Language Arts Indicators	**Assessment Opportunities**
CC1.2 Represent key ideas and events, in a logical sequence and with detail, in different ways (including dramatization, pictures, sounds, physical movement, charts, models, and drawings).	Explain 5

BACKGROUND INFORMATION

Recycling is the process of turning materials that would otherwise be thrown away as garbage into new products. Recycling is beneficial to our environment and community because it reduces waste and pollution, conserves natural resources, and ultimately, helps sustain our environment for future generations.

Every plastic container is marked with a chasing arrow symbol; however, that does not necessarily mean all plastic containers can be recycled. The information to look at is the number inside the arrows or the letters underneath. The numbers indicate the class of plastic or resin used to make the container. Different resins cannot be processed together, so they must be sorted. Most often, only #1 (PETE) and #2 (HDPE) are recycled. However, different municipalities have different guidelines about what is collected.

***Traditional* Knowledge**

The place-based knowledge that many First Nations and Métis peoples traditionally had about the uses for plant and animal materials was extensive, and their survival depended upon it. From daily comforts such as good herbs for seasonings in foods to herbal medicines and even weaponry, all parts of their lives would have been inextricably interwoven with nature. Knowing the properties that made a material useful would have been a skill that was integral to survival. Materials used by First Nations peoples were always treated with respect and no parts were wasted. For example, the roots, stems, leaves, flowers or seeds of a plant would be used, just as all the parts of the animal would be used, not just for meat, but also for clothing and tools.

ASSESSMENT FOR LEARNING

Look for Evidence of Learning	Student-friendly Learning Targets
Can the student: • decide whether a material is correct for a certain job? • choose the correct tools and use them safely when making useful objects? • follow simple instructions to make a useful object from recycled items? • evaluate recycled objects on how well they do their intended jobs? • decide whether an object or a material is more useful after its taste, shape, smell, or other properties have been changed? • use materials to create a useful object, and explain his or her choices in terms of type of material and amount necessary for the task?	(self-assessment) • I can decide which material is the best to use for a task. • I can choose the right tool for a job and use it safely. • I can decide whether my recycled object does the job I want it to. • I can follow simple instructions to make a useful recycled item. • I can use words, drawings, and actions to tell about what I built. • I can sort materials to create a useful object and only use what is necessary.

DI DIFFERENTIATING INSTRUCTION

For EAL

Work one-on-one with students or pair them with another student. Use "I wonder ..." statements as examples of modelling the inquiry process whenever students need additional support to complete an activity or exploration.

For Enrichment

Invite students to keep a journal about the items they reuse, reduce, or recycle for one week. What objects are from their homes? What objects are from school? Invite students to suggest other ways they can use objects and materials wisely.

For Extra Support

Use flexible grouping to group and regroup students based on factors such as content, ability, and assessment results.

CURRICULUM CONNECTIONS

Students will have the opportunity to develop skills and concepts in the following areas:

Mathematics

SS1.2b. Sort a set of familiar 3-D objects using a single attribute determined by the student and explain how the objects were sorted.

Arts Education

CP1.8h. Make decisions about art media, tools, and paper size in creating a visual art expression.

CORE LEARNING OPPORTUNITIES

Engage

1. Activate and Build on Prior Knowledge

- Play a word game to review vocabulary words already listed on the word wall or chart. For example, find words that complete cloze sentences, are opposites, name materials, describe properties, etc.
- In pairs or small groups, have students talk about why we use different materials to do different jobs. Ask students to keep this question in mind while you model silly situations, such as using:
  - a piece of wood to clean up a spill of water.
  - glitter to join two pieces of paper together.
  - paper towel to erase your work.
- Discuss what is wrong with your choices of materials for the tasks you modelled, and have students suggest a material that would be better.
- Ask: Why do you think we should use the right amount of a material when we are doing a job? Model more silly situations, such as using:
  - too much paper towel to clean up a spill.
  - too many staples to join two pieces of paper together.
  - too much glitter on an art project.
  - Allow time for discussion, encouraging students to provide examples of how they can use materials responsibly and why this is important (e.g., sharing with others, caring for the environment). Introduce the terms *responsible/responsibly.*

Literacy Check
Can the student:
- read the "I wonder ..." statements in the class list and identify "I wonder ..." statements for their personal list?
- copy "I wonder ..." statements from the class list onto their personal list?

2. Elicit "I Wonder ..." Statements

- Model an "I wonder ..." form of inquiry. Say: I wonder which of these materials can be reused or recycled. Pick up one or two different materials and make a prediction about whether it can be reused or recycled. Say: I predict this bottle is recyclable because it is plastic. Invite volunteers to do the same with another material.
- Ask students to pose other "I wonder ..." statements. Record these on a chart or strips for a bulletin board and read them together. Choose some statements to discuss and explore. Students can discuss their statements with a partner, and write them on copies of **PM 1: I Wonder ...**
- Ask students to take note of at least two situations at home when they or a family member:
  - used the right material for a task.
  - used "just enough" material.

Explore

Science Check
Can the student:
- demonstrate an understanding of the properties of materials?
- choose appropriate materials for a task or purpose?

3. Plan a Fair Test for Absorbency

- Return to the silly situation of cleaning up spilled water with a piece of wood. Review what was wrong with your choice of material for this task. Then, have students suggest other materials to test for absorbency (e.g., tinfoil, waxed paper, sponge, fabric, cardboard, newspaper).
- Plan to find out whether any of these materials would clean up some water, and which would clean up water most effectively. Talk about the importance of making it a "*fair test*," eliciting the suggestion of having the same amount of water for each material to clean up, and waiting for the same amount of time with each material being tested.
- Display a copy of **PM 3: A Fair Test**, and, in a Shared Writing activity, respond to the first three questions.
- Set up the test area. Have students work with a partner to make predictions and explain their reasoning.
- Ask volunteers to check the materials regularly and record the results on a chart. At a previously agreed-upon time, end the test. As a group, talk about the results, draw conclusions, and complete the shared writing activity.
- As a follow-up, students can choose other materials to test for absorbency (e.g., different kinds of sponges, paper towel, facial tissue paper, dishcloth/washcloth). Have students record the process on copies of **PM 3: A Fair Test.**

4. Think About Footwear

- Gather in a circle to talk about different kinds of footwear (e.g., workboots, moccasins, clogs, ballet shoes, soccer shoes, baby booties, rubber boots, snow boots, slippers, sneakers, snowshoes, etc.). Set out a few examples in the centre, and invite students to add some of their own. Brainstorm a list of other types of footwear.

***Traditional* Knowledge**

- Showing the Traditional Knowledge poster **How are they made?** now would give students the opportunity to discuss the types of materials that have traditionally been used by many First Nations and Métis peoples (e.g., birchbark, corn husk, and animal hide).
- Ask students to consider what properties they would like to see in a shoemaking material. Ask: Would you want the material to be warm? Soft? Hard? Flexible? Light? Heavy? Waterproof?
- Explain to students that the moccasins in the poster are made of animal hide. Animal hide, just like our own skin, can help insulate and keep us warm and dry. It is ideal for clothing and footwear, especially in a Saskatchewan winter.
- Bring students' attention back to the different footwear in front of them. For each type of footwear, talk about the material(s) they are made of (e.g., leather, plastic, rubber, wool, canvas). Discuss how the materials fit the purpose.
- Have students sort the footwear into groups (e.g., outdoor/indoor, adult/young people).
- Talk about the waterproof property, and ask:
  - When would you need waterproof footwear?
  - Which material do you predict would be the most waterproof? How could we test that?
- Have a small group of students set up another fair test, this time focusing on making predictions, using **PM 2: Let's Predict** as an oral or written record.

Explain

Literacy Check
Can the student:
- use picture cues to help read and understand the text?
- recognize and use key topic words?
- participate in discussions?
- sort objects orally and on a Venn diagram?

5. Read and Respond to the Non-fiction Book *Objects Everywhere*

Before: Write the words *Reuse, Reduce,* and *Recycle* on word cards, and ask students what they know about these three actions. Distribute copies of *Objects Everywhere*, explaining that now they'll read about the three Rs.

During: Work as a whole group or in small groups based on students' reading level and needs, using a Shared Reading approach and the Lap Book.

Page 16: Write these key phrases on the blackboard: *more than once, different purposes,* and *reuse materials.* Have students look at each of the illustrations and predict a match between each illustration and one of these key phrases.

- Read each set of sentences aloud or ask an advanced reader to do so. Invite students to chime in, particularly on the key phrases.
- Talk about how materials can be reused, and ask students to add other examples.

Page 17: Repeat the "viewing, reading, and discussing" process for Reduce with the key phrase *use less*, and for Recycle with *make new objects*.
Page 18: Read aloud two sentences at the top of the page. Allow students time to look at the illustrations and captions, and encourage them to keep the first two sentences in mind.
Ask students to list other objects that can be changed. As students name objects, list them on a chart, and ask for suggestions for ways in which each object can be changed.
After: Provide copies of **PM 6: A Venn Diagram**. Have students label the spaces Reused, Both, Recycled, and print the objects in the appropriate space. For students who experience difficulty printing, provide a scribe or make a three-column chart onscreen and let students use a computer.

Science Check
Can the student:
- recognize which materials will help carry out a task effectively?
- demonstrate a sense of the amount of material to use for a task?

6. Use Materials Wisely

- At centres, set out a variety of materials for students to make a picture or greeting card. Include some materials that are reused or recycled.
- Ask students to suggest some rules or guidelines to follow before they begin (e.g., sharing materials, not using too much, keeping some scraps for other art projects, planning and working carefully so they do not have to keep starting over.
- Provide time for students to plan their project and create their picture or card.
- After their projects are completed and everything is cleaned up, review the guidelines that students created. Have students sit with a partner and assess how well they followed these guidelines. Also, ask them to make suggestions for changes and/or additions to the guidelines to be incorporated for another time.
- Lastly, invite students to share their picture or card and talk about the materials they chose, and how they suited the purpose (e.g., why they decided to use certain materials, how they are alike or different).

7. Make Plans for Reusing Materials

- Have students look around the classroom to find ways that objects and materials have been reused. Then, ask them to think of any other classroom needs that could be met by reusing something. Have students record their findings and ideas using words or pictures on **PM 5: Make a T-chart**.

Ways We Currently Reuse	Ideas for The Future
- Save coloured paper scraps	

Science Check
Can the student:
- recognize that the new crayons are easier to use?
- sort the crayons by colour?
- understand that changing the crayon bits into larger pieces makes them more useful?

8. Changing Objects to Reuse Them

- Direct students' attention to a box of crayons. Show students two different crayons: one that is new and another that is small and broken. Ask students which they find more useful for their purpose of colouring.
- Discuss with students how the change in the shape of the crayon from new, long, and sharp to broken, short, and dull has made it less useful.
- Direct students to look again at pages 18 and 19 in *Objects Everywhere* for examples of ways that items that were no longer useful were changed to become useful again.
- Elicit from students which of the methods in the book would be the best to try with the crayon bits to make them useful. Ask students:
  - would painting the broken bits make them useful again?
  - would stretching them make them useful again?
  - would melting the bits together make them useful again?
- Once students have decided that melting the crayon bits is the best option, split the class into groups of three or four, and give each a bag or plate full of broken crayons to sort by colour. Remind students that we also need to sort by material as well, so that only wax goes into the recycled crayons, and all the paper wrappers are sent to the paper recycling bin. Students can put all the wax bits they've sorted into mini muffin baking trays.
- When students have finished sorting the bits by colour into the baking trays, and also sorted out all the paper bits, tell them you will melt all the wax bits using an oven or a microwave to create new recycled crayons. If you use silicone trays, they can go onto a cookie sheet and then into the oven. The new crayons must cool and set before they are used.
- If they stick to the trays, put them in a freezer for a few minutes. Then, turn them over and give the tray a good tap. They'll fall out.
- Have students try using the new crayons, and then identify what kinds of tasks they are best used for.

9. Reflect on Learning

- Invite small groups of students to act out scenarios to illustrate what they have learned, including using the right amount of materials for a project so there is no waste, using the best material to carry out a task, or caring for the environment.
- Have students record evidence of their learning using self-assessment tools such as **PM 13: Look What I've Learned**, a notebook, or an audio recording. Encourage students to note at least two things they learned and something they still wonder about.
- Use **LM 9: This Is What I Can Do** as a self-assessment. Read aloud the learning targets for students to respond to and discuss with you.

OTHER LEARNING OPPORTUNITIES

Extend: Activity Bank

At any time, choose from the following options to replace or supplement the Core Learning Opportunities to meet students' needs and/or interests.

10. Make "We Care" Posters

- Talk about why it is important to care for the environment and how even little things make a difference.
- Working in groups, students can create posters for one of the following: We Care at Home, We Care at School, or We Care in the Community. Students can make their own drawings and/or look through magazines and newspapers for pictures, and then add captions.
- Have groups present their posters and make plans to display them in the school and community.
- Have students summarize three to five important points for home, school, and community, working either independently or in a Shared Writing activity.

11. Explore Other "I Wonder ..." Statements

- Return to any "I wonder ..." statements not yet answered, and any new questions that have come up. With students, set up an inquiry centre to explore an unanswered question.
- Alternatively, ask: I wonder which material would be the best one to repair a rip in this umbrella, clean up an oil spill, or cover a leftover container of soup. Students can record their ideas on **PM 2: Let's Predict.**

12. Use Your Imagination

- Provide a variety of recycled materials from which students can create a mobile, reusing string, fishing wire, coloured paper scraps, twigs, bottle caps, etc.
- In small groups, students can make up and discuss strange "What if" scenarios for new, creative uses of materials, such as a duster made of cardboard or a car tire made of glass. They can then draw cartoons illustrating the scenario and include speech bubbles if possible.

13. Respond to Talk Time

- Complete Talk Time 8 on page 24 in *Objects Everywhere.*

5 Combine, Join, and Create

Time
2–3 hours

Vocabulary
join
fasteners
combine

Program Resources
PM 1: I Wonder ...
PM 13: Look What I've Learned
LM 10: This Is What I Can Do
LM 11: My Fasteners
LM 12: Make a Paper Tube Puppet
LM 13: Which One?
Fiction Book: *A-Maze!*
Non-fiction Book: *Objects Everywhere*

Materials and Equipment
- fasteners of many types, such as buttons, zippers, snaps, shoelaces
- paper tubes for each student
- decorating materials such as feathers, glitter, tissue paper
- container of materials for joining, such as paper, fabric, plastic lids, cardboard
- container of fasteners, such as staples, nails, screws, string, ribbon

GOAL

Students will explore various ways to combine and join materials together, paying close attention to what materials make up the everyday objects in their lives.

ASSESSMENT CHART

Science Indicators	Assessment Opportunities
OM1.2 c. Examine methods (e.g., gluing, stapling, taping, and buttoning) of joining materials of the same and different types.	Engage 1 Explain 5
OM1.2 d. Use appropriate tools (e.g., glue, scissors, and stapler) correctly and safely for manipulating and observing materials and when constructing useful objects.	Explain 5
OM1.2 e. Follow a simple procedure to make a useful object from recyclable materials (e.g., picture frame from old puzzles, holiday ornament from juice can lid, and musical instrument from tissue rolls).	Explain 5
OM1.2 f. Design and construct a useful object that meets a student specified function by selecting, combining, joining, and/or altering materials.	Explain 5
OM1.2 g. Evaluate, using student-identified criteria, personally-constructed objects with respect to their suitability for a particular function.	Explain 5
OM1.2 h. Communicate procedures and results of their design and construction process using drawings, demonstrations, and written and oral descriptions.	Explain 5, 6
English Language Arts Indicators	**Assessment Opportunities**
CR1.1 d. Show awareness of the experiences and ideas of other persons encountered through texts.	Explore 4

BACKGROUND INFORMATION

Different materials can be combined or joined to create a new, useful object. Materials can be joined together in many ways. These joints can be permanent (fixed) or temporary (removable). Materials can be combined and attached by using adhesives such as tape or glue. Metals can also be joined together by soldering or welding. Soldering involves melting a soft metal, usually a mixture of lead and tin, and using this melted material to join two metal surfaces. Welding, on the other hand, involves joining metals by melting their edges and pressing them together when they are hot. Objects can also be joined together to create something new.

***Traditional* Knowledge**

Traditionally, First Nations and Métis peoples have used a variety of materials in order to join objects together. Sinew from animals was used to stitch together clothing. A type of glue was made by boiling animal tissue. This glue was used for many things. Tree branches and grasses were also used as types of fasteners. When Nēhiyawak (Plains Cree) and other peoples needed to make a boat quickly, they made them out of willow and used different objects to fasten the willow together.

ASSESSMENT FOR LEARNING

Look for Evidence of Learning	Student-friendly Learning Targets
Can the student: • recognize how a variety of fasteners and materials can be used to join components or other materials? • demonstrate or explain how joining materials can solve problems? • explain how changing the shape, texture, smell, taste, or other properties of an object can change its use?	(self-assessment) • I can show different ways to join materials together. • I can tell how changing a material can change how it is used. • I can create a useful object by joining materials in different ways.

DI DIFFERENTIATING INSTRUCTION

For EAL

For students needing additional language support when completing the activities in Explore, Explain, and Extend, use dictated or shared writing to provide students with one-on-one assistance. For students who are not able to complete the written exercises, allow opportunities for observations to be discussed verbally or depicted in drawings instead.

For Enrichment

Students interested in finding out more about how objects are made by combining different materials and fasteners can use the Internet to do some research. Websites such as "How Stuff Works" provides images, diagrams, and videos. As a follow-up, students can summarize the steps for a partner.

For Extra Support

Establish stations for inquiry-based, independent learning activities so that students can continue to explore joiners and fasteners.

CURRICULUM CONNECTIONS

In this lesson, students will have the opportunity to develop skills and concepts in the following areas:

Mathematics

SS1.2 b. Sort a set of familiar 3-D objects using a single attribute determined by the student and explain how the objects were sorted.

Arts Education

CP1.8 b. Identify and explore many different textures, shapes, and forms in own surroundings and in art works.
CP1.3 b. Contribute ideas to the drama.

CORE LEARNING OPPORTUNITIES

Engage

1. Activate and Build on Prior Knowledge

- Gather in a circle to introduce the terms *joining* and *fasteners*. In the centre, set five or six examples of fasteners used on clothing and footwear (e.g., buttons, zippers, snaps, shoelaces). Have volunteers demonstrate how these fasteners work and locate other examples of fasteners around the classroom (e.g., on backpacks, pencil cases).
- For each type of fastener, ask: What is this fastener called? How does it work? How does it help to solve a problem? What would you use to fix a rip or hole or put a button back on (e.g., pins, thread, patch)?
- Write names of some common fasteners on a chart or on word cards to add to the word wall. Students can copy these into their word books or electronic dictionaries.
- Provide copies of **LM 11: My Fasteners**. Go over the instructions with students and have them work in pairs or individually. Students can answer the question orally or in writing.

Literacy Check

Can the student:

- read the "I wonder ..." statements in the class list and identify "I wonder ..." statements for their personal list?
- copy "I wonder ..." statements from the class list onto their personal list?

2. Elicit "I Wonder ..." Statements

- Model an "I wonder ..." form of inquiry. Ask: I wonder how else objects are joined together. Show one or two objects and describe how they are joined together (e.g., a stapled booklet, a pair of scissors).
- Have students get into pairs or small groups. In an assigned area, have groups search to find four or five objects that are joined together in different ways.
- Invite students to pose other "I wonder ..." statements. Record these on a chart or strips for a bulletin board. Students can talk about their statements with a partner and record them on **PM 1: I Wonder ...**
- Invite students to work with a family member to find five different joining methods in their homes. They can record their findings with drawings, notes, or a digital camera.

Explore

✓ Science Check
Can the student:
- work effectively in a group and share ideas when sorting materials?
- organize materials on a web?

Safety Check
Remind students to use caution when dealing with sharp materials.

3. Sort Joining Materials

- Set up centres with a variety of joining materials. Include fasteners from the Engage activity, joining materials from *Objects Everywhere,* and other students' suggestions (e.g., staples, nails, screws, string, ribbon, wool, twist-ties, split fasteners, paper clips, glue, pins, and different kinds of tape).
- At each centre, students can sort the materials according to ways they help do things or solve problems (e.g., to make a craft, build something, fix something, hold papers together).
- Have volunteers from each group talk about how they sorted the joining materials. As a class, make a web to illustrate one or two of these sortings using chart paper. Have students create their own web displaying how they sorted their fasteners.

✓ Literacy Check
Can the student:
- gain information from illustrations and text?
- make reasonable predictions?
- recognize steps in a plan?
- make personal connections?

4. Continue to Explore the Fiction Book *A-Maze!*

Before: Distribute copies of *A-Maze!,* asking students to skim through pages 2–11 to review the events so far.
During: With the Lap Book, use a Read Aloud or Shared Reading approach to read pages 12–15.
Pages 12–13: Have students view the illustrations and predict what the next clue will be about.
Page 12: Read the conversation and clue. Ask students what objects they see on the shelf and how they think the friends will use them. Reread the clue together.
Page 13: Look again at the illustration and read the conversation to find out the friends' plans. Review the step-by-step plans.
Page 14: Look at the illustrations, and talk about how the friends made a fishing rod. Ask: Which materials did they use? How did they join them? Were any of the materials reused or recycled? Encourage students to explain their answers. Ask whether any of the materials could be reused or recycled after the friends are finished with them.
Page 15: Have students look at the scene and, with a partner, talk about everything that is going on. Ask students:

- What happened at the end of the maze?
- Is that what you expected?
- Do you think the friends expected that?
- Why or why not?

After: Ask what students thought about the ending and how they might change it.

- Have students draw a picture illustrating a different ending. They can write a few sentences about their ending and/or tell a partner about it.
- Complete Talk Time 4, 5, and 6 on page 16 of *A-Maze!*

Explain

✓ **Literacy Check**
Can the student:
- participate in a shared reading of the text?
- discuss illustrations and text?
- use personal experiences and knowledge to respond to questions?

5. Read and Respond to the Non-fiction Book *Objects Everywhere*

Before: Review fasteners from the Engage activities in a discussion and/or with flash cards or the word wall.

During: Work as a whole group or in small groups based on students' reading level and needs. Distribute copies of *Objects Everywhere.*

Page 20: Read aloud the sentence at the top of the page or ask a student to read it. Have students look at each of the joining materials and read the names silently or to a partner. Ask students:
- What joining materials here could be used on clothes or footwear?
- Which ones should you not use for that purpose? Why?
- What other uses can you think of for a zipper? For string?
- What could you use the other joining materials on this page for?

Page 21: Have students first look at each of the objects pictured here.
- Talk about the objects one at a time, noting the names below each photo and asking what the object is used for (e.g., tree house to feed birds).
- Use a Shared Reading approach for the sentences at the top of the page. Go back to each of the objects, asking what materials could be used to join the parts together (e.g., nails, glue, screw).

After: Together, reread the sentences on page 21. Tell students that they are going to make a puppet made from a paper tube so they can use it to put on a play.
- Set out the materials listed on **LM 12: Make a Paper Tube Puppet**, along with other decorating materials (e.g., feathers, glitter, tissue paper, pipe cleaners). Include large construction paper pieces for the tube body. Distribute the line master.
- Read the instructions aloud to get students started. Some students will be able to continue on their own or in pairs, while others may need step-by-step guidance.
- When their puppets are complete, gather as a whole group to discuss what students like about their puppets and the problems and successes they had with the joining methods they used. Then, have students complete the two assessment questions at the bottom of the line master.
- Provide an opportunity for students to form groups and put on plays with their puppets.

✓ **Science Check**
Can the student:
- make and record relevant observations?
- make and check predictions?

6. Compare Joining Methods

- Put students into small groups and provide each group with two containers holding:
  - materials or objects to be joined at each group's table (e.g., paper, fabric, plastic lids, cardboard, piece of rubber, tinfoil).
  - joining materials from previous explorations, adding others if you wish (e.g., magnets).
- Explain to students that they will be predicting the best method to join two selected objects or materials and testing their prediction using two joining methods.

- Remind students of the importance of a fair test (e.g., same amount of waiting time before trying to pull the objects or materials apart).
- Using a Think Aloud strategy to model the process, choose two objects to be joined and one joining method to use.
- Display a copy of **LM 13: Which One?** to demonstrate how to record the test and results.
- Have students work in groups to complete the line master. Members can volunteer for roles (e.g., reader, recorder, tutor). Some students will benefit from having you work through the entire process with them.

7. Reflect on Learning

- Ask students to comment on how their explorations have helped answer the following questions: What are some different ways to join materials together? How do fasteners and joining materials help me to solve problems?
- Return to "I wonder ..." statements. Discuss what answers students have discovered, what they are still wondering about, and new questions that have come up during their explorations.
- Have students record evidence of their learning using self-assessment tools such as **PM 13: Look What I've Learned**, a journal, or an audio recording. Encourage students to note at least two things they learned about observing objects and materials and something they still wonder about.
- Use **LM 10: This Is What I Can Do** as a tool for self-assessment. Read aloud the learning targets for students to respond to and discuss with you.

OTHER LEARNING OPPORTUNITIES

Extend: Activity Bank

At any time, choose from the following options to replace or supplement the Core Learning Opportunities to meet students' needs and/or interests.

8. Create Unusual Structures

- Provide a collection of unusual materials for students to join together (e.g., spaghetti noodles, newspapers, straws, marshmallows, paper clips, ribbons, glue, staples, toothpicks, safety pins of all sizes).
- Encourage students to use their imaginations to design and build a tall tower or other structure with the joining materials they have chosen from your collection.

9. Explore Other "I Wonder ..." Statements

- Return to "I wonder ..." statements not yet answered and new questions that have come up. With students, plan and set up centres at which they can carry out explorations for these and make and test predictions.

10. Make a Hat for a Parade

- At a centre, set out a variety of materials students can use to create a silly hat for a parade (e.g., coloured paper, fabric, newspaper, feathers, tinfoil, paper plate, small box). To join these materials, students can use glue, tape, ribbon, twist-ties, a stapler, string, or paper clips.
- Have students use at least three joining methods and three hat materials for their creation.

11. Make a Plan

- In a Shared Writing activity, record three or four steps to join a handle to a container (e.g. margarine tub, paper bag, sandwich bag).
- Students can follow the steps at home and show a family member how they can join materials together.

12. Respond to Talk Time

- Complete any unfinished Talk Time activities, specifically Talk Time 7 on page 24 in the non-fiction book *Objects Everywhere*.

UNIT 2

Unit Closer: Putting It All Together

Time
1–2 hours

Unit Resources
PM 4: Finding Out
PM 9: I Found Out
LM 14: Rate Your Learning
LM 15: Not Like the Rest
LM 16: Read and Find
LM 17: Coming Soon!
LM 18: Present Your Invention
Fiction Book: *A-Maze!*
Non-fiction Book: *Objects Everywhere*
Lap Book
Skills Poster: Finding Out
Skills Poster: Safety in Science Class

Looking Back

1. Consider the Learning Targets

- Display the learning targets that were introduced in the Unit Opener on a chart or screen. Explain that these are the big ideas about the properties of objects and materials.
- Read the learning targets aloud. Stop after each one, asking students to provide examples that illustrate the learning target.
- Ask students to think about how well they can do the things on the list. Explain the term *rate*, saying that it is a way of judging how well you can do something. Use a Think Aloud strategy and a copy of **LM 14: Rate Your Learning** to model how students should rate themselves.
- Distribute copies of the line master for students to complete as you read each of the learning targets. Some students may be able to read and complete it on their own.

2. Reread the Fiction Book *A-Maze!*

Before: Ask students to talk about what they thought of the book *A-Maze!* What did they like about the book? What did they learn from the book?
During: Distribute copies of *A-Maze!* In a Shared or Paired Reading, students can read through the book for enjoyment, and talk about it. More proficient readers could take the roles of the narrator and children in the story. They could record the story to be used at a listening centre.
After: Have students make up new "same and different" picture choices for the riddle on page 8, using **LM 15: Not Like the Rest**. They can do this on paper or at a computer centre, using clip art for the pictures. Choose activities and discussion questions provided on page 16 to meet students' interests, needs, and abilities. As an open-ended activity, challenge students to create their own maze either on the floor or on paper. They should include stopping points on their maze path, where questions about objects and materials are asked.

3. Consider "I Wonder ..." Statements

- Ask students to think back on the things they have wondered about throughout the lessons. Review students' copies of "I wonder ..." statements. Have students pick one important question that has been answered and tell a partner about it.
- Students can record their "I wonder ..." statement and what they learned about it on **PM 9: I Found Out.**
- If time permits, select an unanswered statement and present it to the whole group. Review the Skills poster **Finding Out** and, with students, plan an exploration that follows the inquiry steps. Set up the inquiry for students to experience in small groups at a centre. Provide copies of **PM 4: Finding Out** for students to complete as a group while following the steps.

Literacy Check
Can the student:
- use illustrations to gather information and read the text?
- read the text with assistance or without assistance?
- answer the questions?
- follow a step-by-step procedure?

4. Use Reading Task Cards for *Objects Everywhere*

Before: Make a copy of the task cards on **LM 16: Read and Find**. Cut out the cards and distribute one each to six small groups, keeping in mind students' reading/ability levels.
During: Distribute copies of *Objects Everywhere.* Have students in each group turn to the pages indicated on their task card and look at and talk about the illustrations to help recall the information and text. Tell students to read the pages on their own or as a group. Then, have them discuss answers to the questions on the task cards with the members of their group.
After: Invite students to share their responses to the task cards. Call each group in order, reading the questions and asking students in the group to respond.

5. Finish Reading the Non-fiction Book *Objects Everywhere*

- Using the Lap Book, or in small groups, finish reading *Objects Everywhere.*

Pages 22–23: Use a Shared Reading or Read Aloud strategy to introduce and discuss the open-ended project "Make a Pencil Holder." Note the parts of the instructions that leave decisions up to students (e.g., "Materials you may need," "You can use"). Encourage students to work as independently as possible but provide assistance when needed.
Page 24: Choose activities and discussion questions to meet students' interests, needs, and abilities.

Going Further

6. Hold an "Invention Convention"

Introduction

- Tell students that they acted like engineers in this unit by learning about the properties and uses of materials and objects and how certain materials and objects can be combined and joined to create new useful objects.
- Invite them now, as engineers, to be part of an "Invention Convention." Ask students what they think that is and what they might be expected to do.

Tip
You may wish to have all groups create the same object, but use their own design and process, or you can invite adult volunteers to work with the groups to guide and assist them with their invention.

Preparation

- Present **LM 17: Coming Soon!** Use a Shared Reading strategy to introduce the project.
- Brainstorm ideas with the whole group for objects teams could create. Perhaps get students started with a suggestion such as a storage place for a rock collection, a musical instrument, or a birdhouse.
- Explain that it is important for their object to meet certain requirements/criteria. Talk about what those might be for a birdhouse (e.g., can hang from a tree, can hold birdseed, can be reached by a person who will fill it with food).
- Assign teams and, over the next few days, provide opportunities for students to decide on their invention, gather materials, create a step-by-step plan, and determine criteria. Provide assistance and encouragement as needed.
- Through Shared or Dictated Writing, make criteria charts for each team's invention. Display these when the inventions are presented.
- You may choose to use the Skills poster **Safety in Science Class** to review for students how to work safely during the invention process. Explain to students that using tools and equipment in the proper manner, as well as keeping their workplace neat and orderly, can help keep the environment safe for not only themselves, but also others in the room. Even something as small as a dropped marker on the floor can cause a classroom injury if someone slips on it.

Science Check
Can the student:
- design and create a useful object according to his or her own criteria?
- communicate procedures orally?
- compare and evaluate his or her and other teams' inventions?
- communicate with team members while creating their team's invention?

Presentation

- To prepare teams for their presentation:
  - Provide students with **LM 18: Present Your Invention**.
  - Have students decide on and practise roles (e.g., set up, introduce, explain steps, answer questions).
- Have teams present their invention one at a time. If needed, read aloud the points on the line master and/or the criteria chart.

Evaluation

- Have the teams take on the role of judges. First, they should evaluate their own team's invention and presentation, checking to see whether their invention met the criteria. Then, have teams tell two things they like about their presentation and one that needed improvement. After each team's presentation, have the others evaluate the team's invention and presentation in the same way.

UNIT 2

USING OBJECTS AND MATERIALS

Table of Contents

Name:____________________________________

Learning Targets

Put a check mark to show what you can do.

☐	I can name objects and describe their properties.
☐	I know what objects are used for.
☐	I know what materials objects are made from.
☐	I can describe materials.
☐	I can describe similarities and differences between materials.
☐	I can recycle, reduce, and reuse materials.
☐	I can join materials together to make a useful object.
☐	I can tell when an object is found in nature or constructed.

Name:____________________________________

This Is What I Can Do

Put a check mark to show what you can do.

☐	I can describe where an object is compared to the position of another object.
☐	I can follow directions to place an object in a different position.
☐	I can use directions to find something.
☐	I can follow directions to move to a different position.

Put a  beside what you do best.

Put a blue  beside the one you need to practise.

Name:_____________________________________

Scavenger Hunt

Objects I can write with	Objects I can count with
Objects I can read	Objects I can play with
Objects I can change the shape of	Objects I can fix things with

Name:______________________________________

This Is What I Can Do

Put a check mark to show what you can do.

☐	I can use my senses to describe objects and materials.
☐	I can tell what materials objects are made of.
☐	I can use similarities and differences to sort objects and materials.
☐	I can ask questions and share my ideas.
☐	I can choose materials and objects to explore to find answers.
☐	I can ask questions and share my ideas.
☐	I can tell about what I have learned with words, pictures, and a graph.

Put a  beside what you do best.

Put a blue  beside the one you need to practise.

Name:______________________________

Same and Different

These two objects are the same.	They are both ______________________.
These two objects are the same.	They are both ______________________.
These two objects are the same.	They are both ______________________.

These four objects are all different.

Name:______________________________________

Objects and Materials

Name three objects made with these materials.
Draw the objects in the space.

 wood	
 plastic	
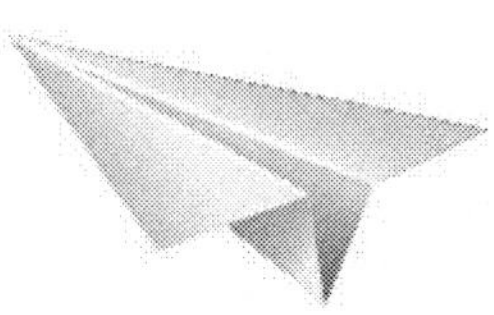 paper	
 rubber	

Pick two materials.
Talk with a partner about how they are different.

Name:__________________________________

This Is What I Can Do

Put a check mark to show what you can do.

☐	I can identify the materials used to make an object.
☐	I can use my senses, science vocabulary, and other tools to compare objects or materials.
☐	I can be a scientist and do an experiment using different materials.
☐	I can make good predictions using what I already know about a material.
☐	I can record my observations using pictures and words.
☐	I can ask questions and share my ideas.

Put a  beside what you do best.

Put a blue  beside the one you need to practise.

Name:________________________________

Objects and Materials Hunt

bumpy	smooth	soft
hard	warm	cold
light	dark	fluffy
shiny	dull	bright
heavy	light	strong
weak	dry	wet
bumpy	sharp	flexible
slippery	smelly	solid
hollow	see-through	stretchy
red	yellow	green
blue	orange	white
purple	black	brown

Name:________________________________

Objects and Materials Hunt

something bumpy	something wet	something tasty	something dry
something slippery	something shiny	something bright	something small
something cold	something fluffy	something big	something flexible
something sharp	something smooth	something warm	something cold

Which ones are opposites? ____

____

Name:____

This Is What I Can Do

Put a check mark to show what you can do.

- ☐ I can decide which material is best to use for a task.
- ☐ I can be careful and not use too much of a material (reduce).
- ☐ I can find ways to use materials over again (reuse and recycle).
- ☐ I can make predictions, test them, and explain the results.
- ☐ I can record my observations using pictures and words.
- ☐ I can ask questions and share my ideas.

Put a  beside what you do best.

Put a blue  beside the one you need to practise.

Name:________________________________

This Is What I Can Do

Put a check mark to show what you can do.

☐	I can show different ways to join materials together.
☐	I can follow a step-by-step plan.
☐	I can create a useful object by joining materials in different ways.
☐	I can record my observations using pictures and words.
☐	I can ask questions and share my ideas.

Put a  beside what you do best.

Put a blue  beside the one you need to practise.

Name:__________________________________

My Fasteners

Draw three objects for each fastener. Write the names under each one.

zipper	
buttons	
Velcro	
snaps	
ties or laces	

Here is how one of them helps me solve a problem:

____

____

____

Name:______________________________________

Make a Paper Tube Puppet

You Will Need

– scissors
– glue
– tape
– split fasteners
– coloured paper
– tissue paper
– sequins or beads
– other things for decorating

What You Do

1. Take a big piece of coloured paper.
   Make a tube shape.
2. Cut out arms and hands.
3. Put on the arms with the fasteners.
4. Add a face.
5. Put clothes on the puppet.
6. Add other things for decoration.

What do you like about your puppet?

Why did you need the split fasteners?

Name:______________________________

Which One?

What will you try to join?

Try four different joining materials.

Predict which one will work best.______________________________

Talk about what you did to find out.

JOINING MATERIAL	HOW IT WORKED
1.	
2.	
3.	
4.	

Which one worked best? ______________________________

Did you predict the right one? ______________________________

Name:______________________________

Rate Your Learning

Circle the number that tells about you.

1 means I can do it very well.

2 means I can do it, but I need some practice.

3 means I need a lot more practice.

1	2	3	I can name objects and describe their properties.
1	2	3	I know what objects are used for.
1	2	3	I know what materials objects are made from.
1	2	3	I can describe materials.
1	2	3	I can describe similarities and differences between materials.
1	2	3	I can recycle, reduce, and reuse materials.
1	2	3	I can join materials together to make a useful object.
1	2	3	I know when an object is found in nature or constructed.

Name:____

Not Like the Rest

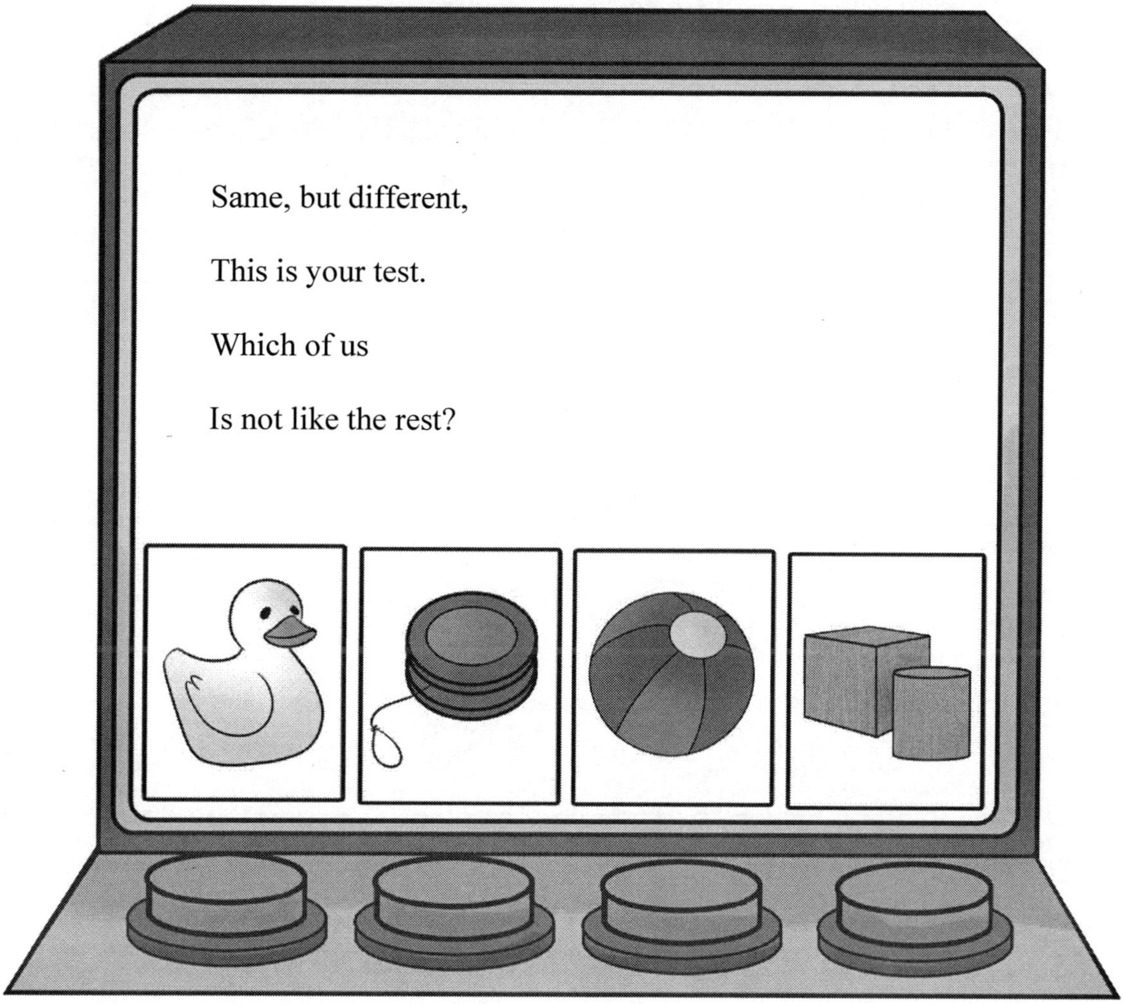

1. They are all ____.

2. The ______________________ and ______________________ are alike.

They are both ____.

3. The ______________________ and ______________________ are alike.

They are both ____.

4. The ______________________ is different.

Name:________________________________

Read and Find

Objects Everywhere

Read pages 2 to 7. Find out:

What do we use objects for?	How do objects help solve problems? Find examples.

Read pages 8 to 11. Find out:

What are five kinds of materials?	How do we learn about the properties of objects and materials?

Read pages 12 to 15. Find out:

What does it mean to reuse?	What does it mean to recycle?	Name five objects that can be recycled.

Read pages 16 to 19. Find out:

How can we change some materials and objects?	Name two materials and two objects that can be changed.

Read pages 20 to 23. Find out:

What joining material is used on clothes?	What joining material is used for crafts?	What object needs nails to join wood?

Name:______________________________

Coming Soon!

The Objects and Materials
Invention Convention

Be sure to enter a team.
It will be fun!

What to do:

1. Create an object that solves a problem.

What to do:

2. You can use all kinds of materials.

Some can be recycled.

Some can be new.

Some can be from nature.

What to do:

3. Use three or more ways to join things together.

What to do:

4. Give your object a name.

Name:__________________________________

Present Your Invention

1. Name the members of your team.

2. Talk about your invention.

Talk about its name.

Talk about what problem it helps solve.

Talk about what steps you followed to make it.

3. Ask if anyone has a question to ask.

Answer the questions.

UNIT 3

USING OUR SENSES

Table of Contents

Unit Indicators Correlation Chart — Using Our Senses*

Indicator	Assessment Opportunities
By the end of grade 1, students will be able to:	
SE1.1 Investigate characteristics of the five traditional external senses (i.e., sight, sound, smell, touch, and taste) in humans and animals.	
a. Identify each of the senses and associate those senses with parts of humans or other animals, including sight and eyes, smell and nose, hearing and ears, taste and tongue/nose, and touch and skin.	Lesson 1: 1, 3, 4, 5 Lesson 2: 2, 4, 9 Lesson 4: 3, 6 Lesson 5: 1, 4, 5, 7, 8
b. Identify characteristics used to describe the range of observations related to each sense (e.g., sounds can be described as loud or soft, high pitch or low pitch; tastes related to the tongue can be described as sweet, sour, salty, or bitter; textures can be described as hard or soft, smooth or rough, sticky or not sticky; smells can be described as musky, aromatic, pungent, or putrid; and appearance can be described in terms of shape, colour, and lustre).	Lesson 1: 1, 3, 8 Lesson 2: 1, 3, 4 Lesson 3: 1, 5 Lesson 4: 1, 3, 5, 6, 7 Lesson 5: 1, 3, 4
c. Provide examples of their favourite and least favourite sounds, smells, tastes, colours, and textures.	Lesson 2: 3 Lesson 3: 1, 4 Lesson 4: 3, 6
d. Discriminate among various natural and artificial sounds that humans can hear.	Lesson 2: 1, 3, 9, 10
e. Explain the purposes (e.g., detecting danger, navigation, and communication) of hearing in animals and humans.	Lesson 2: 5, 6, 9, 11
f. Investigate the sensitivity of different parts of the body to the touch of various materials (e.g., sandpaper, metal, cloth, satin, leaves, and wood).	Lesson 5: 3, 4, 5, 6, 7, 8
g. Assess the ability of humans and other animals to distinguish among various smells.	Lesson 3: 1, 3, 4, 6, 7, 9
h. Categorize foods as sweet, sour, salty, or bitter, and compare results with others.	Lesson 4: 3, 4, 5, 6, 7
i. Sort objects and materials according to characteristics (e.g., colour, shape, texture, odour, sweetness, and loudness) related to one or more senses.	Lesson 1: 3 Lesson 3: 1, 4, 9 Lesson 4: 5, 6, 7, 8
j. Communicate questions, ideas, and intentions while conducting explorations of the human senses.	Lesson 2: 3, 7, 8 Lesson 3: 4, 6, 7

Indicator	Assessment Opportunities
SE1.2 Explore how humans and animals use their senses to interact with their environment.	
a. Pose questions that lead to exploration and investigation of human and animal senses.	Lesson 2: 2, 5, 6
b. Record observations about specific objects (e.g., apple, pencil, shirt, and tree) in their environment using all of their senses as appropriate.	Lesson 4: 4, 7 Unit Closer: 4, 5
c. Record observations of various environments (e.g., classroom, gymnasium, school yard, library, and cafeteria) using all of their senses as appropriate.	Lesson 2: 3 Lesson 5: 6
d. Imagine, and compare with others, possible sensations that students would likely experience in other environments based on representations (e.g., stories, pictures, and videos) of those environments.	Lesson 5: 7, 8
e. Explain and follow given safety procedures and rules when using the senses to observe (e.g., explain the danger to health of tasting unknown materials and the reasons for wafting odours towards the nose rather than smelling directly).	Lesson 3: 3, 8 Lesson 4: 1, 6, 8
f. Assess the function of aids (e.g., glasses, hearing aids, raised Braille alphabet, sign language, and guide dogs) that support peoples' differing abilities to sense their environment.	Lesson 2: 8 Lesson 1: 5, 7
g. Experience changes in ability to explore the environment after the simulated loss of one or more senses (e.g., blindfold, earplugs, nose clip, and socks over both hands).	Lesson 2: 6, 7, 8
h. Suggest how a human or animal might function if they were totally or partially missing one or more of the five senses.	Lesson 1: 7 Lesson 2: 6, 8 Lesson 5: 6
i. Explain how each of the senses helps us to recognize, describe, and safely use materials, and recognize potential dangers in the environment (e.g., colour and smell help determine whether fruit is healthy or bruised, ripe or overripe; machine noises may indicate it needs repair or is not being used correctly; and sirens and flashing lights may indicate an emergency vehicle).	Lesson 4: 1, 8
j. Discuss dangers associated with using the senses to examine the environment (e.g., eating some foods may cause allergic reactions, breathing in certain odours may cause illness, sharp edges can cut skin, extremely loud sounds can damage hearing, and looking at the sun can cause eye problems).	Lesson 2: 7 Lesson 3: 3, 8, 9
k. Describe different sense organs and/or adaptations that enable various animals to accomplish their daily tasks (e.g., bats use echolocation to find prey, cat's pupils dilate to see in low light, bees can sense ultraviolet light, scorpions can have up to 12 eyes, elephants can hear extremely low sounds, and hawks have excellent vision).	Lesson 1: 5, 6 Lesson 2: 5, 6, 9, 11
l. Provide examples of how the senses are important to people in their hobbies and jobs.	Lesson 3: 1, 6

* Indicators are met in multiple lessons, but this correlation only identifies lessons in which the indictors are focused on.

Unit Planning Chart — Using Our Senses

Lesson and Time*	Activities	Program Resources	Materials and Equipment*
Unit Opener: Getting Started 1 hour	**Introduce the Unit:** 1. Set Up an Ongoing Bulletin Board Display **Introduce the Books:** 2. Motivate Using the Fiction Book *On the Trail* 3. Motivate Using the Non-fiction Book *Exploring With Our Senses* **Introduce the Learning Targets:** 4. Post the Student-friendly Learning Targets	PM 1: I Wonder ... LM 1: Learning Targets Fiction Book: *On the Trail* Non-fiction Book: *Exploring With Our Senses* Lap Book Science Poster: Which senses do you use? Skills Poster: Observing and Recording	• bulletin board • large chart paper • glue
1: Sense of Sight 4–5 hours	**Engage:** 1. Activate and Build on Prior Knowledge 2. Elicit "I Wonder ..." Statements **Explore:** 3. Play I Spy 4. Use Senses to Catch Beanbags **Explain:** 5. Read and Respond to the Non-fiction Book *Exploring With Our Senses* 6. Test Your Field of Vision 7. Read and Respond to the Non-fiction Book *Exploring With Our Senses* 8. Categorize Objects By Colour, Shape, Lustre 9. Reflect on Learning **Extend:** 10. Make a Collage 11. Play Twister 12. Listen to a Guest Speaker	PM 1: I Wonder ... PM 13: Look What I've Learned LM 2: Braille Alphabet LM 3: This Is What I Can Do Non-fiction Book: *Exploring With Our Senses* Lap Book Science Poster: Which senses do you use?	• small objects of varying colour, lustre, and shape • beanbags, blindfolds • reflective surface (e.g., a mirror or a piece of cardboard covered with aluminum foil), light source (e.g., a flashlight) • kraft paper • glue in plastic squeeze bottles (not glue sticks)
2: Sense of Hearing 3–4 hours	**Engage:** 1. Activate and Build on Prior Knowledge 2. Elicit "I Wonder ..." Statements **Explore:** 3. Go on a Sound Scavenger Hunt 4. Describe the Sound 5. Research the Hearing of Animals 6. Explore Bats and Echolocation 7. Make Safety Rules for Our Ears 8. Try Lip-reading **Explain:** 9. Read and Respond to the Non-fiction Book *Exploring With Our Senses* 10. Make a Venn Diagram 11. Read and Respond to the Fiction Book *On the Trail* 12. Reflect on Learning **Extend:** 13. Guess What Made That Sound 14. Have an Animal Ear Parade 15. Invite a Knowledge Keeper or Elder to Talk About Listening and to Tell Stories 16. Invite a Class Visitor to Talk About Hearing Loss 17. Create a Device 18. Explore Other "I Wonder ..." Statements	PM 1: I Wonder ... PM 6: A Venn Diagram PM 13: Look What I've Learned LM 4: Sound Scavenger Hunt LM 5: How Animals Use Their Hearing LM 6: What Do Animal Ears Do? LM 7: Keeping My Ears Safe LM 8: American Sign Language Alphabet LM 9: Loud and Soft Sounds LM 10: This Is What I Can Do Fiction Book: *On the Trail* Non-fiction Book: *Exploring With Our Senses* Lap Book Science Poster: Which senses do you use? Skills Poster: Observing and Recording	• clipboards, pencils • research resources such as levelled reading materials, pictures in books • blindfolds • disposable earplugs, music, boom box

Lesson and Time*	Activities	Program Resources	Materials and Equipment*
3: Sense of Smell 5–6 hours	**Engage:** 1. Activate and Build on Prior Knowledge 2. Elicit "I Wonder ..." Statements **Explore:** 3. Be Safe When Smelling 4. Identify Mystery Smells 5. Match Animal Noses 6. Work With Our Noses 7. Respond to Smells **Explain:** 8. Make a Safety Video 9. Identify Dangerous Smells 10. Reflect on Learning **Extend:** 11. Invite a Guest Speaker 12. Make Spice Paintings 13. Make a Literature Link 14. Explore Other "I Wonder ..." Statements	PM 1: I Wonder ... PM 13: Look What I've Learned LM 11: Mystery Containers LM 12: How Do They Smell? LM 13: Different Smells LM 14: This Is What I Can Do Non-fiction Book: *Exploring With Our Senses* Skills Poster: Safety in Science Class Skills Poster: Observing and Recording	• magazines • clear containers, water, clear dish soap, white vinegar, red vinegar, cider vinegar • variety of food substances with strong scents (e.g., curry powder, vanilla extract, onion), opaque containers with lids • Sesame Street video *Troy Polamalu Talks Fragrance with Elmo* • containers, water, coffee filters, funnel, strong smelling flowers, vanilla extract, cinnamon, cloves • object with a distinct smell (e.g., pine bough, fresh cut grass, fresh baked goods), paper bag
4: Sense of Taste 3–4 hours	**Engage:** 1. Activate and Build on Prior Knowledge 2. Elicit "I Wonder ..." Statements **Explore:** 3. Investigate Our Tongues 4. Do a Jelly Bean Taste Test 5. Respond to the Traditional Knowledge Poster: Berries **Explain:** 6. Read and Respond to the Non-fiction Book *Exploring With Our Senses* 7. Determine Different Tastes 8. Identify If It Is Good for Me or Bad for Me 9. Reflect on Learning **Extend:** 10. Talk With a Guest Speaker 11. Do a Gourmet Jelly Bean Taste Test 12. Watch a Food Program 13. Respond to Literature	PM 1: I Wonder ... PM 6: A Venn Diagram PM 7: Make a Bar Graph PM 13: Look What I've Learned LM 15: Our Taste Likes and Dislikes LM 16: Jelly Bean Taste Test LM 17: Tastes LM 18: How Does My Lunch Taste? LM 19: Good for Me or Bad for Me? LM 20: This Is What I Can Do Non-fiction Book: *Exploring With Our Senses* Lap Book Skills Poster: Safety in Science Class Traditional Knowledge Poster: Berries	• sweet foods (sugar, honey, maple syrup), sour foods (lemon, lime, dill pickles), bitter foods (unsweetened chocolate, cocoa, black coffee), salty foods (sea salt, pretzels, plain chips), water • jelly beans of various colours • fresh and dried berries • *Berry Magic* by Teri Sloat and Betty Huffmon or *Blueberries for Sal* by Robert McCloskey • blindfold, food items such as lemons, grapes, cranberries, olives
5: Sense of Touch 4–5 hours	**Engage:** 1. Activate and Build on Prior Knowledge 2. Elicit "I Wonder ..." Statements **Explore:** 3. Investigate Mystery Bags 4. Feel With Our Feet 5. Feel With Sock Hands 6. Role-play Using Touch Like Animals **Explain:** 7. Read and Respond to the Non-fiction Book *Exploring With Our Senses* 8. Make Different Observations 9. Reflect on Learning **Extend:** 10. Respond to Literature 11. Make Texture Collections 12. Try a Morning Without Touch 13. Explore Other "I Wonder ..." Statements	PM 1: I Wonder ... PM 13: Look What I've Learned LM 21: Mystery Bags LM 22: Foot Feel LM 23: This Is What I Can Do Non-fiction Book: *Exploring With Our Senses* Lap Book Science Poster: Which senses do you use?	• plastic zip bags with objects and materials of different textures (e.g., mashed bananas, dried beans, fun fur, etc.), baby wipes, paper lunch bags • objects objects with different textures (e.g., bubble wrap, cotton balls, tissue paper, lentils), tile or piece of sturdy cardboard, glue • access to Internet
Unit Closer: Putting It All Together 1–2 hours	**Looking Back:** 1. Consider the Learning Targets 2. Reread the Fiction Book *On the Trail* 3. Consider "I Wonder ..." Statements 4. Finish Reading the Non-fiction Book *Exploring With Our Senses* **Going Further:** 5. Observe Popcorn with Five Senses	PM 4: Finding Out PM 9: I Found Out LM 24: Popcorn LM 25: Rate Your Learning Fiction Book: *On the Trail* Non-fiction Book: *Exploring With Our Senses* Lap Book Science Poster: Which senses do you use? Skills Poster: Observing and Recording	• microwave popcorn or popcorn kernels and a popcorn maker • blindfolds

* Time and materials lists are for Core Learning Opportunities only.

UNIT 3 Unit Opener: Getting Started

Time
1 hour

Program Resources
PM 1: I Wonder ...
LM 1: Learning Targets
Fiction Book: *On the Trail*
Non-fiction Book: *Exploring With Our Senses*
Lap Book
Science Poster: Which senses do you use?
Skills Poster: Observing and Recording

This unit is an exploration of the five senses: sight, hearing, smell, taste, and touch. We use these senses every day and often take for granted all of the information we gather from them. They provide us with information to keep us safe and to help us interact with the environment around us. Other animals rely on their senses for the same reasons. This unit also explores animal adaptations related to the senses.

***Traditional* Knowledge**

Some Aboriginal peoples believe that there is a sixth sense related to the Spirit world. For example, this is when you get a feeling that someone or something is near you. Animals and plants are closer to the Spirit world because they live and thrive in harmony with Mother Earth. Unlike humans, they don't exploit the earth for its natural resources, don't directly cause other species to become extinct, don't pollute earth's ecosystem. When people misuse the gifts of Creator, Elders teach us that humanity lives out of synch with Mother Earth. This is why Knowledge Keeper Judy Bear's diagram of the natural world in the Program Overview shows that animals and plants are considered closer to the spirit world than humanity. Note that this diagram is based on the teachings of the Elders of the Sweetgrass Cree Nation. They ask that the diagram not be shared directly with students.

Through guided inquiry, students will follow simple procedures to investigate the use of human senses and how animals use their senses. They will record their observations and follow directions in their explorations. They will also have opportunities to explore and practise selecting and safely using materials and tools to carry out explorations, recording observations and measurements, making comparisons, making and testing predictions, designing and carrying out investigations, posing questions and communicating ideas, and collaborating with other students.

Introduce the Unit

1. Set Up an Ongoing Bulletin Board Display

- Begin by displaying the Science poster **Which senses do you use?** Ask students which body part is being used in each of the top photos. Then read the words under the photos and discuss which word(s) best describes what is being sensed in each photo. Finally, ask students: If this poster provides clues about our new unit, what might we be exploring? Record students' suggestions on chart paper or the board. This will assist in activating students' prior knowledge before beginning the unit.
- Make a heading "Five Senses" for the bulletin board and read it to students. Post a large "I wonder ..." bubble like the one on **PM 1: I Wonder ...** and say, "I wonder what we will learn in this unit." Invite students to brainstorm ideas. Record their ideas on a chart or paper strips. Use questions to guide them toward developing "I wonder ..." statements that reflect the big ideas of the unit:

- I wonder what our senses help us to do.
- I wonder how our senses work.
- I wonder how we can use our senses.
- I wonder how someone who has problems with one of the senses deals with this challenge.
- I wonder how animals use their senses.

• Have students start a science journal for the unit and record an "I wonder ..." statement that they want to answer.
• Add vocabulary words, students' work, photos of students involved in investigations of senses, and other related items as the unit progresses.

Introduce the Books

Notes
• This is a brief introduction to the books and unit. Key concepts will be explored in more depth throughout the unit.
• This initial look at the book(s) can take place as a whole group, using the Lap Book, with small groups, at a centre, or during the literacy block of time.

2. Motivate Using the Fiction Book *On the Trail*

Before: Ask students if they have ever had the opportunity to go camping. Show the cover of the book to students and read the title. Ask students what they think the book might be about based on the picture and the title.
During: Distribute copies of the book or use the Lap Book.
Pages 2–13: Use a Picture Walk to give students a preview of the book. Stop at each two-page spread and ask students to describe what they see on the pages, what they think is happening, and what might happen next. Through discussion, elicit that the children are following a dog that has noticed something using his senses.
After: Stop after page 13 to avoid revealing the ending. Assure students that they will have other opportunities to read the book and learn what the children find while they are hiking on the trail.

3. Motivate Using the Non-fiction Book *Exploring With Our Senses*

Before: Show students the cover of the book, read the title aloud, and invite students to discuss the cover images. Ask students what they think the book will be about. Explain that this is a non-fiction book. Non-fiction books provide facts and information.
During: Distribute copies of *Exploring With Our Senses* or use the Lap Book.
Pages 2–7: Start students on a Picture Walk through pages 2–7. Stop at each two-page spread to briefly discuss the questions:
- What do you think you are going to learn about from these pages?
- What do you think you will learn from this unit?
- What other things do you know about the senses?

After: Refer to Talk Time 6 and 9 to introduce students to the idea of how senses keep them and other animals safe.

Notes
• These Unit Targets are developed from the Sciences outcomes for this unit. If they seem overwhelming, leave them for now or choose key points to discuss.
• Lesson-specific learning targets are provided for each lesson.

Introduce the Learning Targets

4. Post the Student-friendly Learning Targets

• Make and post a chart of the learning targets on **LM 1: Learning Targets** for students to view. Read them with students and refer to them throughout the unit to encourage students to reflect on their learning.

1 Sense of Sight

Time
4–5 hours

Vocabulary
colour
shape
lustre
pupil
braille
adapt

Program Resources
PM 1: I Wonder ...
PM 13: Look What I've Learned
LM 2: Braille Alphabet
LM 3: This Is What I Can Do
Non-fiction Book: *Exploring With Our Senses*
Lap Book
Science Poster: Which senses do you use?

Materials and Equipment
- small objects of varying colour, lustre, and shape
- beanbags, blindfolds
- reflective surface (e.g., a mirror or a piece of cardboard covered with aluminum foil)
- light source e.g., a flashlight)
- kraft paper
- glue in plastic squeeze bottles (not glue sticks)

GOAL

Students will associate the eyes with the sense of sight, and use colour, shape, and lustre to sort objects. They will also explore how animals use their sight.

ASSESSMENT CHART

Science Indicators	Assessment Opportunities
SE1.1 a. Identify each of the senses and associate those senses with parts of humans or other animals, including sight and eyes, smell and nose, hearing and ears, taste and tongue/nose, and touch and skin.	Engage 1 Explore 3, 4 Explain 5
SE1.1 b. Identify characteristics used to describe the range of observations related to each sense (e.g., appearance can be described in terms of shape, colour, and lustre).	Engage 1 Explore 3 Explain 8
SE1.1 i. Sort objects and materials according to characteristics (e.g., colour, shape, texture) related to one or more senses.	Explore 3
SE1.2 f. Assess the function of aids (e.g., glasses, hearing aids, raised Braille alphabet, sign language, and guide dogs) that support peoples' differing abilities to sense their environment.	Explain 5, 7
SE1.2 h. Suggest how a human or animal might function if they were totally or partially missing one or more of the five senses.	Explain 7
SE1.2 k. Describe different sense organs and/or adaptations that enable various animals to accomplish their daily tasks (e.g., bats use echolocation to find prey, cat's pupils dilate to see in low light, etc.).	Explain 5, 6
English Language Arts Indicators	**Assessment Opportunities**
CR1.1 b. Make and share connections among texts, prior knowledge, and personal experiences (e.g., family traditions).	Engage 1 Explain 7
CR1.3 h. Listen to and carry out directions with four to six simple steps.	Explore 4 Explain 6, 7

BACKGROUND INFORMATION

We see things because light bounces off objects and enters our eye. The amount of light that enters our eye is controlled by the iris. This light goes through the lens, which focuses the light onto the retina. Embedded in the retina are specialized cells called rods and cones. The rods help us see the difference in light conditions. The cones work in a similar way to help us see colours and details. The more light there is, the better the cones work. This is why it is difficult to perceive colour in low light.

All living things have adaptations which help them survive. Adaptations to the sense of sight are anatomical. Animals' eyes vary in shape, number, location, and function. For example, some aquatic animals have special eyelids that help them see while in the water, and nocturnal animals may have bigger pupils that help them see in low light conditions.

ASSESSMENT FOR LEARNING

Look for Evidence of Learning	Student-friendly Learning Targets
Can the student: • associate the eyes with the sense of sight? • identify the characteristics they can see? • explain how our eyes help us identify objects and materials and warn us of possible danger? • describe how other animals have adapted vision to help them in their different environments?	(self-assessment) • I know that my eyes and animal eyes are used for sight. • I can sort objects into groups according to what I see. • I can explain how my eyes help me to know what is safe and what is not safe. • I can discuss different ways that animals use their eyes.

DI DIFFERENTIATING INSTRUCTION

For EAL
Before beginning this lesson, determine students' understandings of the basic colour words and shapes. Make flashcards showing animals that you will be studying and their correct names.

For Enrichment
Use students' "I wonder ..." statements to guide an inquiry project. Have them choose a specific animal to research and present their findings about animal vision to the rest of the class.

For Extra Support
Since many of the activities use the same strategies as found in the math curriculum, make and review a visual record of concepts learned previously. These might include photos or drawings created by students or videos.

CURRICULUM CONNECTIONS

Students will have the opportunity to develop skills and concepts in the following area:

Physical Education
PE1.5 e. Throw various small objects (e.g., balls, beanbags) from varying distances, both underhand and overhand, under, over, through, and at obstacles such as nets and hoops, using one hand and then the other.

PE1.10 c. Describe what it looks like and sounds like when people are being respectful and showing consideration for others, while participating in a movement activity.

CORE LEARNING OPPORTUNITIES

Engage

1. Activate and Build on Prior Knowledge

- Use the non-fiction book *Exploring With Our Senses* to activate students' prior knowledge about the sense of sight.

Before: Show students the cover of the book and read the title aloud. Ask students:

- What is the girl on the cover doing?
- What sense is she using?
- What part of her body is she using?

During: With the Lap Book, use a Shared Reading approach to read pages 2–6.

Pages 2–3: As you read about each sense, ask students to point to the body part used for that sense.

Page 4: Read the text on page 4 and then ask students to answer the questions.

Page 5–6: Read the text and draw students' attention to the illustrations. Ask students:

- What is the boy in the picture at the bottom of the page doing to keep himself safe? What sense is he using?
- How else might we use the sense of sight to keep ourselves safe? (We use caution when we see flashing lights, we don't eat foods that are discoloured or that have mould on them, we avoid obstacles we see in the street, etc.)
- What can we do to protect our eyes? (Wear sunglasses, wear safety goggles.)

After: In pairs, have students find examples in the classroom of the different shapes and colours mentioned in the book (square, circle, triangle, rectangle; blue, red, green, yellow, white, black). In pairs, students can do Talk Time 2.

Literacy Check
Can the student:
- read the "I wonder ..." statements in the class list and identify "I wonder ..." statements for his or her personal list?
- copy "I wonder ..." statements from the class list onto his or her personal list?

2. Elicit "I Wonder ..." Statements

- Model an "I wonder ..." form of inquiry with a statement such as: "I wonder if dogs' eyes work the same as our eyes?"
- Invite students to offer other "I wonder ..." statements. Record these on a chart or paper strips, and read them together. Provide students with copies of **PM 1: I Wonder ...** to record statements that interest them. Some students may require individual or small group assistance to identify statements and record them.

Science Check
Can the student:
- associate the eye with the sense of sight?
- identify the characteristics they see?
- categorize objects and materials according to the characteristics they see?

Explore

3. Play I Spy

- Briefly discuss observations we can make about objects using our sense of sight to help us to describe how an object looks (shape, colour, and lustre) and show students real examples of each. Some students may have difficulty with the concept of lustre, so explain to them that lustre refers to how shiny an object is.

- In pairs, have students challenge each other to identify and sort objects by giving clues based on characteristics they can see: "I spy with my little eye, something this is shiny." Or red, or round, or any other characteristic that can be seen. Encourage them to tell you which characteristic they are using to do their sorting.

Safety Check
Ensure that blindfolded students are pointing at the targets before they toss and that all other students are well behind the throwing line.

4. Use Senses to Catch Beanbags

- In this activity, students will experience how important their sense of sight is. Place several targets on the ground in a large open space such as a gym or in the school yard. Have blindfolded students individually try to hit a target with a beanbag. After removing the blindfold, give students a couple more tries to hit the target.
- Bring students back into the circle to discuss what they experienced. Ask students:
  - Was it harder to hit the target and throw when your eyes were covered? Why?
  - What senses did you use when your eyes were covered?
  - How many times did you hit the target when your eyes were covered compared to when you were able to see?

Explain

5. Read and Respond to the Non-fiction Book *Exploring With Our Senses*

Before: Ask students what they would have trouble doing if they lost their sense of sight. They will likely mention that they would have trouble walking and that they would not be able to read.

During: With the Lap Book, use a Shared Reading approach to read and discuss page 6.

Page 6: Ask students if anyone can tell us something about Braille. Explain that it is a system of raised dots that represent the letters of the alphabet. People who have problems seeing can feel the dots and read the text. Ask students: Which sense is being used to read Braille?

After: Using **LM 2: Braille Alphabet**, have students place one dot of puff paint on each of the black dots. Tell them not to touch the dots until the paint is dry. Once the paint is dry, they will be able to feel the raised dots with their fingertips.

- Have students use the Braille alphabet to spell out their names. This might work best if they use a pencil to copy the letters of their names in Braille first on a new sheet of paper. After the paint dries, have students work in small groups to exchange sheets and see if they can read one another's names. Discuss other tools or strategies that visually impaired people use to help them in their everyday lives (e.g., Seeing Eye dogs, white canes, special computers).

***Traditional* Knowledge**

- In First Nations, Métis, and Inuit cultures it was understood that if someone lost their capacity of sight, everyone would help out in a respectful way that allowed the person to maintain his or her dignity. This was so that the person would not feel like he or she was a burden.

✓ Science Check
Can the student:
- describe what peripheral vision is?
- identify why peripheral vision is important?

6. Test Your Field of Vision

- Explain to students that many animals, such as horses, deer, and goats, can see what is beside them even when facing forward, because their eyes are on the sides of their heads. Seeing what is beside you is called peripheral vision. In this activity, students will test their own peripheral vision, or field of vision, in small groups.
- Before breaking into small groups, model the activity. Have a volunteer stand on a large sheet of kraft paper while another student draws a semicircle on one side of the volunteer, an arm's length away from the volunteer's body. Then, the volunteer looks straight ahead while the other student holds an object at eye level and starting behind the volunteer, slowly walks around the semi-circle. When the volunteer first sees the object, he or she can ask the other student to stop walking and mark an X on the kraft paper on that spot. Model how to record their results in their journals by drawing a small circle to represent them from above and then an X beside their bodies where they first saw the object.
- Have students work in small groups to do the activity and record their results. Afterward, ask students:
  - How might peripheral vision help us to stay safe?
  - Why might it be important for animals to have good peripheral vision? (It can help them watch out for predators.)

✓ Science Check
Can the student:
- describe how the vision of some animals has adapted to help them survive in different environments?
- explain how his or her eyes help to identify things in the environment and warn of possible danger.
- describe adaptations that help animals in their daily lives?

7. Read and Respond to the Non-fiction Book *Exploring With Our Senses*

Before: Ask students to share what they know about how animals use their sense of sight to do daily tasks such as finding their way around, finding food, or watching out for other animals.
During: Distribute copies of *Exploring With Our Senses* to students. Use a Shared Reading approach to work as a whole group or in small groups based on reading level and needs.
Page 7: Read the text. Ask students for answers to the question on the page. (They use their sight to find food.)
After: Explain to students that animals that are active at night (nocturnal) have special adaptations for living in the dark. Adaptations are different body forms or structures that help living things survive. For example, owls have large eyes and pupils that let in a lot of light, allowing them to see better in the dark. Ask students why this is a useful adaptation. (When owls fly around at night, they won't bump into things and they can see the animals they are hunting.)

- Ask students if they have they ever noticed how some animals have eyes that seem to glow in the dark, and ask for specific examples. (Many will give the examples of cats and dogs, some might mention deer or other nocturnal animals like the tiger shown in the book.)
- Explain that these animals have a special membrane in their eyes. It works like a mirror. Even at night there is a little bit of light, and this light goes into the animal's eye, hits this membrane, and is reflected back inside the eye. This lets the animal's eye have a second chance to collect information from the light to help them see.
- Demonstrate or have students use a mirror or other reflective surface to reflect light. In a darkened room, shine a light source, such as a

flashlight, toward a reflective surface to illuminate a specific object or area. Ask students if the object or area seemed brighter when the light was reflected. Ask them why this would be good for animals that are awake at night. They should come to the conclusion that it allows the animals' eyes to use more light.

Traditional **Knowledge**

- You might ask an Elder or Knowledge Keeper to visit the class to tell stories about animal sight.

Science Check
Can the student:
- categorize objects according to the characteristics they see?

8. Categorize Objects by Colour, Shape, Lustre
- Have students look at the Science poster **Which senses do you use?**
- Ask students to group and categorize the objects they see using the characteristics they see (colour, shape, lustre). Ask students:
  - Why are some objects harder to group than others?
  - Do some objects have more than one shape/colour?

9. Reflect on Learning
- Have students record evidence of their learning on **PM 13: Look What I've Learned.** They can also record in their journal or with a video or audio recording on a smart device or camera. Encourage them to note at least two things they learned about sight and something they still wonder about.
- Use **LM 3: This Is What I Can Do** as a self-assessment. Read the learning targets with students and have them respond on their own. Some students may need assistance.

Literacy Check
Can the student:
- speak clearly about ideas and experiences in a logical sequence?
- represent key ideas and events using pictures, dramatization, and models?

OTHER LEARNING OPPORTUNITIES

Extend: Activity Bank

At any time, choose from the following options to replace or supplement the Core Learning Opportunities to meet students' needs and/or interests.

10. Make a Collage
- Choose one of the characteristics that can be sensed by sight (shape, colour, lustre) and have students create collages using pictures from magazines and objects. Students can make other collages based upon the characteristics that you want to evaluate (e.g., a collage of only square objects, a collage of only blue objects).

11. Play Twister
- Play the game Twister to help students with recognizing colours and shapes.

12. Listen to a Guest Speaker
- Invite an individual who is visually impaired to speak to the class. Ask this guest to share examples of aids (e.g., books in Braille) that help him or her sense the environment.

2 Sense of Hearing

Time
3–4 hours

Vocabulary
pitch
natural
artificial
echolocation

Program Resources
PM 1: I Wonder ...
PM 6: A Venn Diagram
PM 13: Look What I've Learned
LM 4: Sound Scavenger Hunt
LM 5: How Animals Use Their Hearing
LM 6: What Do Animal Ears Do?
LM 7: Keeping My Ears Safe
LM 8: American Sign Language Alphabet
LM 9: Loud and Soft Sounds
LM 10: This Is What I Can Do
Fiction Book: *On the Trail*
Non-fiction book: *Exploring With Our Senses*
Lap Book
Science Poster: Which senses do you use?
Skills Poster: Observing and Recording

Materials and Equipment
- clipboards, pencils
- research resources such as levelled reading materials, pictures in books
- blindfolds
- disposable earplugs, music, boom box

GOAL

Students will identify and categorize different types of sounds and recognize the importance of hearing to all living things.

ASSESSMENT CHART

Science Indicators	Assessment Opportunities
SE1.1 a. Identify each of the senses and associate those senses with parts of humans or other animals, including sight and eyes, smell and nose, hearing and ears, taste and tongue/nose, and touch and skin.	Engage 2 Explore 4 Explain 9
SE 1.1 b. Identify characteristics used to describe the range of observations related to each sense (e.g., sounds can be described as loud or soft, high pitch or low pitch; tastes related to the tongue can be described as sweet, sour, salty, or bitter; textures can be described as hard or soft, smooth or rough, sticky or not sticky; smells can be described as musky, aromatic, pungent, or putrid; and appearance can be described in terms of shape, colour, and lustre).	Engage 1 Explore 3, 4
SE 1.1 c. Provide examples of their favourite and least favourite sounds, smells, tastes, colours, and textures.	Explore 3
SE1.1 d. Discriminate among various natural and artificial sounds that humans can hear.	Engage 1 Explore 3 Explain 9, 10
SE1.1 e. Explain the purposes (e.g., detecting danger, navigation, and communication) of hearing in animals and humans.	Explore 5, 6 Explain 9, 11
SE1.1 j. Communicate questions, ideas, and intentions while conducting explorations of the human senses.	Explore 3, 7, 8
SE1.2 a. Pose questions that lead to exploration and investigation of human and animal senses.	Engage 2 Explore 5, 6
SE 1.2 c. Record observations of various environments (e.g., classroom, gymnasium, school yard, library, and cafeteria) using all of their senses as appropriate.	Explore 3
SE 1.2 f. Assess the function of aids (e.g., glasses, hearing aids, raised Braille alphabet, sign language, and guide dogs) that support peoples' differing abilities to sense their environment.	Explore 8
SE1.2 g. Experience changes in ability to explore the environment after the simulated loss of one or more senses (e.g., blindfold, earplugs, nose clip, and socks over both hands).	Explore 6, 7, 8
SE1.2 k. Describe different sense organs and/or adaptations that enable various animals to accomplish their daily tasks (e.g., bats use echolocation to find prey, etc.).	Explore 5, 6 Explain 9, 11
English Language Arts Indicators	**Assessment Opportunities**
CR1.2 a. Identify and locate the key information in pictures, charts, and other visual forms (e.g., photographs, physical movement, icons) including traditional and contemporary First Nations and Métis resources and performances.	Explore 4, 5, 8 Explain 9, 10, 11
CC1.3 f. Listen courteously and attentively to understand the meaning and intent of others.	Engage 1 Explore 3, 6, 8 Explain 9, 11

BACKGROUND INFORMATION

Sound is created by vibrations from the motion of objects. Waves of sound travel through a medium such as air or water.

Animal ears vary in size, placement, and function. Animals such as rabbits, horses, and deer have elongated outer ears, which are able to rotate in different directions. This helps them hear noises in different directions and decide if the noise is a threat. Birds have ears that are located behind and slightly below the eyes. Their ears are covered with special feathers that protect them from turbulence when flying but still allow them to hear.

***Traditional* Knowledge**

Aboriginal children are taught the importance of listening and observing. First Nations women swaddled their babies and bundled them tightly into moss bags. Babies in moss bags have only their eyes, ears, and nose exposed. This was so that, even at an early age, babies could observe the environment around them.

ASSESSMENT FOR LEARNING

Look for Evidence of Learning	Student-friendly Learning Targets
Can the student: • connect the sense of hearing to the ears? • discriminate between the characteristics used to describe different types of sounds? • provide examples of his or her favourite and least favourite sounds? • discriminate between natural and artificial sounds? • explain why hearing is important for humans and animals?	(self-assessment) • I know that I hear with my ears. • I can show you how to make loud/quiet sounds and high/low sounds. • I know which sounds I like and which sounds I don't like. • I know which sounds are made by nature and which ones are made by people and their machines. • I know that humans and animals use their ears to listen for danger, to help them get around, and to communicate.

DI DIFFERENTIATING INSTRUCTION

For EAL

Have students draw pictures representing important vocabulary word on index cards. Write the words on the back of the cards.

For Enrichment

Have students collect sounds at home for other students to identify. If they are unable to use a sound recording device to do this, ask them to "act out" the sounds they heard.

For Extra Support

To help students understand echolocation, have them roll a tennis ball against a wall with their eyes closed or blindfolded. They can gauge the distance to the wall based upon how long it takes the ball to return.

CURRICULUM CONNECTIONS

Students will have the opportunity to develop skills and concepts in the following area:

Arts Education

CP1.6 f. Identify and respond to loud/soft and louder/softer sounds (dynamics) in speech, music, and the environment.

CORE LEARNING OPPORTUNITIES

Engage

1. Activate and Build on Prior Knowledge

- Play a video of different animals and objects making various sounds. Have students close their eyes as they listen. Pause the video after each sound, and ask them what animal or object made the sound. Record their ideas in a list on chart paper. After listening to 8–10 different sounds, ask them to help you divide the list into groups such as soft/loud, pretty/scary, natural/artificial, high/low pitch. Explain to students that you are making observations using their sense of hearing.
- Ask students how they think animals use their ears. Have them use their hands to mimic those animals and how they might use their ears. Ask students:
  - What were the different types of animals that we acted out?
  - Why do you think animals have many different types of ears?
- Remind students that our hearing is an important part of communication. Ask students how animals might use their hearing for communicating with each other. Encourage them to give specific examples (e.g., kittens mewing for their mother, coyotes howling).
- Explain to students that animals use their hearing to warn them of danger. Ask students if they think humans use their hearing to warn them of danger. Brainstorm warning sounds, such as fire alarms, beeping from a smoke detector, or police car sirens.

Tip
- Be aware that some First Nations children are traditionally taught to observe and listen as a way of acquiring knowledge. Even if they are not being verbally interactive, they are still participating in learning. Keep this in mind when assessing students.

2. Elicit "I Wonder ..." Statements

- Model an "I wonder ..." form of inquiry with statements such as: "I wonder if owls have ears, because I can't see any ears."
- Invite students to offer other "I wonder ..." statements. Record these on a chart or paper strips, and read them together. Provide students with copies of **PM 1: I Wonder ...** to record statements that interest them. Some students may require individual or small group assistance.

Literacy Check
Can the student:
- read the "I wonder ..." statements in the class list and identify "I wonder ..." statements for his or her personal list?
- copy "I wonder ..." statements from the class list onto his or her personal list?

Explore

3. Go on a Sound Scavenger Hunt

- Explain to students that they will be going on a scavenger hunt to search for different sounds. Show them the Skills poster **Observing and Recording**. Tell them that sometimes we use all of our senses to make observations, but today we will be using our sense of hearing to observe sounds. You might introduce this activity by referring to Talk Time 8 in the non-fiction book *Exploring With Our Senses*.
- Put students in small groups with a pencil and a copy of **LM 4: Sound Scavenger Hunt** on a clipboard. Read the text together. Then guide students through the school and around the playground encouraging them to notice all the different types of sounds they are hearing.
- When students return, discuss what they heard. Make a large version of **LM 4** on a chart or on the board. Ask students to take turns sharing the different sounds they heard in the categories from **LM 4** (i.e., scary, happy, nature). Ask students which sound was their favourite and

Science Check
Can the student:
- record observations using his or her senses?
- discriminate between natural and artificial sounds?
- provide examples of his or her favourite and least favourite sounds?

encourage them to explain why. They may also want to classify the sounds they heard as loud or soft.

4. Describe the Sound

- Show students the Science poster **Which senses do you use?** Ask them to identify a photo that shows something they could use their hearing to sense if they were in the photo. (The cat purring, thunder rumbling, fire crackling, waves crashing, child whispering, drum beating.) Encourage them to describe the sounds. Were the sounds loud or soft? High pitched or low pitched?

Traditional **Knowledge**

- Tell students that the drum shown is a drum made and being played by a First Nations person. Ask them for words to describe what the drum playing would sound like. Then, tell them that when First Nations people are at powwows, they try to stand close to the drums so that they can also feel the vibrations of the drums.

Literacy Check
Can the student:
- comprehend and respond to a variety of grade-appropriate texts?
- speak clearly about ideas and experiences in a logical sequence?

5. Research the Hearing of Animals

- Have students choose an animal to research. Depending on the resources available and your students' readiness for research, the class could research a variety of animals or one specific animal, such as a bat.
- Make resources available to students to do their research. This may include levelled reading materials, pictures in books and on the Internet, and YouTube videos.
- Have students use **LM 5: How Animals Use Their Hearing** to record their information. Be sure that they describe their animal's environment under the "Lives" heading. Help students understand adaptations by asking questions such as:
  - How are your animal's ears adapted to where it lives?
  - How do animals use their ears to avoid danger?
- To help reinforce the different uses of ears, have students complete **LM 6: What Do Animal Ears Do?** Students' answers may vary depending on if they make certain connections to their learning.

Science Check
Can the student:
- describe adaptations that help animals in their daily lives?
- ask questions while learning about an animal's sense of hearing?

Safety Check
Students will be blindfolded, so they will need a clear space to move around in.

Science Check
Can the student:
- describe how bats use echolocation?
- explain why echolocation is important for bats?

6. Explore Bats and Echolocation

- Show students a few images of bats and explain to them that bats have very bad vision. Ask students: If they can't see well, how do they find their way around in the dark?
- Have students role-play being bats. In the gym, or another open space, blindfold half of the students. Assign a safety buddy to each blindfolded student to ensure that he or she won't get hurt while moving quietly around the gym.
- Have the partners switch. After everyone has had a chance to be blindfolded, discuss the experience. Ask students:
  - How did it feel to be blindfolded?
  - What senses did you use more than others?
  - Why was it important for everyone to move quietly? (They couldn't have used their sense of hearing to help them navigate if it was very loud.)
- For the second part of the activity, explain to students that bats use *echolocation*. This is when a bat makes a sound as it flies. The sound it

makes bounces off of an object, such as a tree, house or even an insect. When the sound comes back to the bat, it knows how far away the object is, what direction it is, and what size and shape it is. (See **For Extra Support** if students are struggling with this concept.)

7. Make Safety Rules for Our Ears

- Explain to students the importance of protecting our hearing. Ask students for examples of safety equipment that protects our hearing (e.g., earplugs, earmuffs). Elicit that these work by preventing sound waves or vibrations from entering our ears. Provide some examples of sounds that can damage hearing, from a hearing loss organization such as www.dangerousdecibels.org.
- Have students insert disposable earplugs into their ears. Play some music at a loud volume. Then have students remove their earplugs. Play the same music at the same volume as before. Using **LM 7: Keeping My Ears Safe**, students can record how they felt listening to the loud music with and without earplugs.
- Ask students what they can do to keep their ears safe (e.g., listen to music at low volumes, limit the use of headphones, wear earplugs at loud concerts). They can write down their safety rules for the ears on **LM 7**.

Safety Check
Tell students not to put anything in their ears. If they are using earplugs, ensure that the earplugs are being used for their intended use.

8. Try Lip-reading

- Have students work in pairs. One student will wear foam earplugs, while the other can talk quietly about something he or she likes. Have students discuss how well they could hear their partner and how much they understood. Have students switch roles. Be sure to use new earplugs for each student.
- Discuss with students that lip-reading is just one way that people with hearing loss communicate. Ask them what sense people are using when they lip-read.
- Explain that some people with hearing loss also use sign language. They use their hands and fingers to make words. There are some hand signals that mean certain words and there are also signals for letters of the alphabet which can be used to spell out words.
- Have students use **LM 8: American Sign Language Alphabet** to spell their names and simple words. To help students, you could show them YouTube videos that show how to form the letters. Use the phrase "ASL alphabet" or "American Sign Language" in your search.

Explain

9. Read and Respond to the Non-Fiction Book *Exploring With Our Senses*

Before: Ask students to touch the body part they use to hear. Remind them that there are many different types of sounds. Ask students for examples of how our sense of hearing helps us to communicate and may keep us safe from danger.

Literacy Check
Can the student:
- comprehend and respond to a variety of grade-level texts?
- speak clearly about ideas and experiences in a logical sequence?

During: Work as a whole group or in small groups based on reading level and needs, using a Shared Reading approach using the Lap Book.
Pages 8–9: Have students talk with a classmate about what they see. Read the text. Ask students to name three loud sounds and three quiet sounds. Ask students:
- How is the girl using her sense of hearing?
- Which of the sounds are natural sounds?
- Which sounds are not natural sounds (made by machines)?

Page 10: Read the text. If possible, show students a hearing aid and how it works. Have students make the signs to spell pizza. Ask students: How else do people communicate when they can not hear well?
Page 11: Read the text and then ask students what adaptations owls, hares, and bats use to hear. Explain that owls have asymmetrical ear openings so they receive sounds milliseconds apart, which helps them locate prey.
After: Talk Time 8 could be used to assess students' comprehension.

10. Make a Venn Diagram

- Have students cut out the pictures on **LM 9: Loud and Soft Sounds** and place them on a Venn diagram to show their understanding that some objects make loud noises, some make quiet noises, and others can produce both. Provide copies of **PM 6: A Venn Diagram**.
- You can also have students show their understanding of sounds that are natural and sounds that are made by machines. Have students cut out the pictures and paste them on a larger piece of paper, with the headings "Natural" and "Artificial."

Literacy Check
Can the student:
- comprehend and respond to grade-level texts?
- speak clearly about ideas and experiences in a logical sequence?

11. Read and Respond to the Fiction Book *On the Trail*

Before: Discuss with students what animals use their sense of hearing for. Elicit that animals use their hearing to keep them safe from predators, to find prey, and even to communicate with other animals. Tell them you are going to read a book in which a dog helps some people by using his sense of hearing.
During: Distribute copies of the book. Work as a whole group or in small groups based on reading level and needs, using a Shared Reading approach.
Pages 2–11: Use a Picture Walk to give students a preview of the book. Stop at each two-page spread and ask:
- What do you see here?
- What do the pictures tell you about the characters?
- What do you think is happening?
- What might happen next?

- Have students discuss how the children and Roy the dog used their sense of hearing to observe their environment and stay safe. Ask students to predict what animals the characters think they hear.

Pages 12–15: Continue reading. On page 15, encourage students to recognize the role the sense of smell played in the story.
After: As a group, you could discuss Talk Time 4 and 5. Brainstorm other examples of animals helping humans (e.g., Seeing Eye dogs). Now might be a good time to explore Talk Time 2 as well.

12. Reflect on Learning

- Have students record evidence of their learning on **PM 13: Look What I've Learned.** They can also record in their journal or with a video or audio recording on a smart device or camera. Encourage them to note at least two things they learned about hearing and one thing they would still like to learn.
- Use **LM 10: This Is What I Can Do** as a self-assessment. Read the learning targets with students and have them respond on their own. Some students may need assistance.

OTHER LEARNING OPPORTUNITIES

Extend: Activity Bank

At any time, choose from the following options to replace or supplement the Core Learning Opportunities to meet students' needs and/or interests.

13. Guess What Made That Sound

- Have students collect sounds at home and/or in the community. If they are unable to use a sound recording device to do this, ask students to "act out" the sound they heard using their voices. Other students can take turns guessing what the sound is.

14. Have an Animal Ear Parade

- Provide students with various arts and crafts materials. Tell students they will make the ears of the animal they researched in Explore 5. Put the ears on headbands and have students each parade and explain to others why these ears are well suited for their chosen animal. Be sure to ask students why the shape and/or location of the ears is important to their animal's survival in the wild.

***Traditional* Knowledge**

15. Invite a Knowledge Keeper or Elder to Talk About Listening and to Tell Stories

- Invite a Knowledge Keeper or Elder to visit the class to explain the importance of listening and possibly to tell stories related to how animals use their sense of hearing. One of those stories might be why the rabbit or deer didn't get their voices.
- Some First Nations peoples believe that the voice is sacred and that it has a connection to the Spirit world. Prayer is said in one's own language because the voice is a connection to the Spirit world. The voice is so powerful that when a person speaks or sings, everything listens. When you sing the bear song, you are speaking to Spirit in the bear. It is important that there be a reason for speaking and using your voice. When you speak, it comes from a special place. You are accountable for the things you say.
- Many First Nations, Métis, and Inuit people also believe that everything is connected. A story is not over when it is finished being told. There is a connection to the next thing or lesson. When an

Elder tells a story, it must be told in the same way *they* were told the story. The Elder might add a little humour to the story, but they will tell you what they have personally added to the story. This is part of the storytelling tradition, and how important knowledge has been taught for generations.

16. Invite a Class Visitor to Talk About Hearing Loss

- Invite someone who has hearing loss to visit the class and speak about how he or she uses other senses and supportive aids to accomplish daily tasks. You may want to bring in someone who uses sign language.

17. Create a Device

- Have students brainstorm and create a device to assist people with hearing loss. You may have to help students understand the needs of people with hearing loss. The devices that they create should be reflective of what they have learned in the lesson and help them in communicating or warn them of danger.
- Students can illustrate their device or make a model. They may need to use dictation to explain how their device works and assists those with hearing loss.

18. Explore Other "I Wonder ..." Statements

- Return to the "I wonder ..." statements not yet answered and new wonderings that have come up. With students, plan and set up centres where they can explore these wonderings. Encourage them to make and test predictions.
- Working in small groups, students can rotate to all the centres or focus on one per group. They could share their findings in oral, written, or electronic presentations.

3 Sense of Smell

Time
5–6 hours

Program Resources
PM 1: I Wonder ...
PM 13: Look What I've Learned
LM 11: Mystery Containers
LM 12: How Do They Smell?
LM 13: Different Smells
LM 14: This Is What I Can Do
Non-fiction Book: *Exploring With Our Senses*
Skills Poster: Safety in Science Class
Skills Poster: Observing and Recording

Materials and Equipment:
- magazines
- clear containers, water, clear dish soap, white vinegar, red vinegar, cider vinegar
- variety of food substances with strong scents (e.g., curry powder, vanilla extract, onion), opaque containers with lids
- Sesame Street video *Troy Polamalu Talks Fragrance with Elmo*
- containers, water, coffee filters, funnel, strong smelling flowers, vanilla extract, cinnamon, cloves
- object with a distinct smell (e.g., pine bough, fresh cut grass, fresh baked goods), paper bag

GOAL

Students will associate their nose with the sense of smell and examine how the sense of smell warns us of danger. They will also explore how other animals use their sense of smell.

ASSESSMENT CHART

Science Indicators	Assessment Opportunities
SE1.1 b. Identify characteristics used to describe the range of observations related to each sense (e.g., sounds can be described as loud or soft, high pitch or low pitch; tastes related to the tongue can be described as sweet, sour, salty, or bitter; textures can be described as hard or soft, smooth or rough, sticky or not sticky; smells can be described as musky, aromatic, pungent, or putrid; and appearance can be described in terms of shape, colour, and lustre).	Engage 1 Explore 5
SE1.1 c. Provide examples of their favourite and least favourite sounds, smells, tastes, colours, and textures.	Engage 1 Explore 4
SE1.1 g. Assess the ability of humans and other animals to distinguish among various smells.	Engage 1 Explore 3, 4, 6, 7 Explain 9
SE1.1 i. Sort objects and materials according to characteristics (e.g., colour, shape, texture, odour, sweetness, and loudness) related to one or more senses.	Engage 1 Explore 4 Explain 9
SE1.1 j. Communicate questions, ideas, and intentions while conducting explorations of the human senses.	Explore 4, 6, 7
SE1.2 e. Explain and follow given safety procedures and rules when using the senses to observe (e.g., explain the danger to health of tasting unknown materials and the reasons for wafting odours towards the nose rather than smelling directly).	Explore 3 Explain 8
SE1.2 j. Discuss dangers associated with using the senses to examine the environment (e.g., breathing in certain odours may cause illness).	Explore 3, 9 Explain 8
SE1.2 l. Provide examples of how the senses are important to people in their hobbies and jobs.	Engage 1 Explore 6
English Language Arts Indicators	**Assessment Opportunities**
CC1.2 a. Understand that making pictures, illustrations, and other representations clarify and extend understanding.	Explore 7 Explain 8
CC1.3 a. Use oral language to bring meaning to what is listened to, observed, felt, viewed, and read.	Engage 1 Explore 3, 4, 7 Explain 8

BACKGROUND INFORMATION

Our nose helps us to smell, helps us to taste, and is the gateway to our respiratory system. When we inhale, air enters into our nasal passages before making its way into our nasal cavity. On the roof of our nasal cavity is an area which allows us to sense as many as 10000 different smells. The receptors that gather the information are specifically coded by our DNA, so everyone is unique in his or her sense of smell. Researchers believe this is why some people like certain smells and others do not.

Some people are unable to smell odours due to chemicals blocking or stimulating receptors (e.g., air fresheners or cigarette smoke), sickness (sinus infections or viruses), head trauma, or genetic defects. Other people have a keen sense of smell. For some of those individuals the presence of some scents, such as perfume, can cause headache and nausea.

There are many different types of noses in the animal kingdom that allow animals to adapt and survive in their environment. Koala bears use their sense of smell to help them identify the specific type of gum tree leaves that they eat. The nostrils of rats work independently, allowing them to scan their environment. Their sense of smell is so acute that rats are used to detect landmines. Most dogs can smell 100 times better than a human, and some dogs, such as bloodhounds, can smell 300 times better.

It is believed that sharks have the best sense of smell of all animals. They can smell a drop of blood or the faint smell of fish in the water from a great distance. They have two nostrils on either side of their snouts and almost two-thirds of a shark's brain is devoted to its sense of smell. Snakes have very poor eyesight and almost no hearing, so they rely on their sense of smell. They don't have a nose. They use their tongues to smell the air around them.

ASSESSMENT FOR LEARNING

Look for Evidence of Learning	Student-friendly Learning Targets
Can the student: • associate the nose with the sense of smell? • identify the characteristics associated with smell and categorize objects and materials according to those characteristics? • demonstrate the correct safety procedures to use when smelling substances? • give examples of how our sense of smell helps us to recognize danger? • explain how some smells are dangerous?	(self-assessment) • I know that my nose is used for smelling. • I know that some objects and materials smell differently. • I can put objects in groups based on how they smell. • I can show you how to smell safely. • I can explain how our sense of smell can keep us safe. • I know that some smells are dangerous.

DI DIFFERENTIATING INSTRUCTION

For EAL

Provide sufficient scaffolding throughout this lesson by collecting a variety of manipulatives and visuals. Word walls, graphic organizers, models, and posters are helpful for introducing and reinforcing more difficult vocabulary. Also consider reteaching concepts and content in mini lessons for students who need additional support.

For Enrichment

Use students' "I wonder ..." statements to guide an inquiry project. Have students choose a specific job that might involve the sense of smell, research the job, and present their findings to the rest of the class. They could also develop a superhero with the power of a super sense of smell. They can either role-play or make an illustration of their superhero.

For Extra Support

Make a word wall using words that are associated with the sense of smell. You may want students to make their own glossary using the words on the wall and images associated with them.

CORE LEARNING OPPORTUNITIES

Engage

1. Activate and Build on Prior Knowledge

• Activate students' prior knowledge of the sense of smell using the non-fiction book *Exploring With Our Senses.*

Before: Ask students to point to the body part they use to smell. Ask them what they use their sense of smell for. In what jobs or hobbies might smelling be an asset? For example, a safety inspector or journalist.

During: Work as a whole group or in small groups, based on reading level and needs, using a Shared Reading approach.

Page 12: Read the text and then ask students for their favourite smells. Record their favourite smells organizing them on a tally chart. Draw their attention to the idea that different people have different favourites.

Page 13: Read the text. Ask students:

- What do you see in the photo? (burning toast, smoke)
- When might it be important to be able to smell smoke? (When there is a fire)
- What are the safety procedures for when there is a fire?
- What are other ways we might use our sense of smell to stay safe? (Smelling that food has gone bad so we don't eat it)

Pages 14–15: Read the text. Ask students:

- What is the dog using its sense of smell to do?
- What might the bear and shark be using their sense of smell for?
- Do sharks, bears, dogs, and humans all have the same sense of smell?

After: Distribute a pile of magazines and have students cut out images of objects that give off a smell. On a folded piece of paper, have them glue the pictures in two categories: "things that we think smell good" and "things that we think smell bad." Ask students to share their charts and some of their favourite and least favourite smells with the class. Remind students that our sense of smell is different from person to person. What smells good to you might not smell good to someone else. Ask students to think of different jobs in which smell might be important.

Literacy Check
Can the student:
• read the "I wonder ..." statements in the class list and identify "I wonder ..." statements for his or her personal list?
• copy "I wonder ..." statements from the class list onto his or her personal list?

2. Elicit "I Wonder ..." Statements

• Model an "I wonder ..." form of inquiry with statements such as: "I wonder how many different kinds of smells I can sense," or "I wonder if animals' noses work the same way that the human nose works."
• Invite students to offer other "I wonder ..." statements. Record these on a chart or paper strips, and then read them together. Provide students with copies of **PM 1: I Wonder ...** and ask them to record statements that especially interest them.

Explore

Science Check
Can the student:
• associate the nose with the sense of smell?
• demonstrate the correct safety procedures to use when smelling substances?

3. Be Safe When Smelling

• Ask students how they think they should go about smelling something. Show students the Skills poster **Safety in Science Class**. Review all of the points and focus on the proper technique to be used when smelling.

Explain to students that our lungs can be very sensitive, and we need to protect them. When we are doing experiments, we need to use a special technique called *wafting* to make sure we don't hurt our lungs. Wafting ensures that only a small amount of the scent enters our body. Model how to waft for students. Put your hand over the substance that you would like to smell with your palm facing you and your hand slightly cupped. Bring your hand forward, pulling the scent toward you. Have students try it themselves a few times. Ask them why we should never smell something directly without knowing if it is safe first. (It could be a poisonous substance.)

- Introduce three clear containers: one filled with water, one with clear dish soap, and one with white vinegar. Have students observe the three liquids and record what they think each might be. Ask for volunteers to come up and smell each container, using the proper wafting technique. Ask students if they can identify the liquids after smelling them:
  - Do the smells remind you of anything?
  - Were you surprised that the three liquids smelled so different even though they looked the same?
- Introduce three more clear containers: one filled with red vinegar, one with white vinegar, and one with cider vinegar. The substances in these containers will all look very different, but because they are all vinegar, will smell very similar. Repeat the procedure from above, and then discuss with students what they observed. Guide them to the conclusion that we need to use a number of senses in order to adequately observe the world around us.

Safety Check
Some students may have allergies and/or sensitivities to some of these items. Be sure to check with parents to ensure the safety of students.

Literacy Check
Can the student:
- select the correct descriptive word to describe each smell?
- clearly record what he or she likes/dislikes about each smell?

4. Identify Mystery Smells

- In this activity, you will be setting up smell stations for students to rotate through. Choose a variety of scents for students to smell (e.g., curry powder, vanilla extract, onion, garlic, cinnamon, oranges, mashed bananas, sauerkraut). Place the substances in opaque containers with a small hole in the lid so they can smell the substance but not see it. Label each of the containers with a number.
- Show students the Skills poster **Observing and Recording**. Tell them that today they are going to be using their sense of smell and recording their observations on a chart.
- Have students rotate through the stations to smell each container. Remind students to use the proper wafting technique as they smell. Have students record whether or not they liked each scent on **LM 11: Mystery Containers**. In a follow-up discussion, encourage students to use descriptive words to describe the scents they prefer.
- In a large group, give students the chance to smell each container again, and then ask for guesses of what each container holds. After several students have guessed, reveal the contents of each container. As a class, have students share which smells they liked and which they disliked. Record responses on a tally chart. Talk about how different people can like or dislike a particular smell.

5. Match Animal Noses

- Animals have many different shapes and types of noses. They use the sense of smell to warn them of danger, mark territory, and find babies, mates, and food. Share some of following information with students supported with visuals:
  - Elephants have long trunks that are able to pick up odours up to 19 km away. Their nostrils are at the end of their trunk, and they move this trunk back and forth to smell things.
  - Pigs also have very sensitive noses. They can detect odours up to 11 km away and smell food that is buried more than 7 m underground. Pigs are often used to dig for truffles, a type of mushroom, because their sense of smell is so good.
  - Moles are animals that live underground. They have very poor eyesight and hearing, so they rely on their special noses to help them locate prey and find their way around.
  - Dogs can smell much better than humans. They use their sense of smell to identify territory, find food, and gather information.
  - Bears have the best sense of smell of all land animals. They can smell 2000 times better than a human. They use this powerful sense of smell to find food and mates, to mark territory, to find their cubs, and to warn them of danger.
  - Sharks can smell a drop of blood or the faint smell of fish in the water from a great distance. This helps them find prey.
  - Snakes have very poor eyesight and must rely on their sense of smell, yet they don't have a nose like other animals. They use their tongue to smell the air around them. Their tongue flicks in and out of their mouth, which collects the scent.
- In pairs, have students cut up **LM 12: How Do They Smell?** and play a memory game. Encourage students to not only match the nose with the correct animal, but also to name one other thing that the animal uses its nose for. Students will need to cut out copies of the line master to do this activity.

Science Check
Can the student:
- correctly match the nose with the animal?
- explain what the animal uses its nose for?
- recognize adaptations that help animals in their daily lives?

6. Work With Our Noses

- Ask students what types of jobs might require a good sense of smell (e.g., chefs need to smell if food smells good, safety inspectors smell for gas or burning materials).
- Explain to students that many of the products we purchase have a *fragrance* added to them. Ask students what they think the word fragrance means. To help with creating a working definition of the word, view the Sesame Street video *Troy Polamalu Talks Fragrance with Elmo*. This video can be found on YouTube. Students should have an understanding that fragrance is a pleasant odour or smell. There are people whose job is creating new and different fragrances. They train for many years. Some work for companies that make the products we use every day like shampoo, but others make perfume.
- Have students create their own perfumes using the sample recipes below. These recipes do not give scents that last but will give students a basic understanding of how perfumes are created:

Recipe 1	**Recipe 2**
240 mL of water 240 mL of strong smelling flowers such as lilac Combine the water and the flowers. Let the mixture sit overnight. Filter the mixture using coffee filters and a funnel.	240 mL of water dash of vanilla dash of cinnamon a few cloves Combine the water and the spices. Let the mixture sit overnight. Filter the mixture using coffee filters and a funnel.

- After students have completed this activity, have them recall the steps that they used to make their scented water. Encourage them to name their perfumes.

7. Respond to Smells
- Choose an object that has a distinct smell. This might be a pine bough, fresh cut grass, fresh baked goods, cinnamon and cloves. Place the object in a paper bag.
- Explain to students that our sense of smell not only warns us of danger, but sometimes it is linked to our memory. Certain smells can help us to remember special times in our lives.
- Have students sit in a circle, close their eyes, and smell what is in the paper bag. Then ask students to share what the smell makes them think of. Remind them not to tell what they think is in the bag, but concentrate on what the smell reminds them of.
- Have students make a painting or drawing of what the smell makes them think of. Some students may want to write a poem instead.

Literacy Check
Can the student:
- represent key ideas in a drawing or poem?

Explain

Science Check
Can the student:
- give examples of how our sense of smell helps us to recognize danger and stay safe?
- explain the important of using the wafting technique when smelling?

8. Make a Safety Video
- Have students work in small groups to create a public service announcement (PSA) video about smelling safely. They should demonstrate how to smell safety and how our sense of smell can help to keep us safe. Be sure that students explain why not using the wafting technique is dangerous. If recording equipment is not available, have students simply write out the script or storyboard for their PSA to share with other groups.

9. Identify Dangerous Smells
- Have students complete **LM 13: Different Smells** to demonstrate their understanding of good, bad, and dangerous smells. Have them explain how some smells are dangerous.

10. Reflect on Learning

- Have students record evidence of their learning on **PM 13: Look What I've Learned**. They can also record in their journal or with a video or audio recording on a smart device or camera. Encourage them to note at least two things they learned about the sense of smell and something they still wonder about.
- Use **LM 14: This Is What I Can Do** as a self-assessment. Read the learning targets with students and have them respond on their own. Some students may need assistance.

OTHER LEARNING OPPORTUNITIES

Extend: Activity Bank

At any time, choose from the following options to replace or supplement the Core Learning Opportunities to meet students' needs and/or interests.

11. Invite a Guest Speaker

- Contact SaskEnergy or the local fire department to have someone visit the class to discuss the dangers of smelling natural gas and what safety procedures to take.

Tip
Spices can stain clothing, so have students wear paint shirts.

12. Make Spice Paintings

- Choose a small variety of spices for students to use. Add a small amount of water to each of the spices. The less water you add, the stronger the colour will be. Using a paintbrush, students can paint a picture using two or three of the spices. Once the spices have dried, the scent can be released by scratching. They can ask a classmate to try to identify the spices used. Provide labelled containers of the spices so they can compare.

Literature Links
Smelly Socks by Robert Munsch
The Nose Book by Al Perkins

13. Make a Literature Link

- Read *Smelly Socks* by Robert Munsch. Ask students to describe how the dirty socks look and how they might smell. Talk about how the animals in the story reacted to the smelly socks. Have students retell the story from the perspective of one of the animals.
- Read *The Nose Book* by Al Perkins. Discuss all the different animal noses in the book. Have students create their own animal noses using clay, papier mâché, or construction paper.

14. Explore Other "I Wonder ..." Statements

- Return to the "I wonder ..." statements not yet answered and any new wonderings that have come up. With students, plan and set up centres where they can explore these wonderings. Encourage them to make and test predictions.
- Working in small groups, students can rotate to all the centres or focus on one per group. They could share their findings in an oral, written, or electronic presentations.

4 Sense of Taste

Time
3–4 hours

Vocabulary
sweet
sour
salty
bitter

Program Resources
PM 1: I Wonder ...
PM 6: A Venn Diagram
PM 7: Make a Bar Graph
PM 13: Look What I've Learned
LM 15: Our Taste Likes and Dislikes
LM 16: Jelly Bean Taste Test
LM 17: Tastes
LM 18: How Does My Lunch Taste?
LM 19: Good for Me or Bad for Me?
LM 20: This Is What I Can Do
Non-fiction Book: *Exploring With Our Senses*
Skills Poster: Safety in Science Class
Traditional Knowledge Poster: Berries

Materials and Equipment
- sweet foods (sugar, honey, maple syrup), sour foods (lemon, lime, dill pickles), bitter foods (unsweetened chocolate, cocoa, black coffee), salty foods (sea salt, pretzels, plain chips), water
- jelly beans of various colours
- fresh and dried berries
- *Berry Magic* by Teri Sloat and Betty Huffmon or *Blueberries for Sal* by Robert McCloskey
- blindfold, food items such as lemons, grapes, cranberries, olives

GOAL

Students will understand how our tongue helps us to identify different tastes.

ASSESSMENT CHART

Science Indicators	Assessment Opportunities
SE1.1 a. Identify each of the senses and associate those senses with parts of humans or other animals, including sight and eyes, smell and nose, hearing and ears, taste and tongue/nose, and touch and skin.	Explore 3 Explain 6
SE1.1 b. Identify characteristics used to describe the range of observations related to each sense (e.g., tastes related to the tongue can be described as sweet, sour, salty, or bitter).	Engage 1 Explore 3 Explain 5, 6, 7
SE 1.1 c. Provide examples of their favourite and least favourite sounds, smells, tastes, colours, and textures.	Explore 3 Explain 6
SE1.1 h. Categorize foods as sweet, sour, salty, or bitter, and compare results with others.	Explore 3, 4, 5 Explain 6, 7
SE1.1 i. Sort objects and materials according to characteristics (e.g., colour, shape, texture, odour, sweetness, and loudness) related to one or more senses.	Explore 5 Explain 6, 7, 8
SE1.2 b. Record observations about specific objects (e.g., apple, pencil, shirt, and tree) in their environment using all of their senses as appropriate.	Explore 4 Explain 7
SE1.2 e. Explain and follow given safety procedures and rules when using the senses to observe (e.g., explain the danger to health of tasting unknown materials).	Engage 1 Explain 6, 8
SE1.2 i. Explain how each of the senses helps us to recognize, describe, and safely use materials, and recognize potential dangers in the environment (e.g., colour and smell help determine whether fruit is healthy or bruised, ripe or overripe).	Engage 1 Explain 8
English Language Arts Indicators	**Assessment Opportunities**
CR1.4 a. Read and interpret own writing, experience charts, labels, symbols, and print in environment.	Explore 3, 4, 5 Explain 6, 7, 8, 9
CC1.3 d. Share and talk about what is being learned, and stay on topic when speaking.	Engage 1, 2 Explore 4, 5 Explain 6, 7, 8, 9

BACKGROUND INFORMATION

Our sense of smell and taste both rely on receptors that respond to the presence of certain chemicals in the environment. In the case of taste, the receptors are located on the tongue. We often refer to these microscopic receptors as taste buds. We have four basic types of taste cells: sweet, sour, salty, and bitter. Many scientists believe that there is a fifth taste called umami. Umami is often described as a savoury or meaty taste. It is believed to enhance the other tastes.

When a taste cell is stimulated, it sends an impulse to taste nerves which send the impulse to the brain. The nerves can be triggered by more than one type of taste cell. This allows us to taste different combinations and flavours, such as bacon-topped chocolate brownies (salty, sweet, and bitter).

***Traditional* Knowledge**

Many First Nations and Métis peoples would identify five tastes: sweet, sour, bitter, salty, and smokiness. The taste of smokiness comes from the way that meat and fish can be preserved using smoke and fire. In the past, First Nations and Métis peoples would gather salt from salt deposits. For some, salt was seen as a medicine, rather than a seasoning.

Food aversions will often occur if a person becomes ill after consuming a particular food. Our body's needs may also affect our taste preferences, causing us to have cravings for certain types of foods.

ASSESSMENT FOR LEARNING

Look for Evidence of Learning	Student-friendly Learning Targets
Can the student: • associate the tongue with the sense of taste? • identify the characteristics that can be tasted? • identify his or her favourite taste and least favourite taste? • categorize objects and materials according to the characteristics that can be tasted? • give examples of how our sense of taste helps us to recognize danger? • explain how some tastes are dangerous?	(self-assessment) • I know that my tongue is used for tasting. • I can sort tastes into four main groups: sweet, sour, salty, and bitter. • I know why I like one taste and why I don't like another. • I can put objects into groups according to what I taste. • I understand why it is important to know if something is safe before I taste it. • I know why some tastes are dangerous.

DI DIFFERENTIATING INSTRUCTION

For EAL

Provide visuals to help reinforce vocabulary and link material to students' existing knowledge.

For Enrichment

Students could do research projects based on their "I wonder ..." statements. Have them prepare a report or video based on their findings and present them to the class. They might also develop an experiment to test things they wonder about.

For Extra Support

Access and explore new information through Retell-Reflect-Relate activities and videos found on YouTube.

CURRICULUM CONNECTIONS

Students will have the opportunity to develop skills and concepts in the following area:

Health Education

DM1.1 d. Recognize the importance of thinking before acting.

CORE LEARNING OPPORTUNITIES

Engage

> **Safety Check**
> Be sure you are aware of student allergies or other dietary restrictions before beginning this lesson.

1. Activate and Build on Prior Knowledge

- In partners or small groups, have students draw pictures of their favourite foods. Encourage them to tell their partners what they like about the taste of that particular food (e.g., It is a bit salty and sweet.). Explain to students that different people like different tastes, but that we all have five basic characteristics to describe taste: sweet, sour, bitter, umami, and salty. Make an anchor chart defining each of these four characteristics, with pictures and examples for each, for students to refer back to.
- Talk with students about safety concerns associated with the sense of taste. Review the Skills poster **Safety in Science Class**, focusing on the importance of only tasting or smelling with a teacher's permission. Ask students:
  - Is it okay to eat anything that you find? Why not?
  - How can you know if something is safe to eat? (A parent, teacher, or caregiver will say so.)
  - What are the dangers of tasting or eating something you don't know is safe? (You could have an allergic reaction, it could be poisonous, or it might have gone bad.)
- Explain to students that their sense of taste, just like their other senses, can warn them of danger. Usually things that are dangerous to eat don't taste very good, such as food that has gone bad. However, sometimes they might taste okay. That is why it is important to check with parents, teachers, or caregivers to be sure something is safe to eat.
- Explain to students that they should not taste anything in a science lab unless their teacher gives them permission.
- Note that some of these safety concerns will be prior knowledge for some students, but not for others. Explain how important they are.

> **Literacy Check**
> Can the student:
> - read the "I wonder ..." statements in the class list and identify "I wonder ..." statements for his or her personal list?
> - copy "I wonder ..." statements from the class list onto his or her personal list?

2. Elicit "I Wonder ..." Statements

- Model an "I wonder ..." form of inquiry with statements such as: "I wonder how many different tastes humans can sense" or "I wonder why people like different foods."
- Invite students to offer other "I wonder ..." statements. Record these on a chart or paper strips, and then read them together. Provide students with copies of **PM 1: I Wonder ...** and ask them to record statements that especially interest them.

Explore

> **Safety Check**
> Some students may have allergies and/or sensitivities to some of these items. Be sure to check with parents to ensure the safety of students. Also be aware of dietary restrictions.

3. Investigate Our Tongues

- Tell students that our tongues have bumps on them called taste buds. We taste food using these taste buds. Have students work with a partner to find their taste buds. Have one partner stick out his or her tongue while the other looks for the taste buds, and then switch.

- As students are looking at each other's tongues, explain that there are different taste buds for sensing different tastes such as sweet like honey, sour like a dill pickle, bitter like coffee, and salty like salt. Write out these words. Explain to students that they are going to be using their tongues to try different tastes.
- Provide students with the following food samples to taste:
  Sweet: sugar, honey, maple syrup
  Sour: lemon, lime, dill pickle
  Bitter: unsweetened chocolate, cocoa, black coffee
  Salty: sea salt, pretzels, plain chips
- Have students place each substance individually on their tongue. After they try each substance, have them drink some water so that the previous taste does not interfere with the next taste.
- Have students collect data about their classmates' taste likes and dislikes. Have students record their data on **LM 15: Our Taste Likes and Dislikes**. Collect the class data and use **PM 7: Make a Bar Graph** to graph the class likes and dislikes of each of the substances tasted.

Literacy Check
Can the student:
- identify vocabulary associated with the four types of taste?

4. Do a Jelly Bean Taste Test

- In this activity, students will be given two sets of two jelly beans each to do taste tests. Each set of jelly beans should be the same colour. Have them record their results on **LM 16: Jelly Bean Taste Test**.
- For the first taste test, students will close their eyes and pinch their noses. Give each student the same colour of jelly bean, and ask them to guess what colour it is based on taste. Have them record the colour they think the jelly bean was. Repeat this procedure for the second jelly bean.
- For the second round of taste tests, students will only close their eyes. After eating each jelly bean, have students record what colour they think each jelly bean is.
- After students have completed recording their results, reveal the colour of the jelly beans. Ask students: Were your guesses more accurate when your nose was plugged or unplugged? Why? Encourage students to make the connection between smell and taste.
- Explain to students that sometimes we need more than one sense to give us accurate information about the world around us. Ask them how the smell or the colour of a jelly bean might have helped them decide on its flavour. Explain how some candy makers might use different colours for different flavours. For example, the taste of green jelly beans can be different.

Science Check
Can the student:
- connect the tongue with the sense of taste?
- identify the characteristics that can be tasted?
- categorize objects and materials according to taste characteristics?

***Traditional* Knowledge**

5. Respond to the Traditional Knowledge Poster: Berries

- Show students the Traditional Knowledge poster **Berries**. Ask them to make observations about the different berries. Ask: How are the berries the same? How are the berries different?
- Tell students that for centuries, First Nations, Métis, and Inuit people have gathered berries to eat. Many of these berries are dried, as seen on the poster, so that they can be stored and eaten later. Dried chokecherries and blueberries can be added to pemmican. (Pemmican is a concentrated mixture of protein and fat that is used as a nutritious food made by First Nations and Métis peoples.) Today, many people

freeze, can, or make jam out of the berries that they pick. Berries can also be made into drinks such as berry tea.

- If possible, have students try both fresh and dried berries. Ask which they prefer and why. As a group, or individually, have students make a Venn diagram to compare the tastes of the dried berries versus fresh berries. You could use **PM 6: A Venn Diagram**.
- Read *Berry Magic* by Teri Sloat and Betty Huffmon or *Blueberries for Sal* by Robert McCloskey to students. *Berry Magic* is about an Inuit girl picking berries. Traditionally, berry picking is work done by women. *Blueberries for Sal* deals with an encounter with a bear while berry picking. First Nations and Métis people would traditionally be silent while in the woods so as not to disturb the animals in their homes. However, noise is made while berry picking as a safety measure to let bears know you're there, since they typically stay away from humans.
- You might invite people in the community to visit the class to demonstrate how they preserve berries or make pemmican.

Literature Links
Berry Magic by Teri Sloat and Betty Huffmon
Blueberries for Sal by Robert McCloskey

Explain

6. Read and Respond to the Non-fiction Book *Exploring With Our Senses*

Literacy Check
Can the student:
- comprehend and respond to a variety of grade-level texts?
- speak clearly about ideas and experiences in a logical sequence?

Before: Ask students for the ways we describe how different foods taste. (Foods can taste sweet, sour, bitter, salty, or a combination of any of these.) Ask: What examples of foods can you suggest for each taste?
During: Distribute copies of *Exploring With Our Senses*. Use a Shared Reading approach and work as a whole group or in small groups based on students' reading level and needs.
Page 16: Read the page. Ask students:
- Have you tasted these foods?
- Do you like them or dislike them?
- What is your favourite food/taste?

Remind students of the dangers of eating or drinking things that are not foods and the need to be careful eating foods that a teacher, parent, or caregiver has not told them is safe to eat.
Page 17: Read the page. Ask students:
- Where are your taste buds?
- What do your taste buds help you to do?
- Why might having a cold change how food tastes?

After: Use **LM 17: Tastes** to assess students' understanding of the four basic tastes: sweet, sour, salty, bitter. Students will circle food examples in different colours to represent the different tastes and then describe the tastes they like best.

7. Determine Different Tastes

- Have students complete **LM 18: How Does My Lunch Taste?** to assess their understanding of different tastes. Have them analyze parts of their lunch or snack to determine which foods might be considered sweet, sour, salty, or bitter.

- Ask students to imagine what it would be like if they had a job that required them to be able to classify tastes very well. Talk about chefs and taste testers for food companies and which senses they use in their jobs. (They use a combination of smell, taste, and sight.) Ask students:
  - Why would it be important to have a good sense of taste in these jobs?
  - What hobbies could people have that require a good sense of taste?

Science Check
Can the student:
- give examples of how his or her sense of taste helps him or her to recognize danger?
- identify the characteristics that can be tasted?
- communicate questions and ideas while exploring the senses?

8. Identify If It Is Good for Me or Bad for Me
- Use **LM 19: Good for Me or Bad for Me?** to assess students' understanding of how our sense of taste keeps us safe, and why it is important to use safety rules when trying new things.
- Ask students why certain items on the line master are items that they should never taste. This may also be a good time to discuss with students how it can be dangerous for some people to taste certain foods because of severe allergies.

9. Reflect on Learning
- Have students record evidence of their learning on **PM 13: Look What I've Learned**. They can also record in their journal or with a video or audio recording on a smart device or camera. Encourage them to note at least two things they learned about the sense of taste and something they still wonder about.
- Use **LM 20: This Is What I Can Do** as a self-assessment. Read the learning targets with students and have them respond on their own. Some students may need assistance.

OTHER LEARNING OPPORTUNITIES

Extend: Activity Bank

At any time, choose from the following options to replace or supplement the Core Learning Opportunities to meet students' needs and/or interests.

10. Talk With a Guest Speaker
- Have a chef or baker come in to talk about how his or her job requires him or her to have a good sense of taste. Ask the guest speaker to explain how some tastes go well together and others do not.

11. Do a Gourmet Jelly Bean Taste Test
- Gourmet jelly beans come in a wide range of flavours. The makers of these candies usually provide a chart to identify their different flavours. Give each student a handful of jelly beans and have students taste each jelly bean to try to identify its flavour.

- Ask students to make a chart which lists the flavour of the jelly beans they taste and how many times they have that particular flavour in their sample. Have students compare results and as a group determine which jelly bean flavour was in the mix the most and which jelly bean flavour was in the mix the least.
- You could also have students conduct a survey to find out the class's favourite and least favourite flavours.

12. Watch a Food Program

- Watch a program called *Taste Buds* by Marblemedia. It focuses on cooking, tasting, and kitchen safety. One particular episode that you might want students to view and respond to is entitled *Foods That Make You Pucker.*

Literature Link
Bread and Jam for Frances
by Russell Hoban

13. Respond to Literature

- As a class, read *Bread and Jam for Frances* by Russell Hoban. Use a Shared Reading approach to work as a whole group or in small groups based on students' reading level and needs. *Bread and Jam for Frances* is a story about a little badger who will not try new foods. She will only eat bread and jam.

Safety Check
Be aware of possible food allergies.

- This is an opportunity for students to talk about trying new foods. If possible, have students bring in foods that other students may not have tried. Be sure to consider allergies before beginning, and remind students that everyone has different tastes and to be respectful of others.
- If it is not possible for students to bring in different foods, then you may wish to bring in one or two unique items, such as dragon fruit or star fruit. Have students reflect on this taste experience and record their reactions through writing, illustration, or using a video camera.

5 Sense of Touch

Time
4–5 hours

Vocabulary
texture

Program Resources
PM 1: I Wonder ...
PM 13: Look What I've Learned
LM 21: Mystery Bags
LM 22: Foot Feel
LM 23: This Is What I Can Do
Non-fiction Book: *Exploring With Our Senses*
Lap Book
Science Poster: Which senses do you use?

Materials and Equipment
- plastic zip bags with objects and materials of different textures (e.g., mashed bananas, dried beans, fun fur) baby wipes, paper lunch bags
- objects with different textures (e.g., bubble wrap, cotton balls, tissue paper, lentils), tile or piece of sturdy cardboard, glue
- access to Internet

GOAL

Students will associate the sense of touch with the skin, identify and categorize different types of textures, and develop the understanding that all parts of the body experience touch.

ASSESSMENT CHART

Science Indicators	Assessment Opportunities
SE1.1 a. Identify each of the senses and associate those senses with parts of humans or other animals, including sight and eyes, smell and nose, hearing and ears, taste and tongue/nose, and touch and skin.	Engage 1 Explore 4, 5 Explain 7, 8
SE1.1 b. Identify characteristics used to describe the range of observations related to each sense (e.g., sounds can be described as loud or soft, high pitch or low pitch; tastes related to the tongue can be described as sweet, sour, salty, or bitter; textures can be described as hard or soft, smooth or rough, sticky or not sticky; smells can be described as musky, aromatic, pungent, or putrid; and appearance can be described in terms of shape, colour, and lustre).	Engage 1 Explore 3, 4
SE1.1 f. Investigate the sensitivity of different parts of the body to the touch of various materials (e.g., sandpaper, metal, cloth, satin, leaves, and wood).	Explore 3, 4, 5, 6 Explain 7, 8
SE1.2 c. Record observations of various environments (e.g., classroom, gymnasium, school yard, library, and cafeteria) using all of their senses as appropriate.	Explore 6
SE1.2 d. Imagine, and compare with others, possible sensations that students would likely experience in other environments based on representations (e.g., stories, pictures, and videos) of those environments.	Explain 7, 8
SE1.2 h. Suggest how a human or animal might function if they were totally or partially missing one or more of the five senses.	Explore 6

English Language Arts Indicators	Assessment Opportunities
CR1.2 a. Identify and locate the key information in pictures, charts, and other visual forms (e.g., photographs, physical movement, icons) including traditional and contemporary First Nations and Métis resources and performances.	Explore 6 Explain 7, 8
CC1.3 e. Participate in small-group work.	Engage 1 Explore 3, 5

BACKGROUND INFORMATION

Our sense of touch is controlled by a system of nerve endings in our body and touch cells in our skin. Pain receptors detect pain or stimuli that could cause damage to the skin and other tissues. They detect mechanical stimuli such as cuts or scrapes, thermal stimuli such as burns, and chemical stimuli such as insect bites.

There are also cold receptors and heat receptors. Cold receptors are activated when the skin surface drops below 35 °C. The greatest concentration of cold receptors is in our face and ears. Heat receptors are activated when our skin temperature rises above 30 °C. Beyond 45 °C, the pain receptors take over and the heat receptors quit working. Other receptors receive messages relating to pressure, vibrations, and texture. They are found in our skin and also in our joints, tendons, and muscles. These help us to do physical activity.

Other animals use paws, fingers, whiskers, antennae, feathers, and hair to help them find their way around. Animals with whiskers, such as cats, use these and other hairs on their bodies to help them sense and feel their way around in the dark. Catfish have very smooth skin and special hair. This helps them sense their surroundings in murky water. Crocodiles and alligators have thousands of tiny receptors along their jawlines that help them sense their prey's movement in water.

***Traditional* Knowledge**

Using touch is an important way to understand the world around us, but for some First Nations and Métis peoples, there are some protocols around touch. In some First Nations groups, a woman should never touch a man's hair or his hat. You may want to ask an Elder or Traditional Knowledge Keeper for other protocols that they could share.

ASSESSMENT FOR LEARNING

Look for Evidence of Learning	Student-friendly Learning Targets
Can the student: • associate the sense of touch with skin? • make the connection that it is not just our hands that can sense touch? • discriminate between the characteristics used to describe different types of textures? • provide examples of favourite textures and least favourite textures? • sort objects and materials based upon the characteristics of texture?	(self-assessment) • I know that my sense of touch comes from something touching my skin. • I can feel textures with different parts of my body. • I can show you things that have different textures and describe the texture. • I can describe which textures I like and which textures I don't like.

DI DIFFERENTIATING INSTRUCTION

For EAL

Students may have difficulties with the proper names of textures. Have these students draw or paste pictures representing textures on index cards. Write the correct name on the back of the card. These cards could be used for language reinforcement at a later date. To enrich vocabulary, have students make their own sensory tiles using objects familiar to them and/or their culture.

For Enrichment

Have students research how other animals use their sense of touch. Have them create an information poster, and present it to the class.

For Extra Support

Providing visual symbols for vocabulary words will help students who require extra support. Use strategies similar to those suggested for EAL students.

CORE LEARNING OPPORTUNITIES

Engage

1. Activate and Build on Prior Knowledge

- Ask students what touch is. Many will say it is how you feel with your hands. Ask students:
  - Are your hands the only place where you can feel things?
  - Where else can you feel things on your body?
  - What are some examples of things you can feel?
- Ask students what all of the body parts they listed have in common. (They are all covered in skin.) Explain that our skin is an organ that helps us experience touch all over our bodies.
- Then ask students if touch is the only sensation that their skin can feel.
  - What are other sensations that you can feel?
  - What are some of your favourite things to feel?
- Guide students into making a list that includes words such as cold and hot, soft and hard, or even pain. Explain to them that our sense of touch helps us to make observations about the world around us. The things we touch may be smooth or rough, sticky or not sticky, wet or dry.
- In pairs, have students use their finger to draw a shape or a letter of the alphabet onto their partner's back and then into the palm of their hand. Have students guess what shape was drawn and then switch.
- Ask students whether it was easier to guess the shape/letter on their back or their hand and why.

Literacy Check
Can the student:
- read the "I wonder ..." statements in the class list and identify "I wonder ..." statements for his or her personal list?
- copy "I wonder ..." statements from the class list onto his or her personal list?

2. Elicit "I Wonder ..." Statements

- Model an "I wonder ..." form of inquiry with statements such as: "I wonder if my elbow is more sensitive to touch than my knee."
- Invite students to offer other "I wonder ..." statements. Record these on a chart or paper strips, and then read them together. Provide students with copies of **PM 1: I Wonder ...** and ask them to record statements that especially interest them.

Explore

3. Investigate Mystery Bags

Safety Check
Make sure that you are aware of any possible allergies.

- Tell students they will be using their hands to feel different objects and then try to identify them by touch in Touch Centres.
- Prepare plastic zip bags with objects and materials that have different textures (e.g., mashed bananas, dried beans, fun fur, whipped cream or shaving cream, ice cubes, marbles, bubble wrap, jello, cold cooked spaghetti). You will also need baby wipes for clean up. Place the plastic zip bags into paper lunch bags so students cannot see the contents.
- Have students work in small groups to rotate through the centres, and feel the contents of each bag without looking into the paper bags. As they feel the contents of each bag, have them complete **LM 21: Mystery Bags**. Ask guiding questions such as: What do you think is in that bag? Is it rough, soft, cold, etc.?
- After everyone has completed the activity, gather the class together and have students share their guesses. Encourage students to describe what

they felt using terms such as hard or soft, wet or dry, smooth or rough. Reveal the object in each bag, and have them record what the actual object or material was on their copy of **LM 21**. Some students may need assistance completing the bottom of the sheet.

Science Check
Can the student:
- associate the sense of touch with skin?
- provide examples of his or her favourite and least favourite textures?
- discriminate between the characteristics of different types of textures?

4. Feel With Our Feet

- To help students understand that we use more than just our hands to experience touch, provide an opportunity for them to touch using their feet. Collect objects with different textures (e.g., bubble wrap, cotton balls, tissue paper, lentils) and glue them to a tile or piece of sturdy cardboard.
- Ask students what words can be used to describe different textures (e.g., hard or soft, smooth or rough, sticky or not sticky). Make a word bank of these words.
- Give each student a copy of **LM 22: Foot Feel**. Have students take turns running their feet over the "texture tiles" and then record their observations on **LM 22**. Ask them which textures are nice to touch and which are not nice to touch. Which is their favourite?
- Ask students how feeling with their feet was different from feeling with their hands.

Science Check
Can the student:
- discuss and explain how other animals use their sense of touch to survive?
- describe the environment using his or her sense of touch?
- discuss how sense of touch can warn of danger?
- make the connection that it is not just the hands that can experience touch?

5. Feel With Sock Hands

- Have students feel the same texture tiles from Explore 4 but while wearing socks or mittens on their hands. They will likely observe that the sense of touch is not as strong when wearing mittens or socks.
- Have students recall in the fiction book *On the Trail* when the children see the thistles (pages 8–9). Ask them what happens when you touch thistles or rose branches.
- Brainstorm as a group ways in which our sense of touch helps to keep us safe. (When we touch a sharp or hot object, we feel pain so we pull our hands away before we are seriously injured.)

6. Role-play Using Touch Like Animals

- Search the Internet for photos of different animals that depict how the animals use their sense of touch. Have students look at the photos and ask:
  - How have you seen animals using touch?
  - What parts of their bodies do they use and for what purpose? (They use their paws, fingers, whiskers, antennae, feathers, and hairs to help them find their way around.)
- Have students imagine that they are tigers. Tigers use their whiskers as touch detectors to help them hunt in the dark. Dim the lights and have students close their eyes. Next, have students stretch out their fingers. Have them feel around and then ask:
  - What do you feel? What does your sense of touch tell you about the environment around you?
  - If you could not see, how could you find your way back to your seat?

Explain

Literacy Check
Can the student:
- comprehend and respond to a variety of grade-level texts?
- speak clearly about ideas and experiences in a logical sequence?

7. Read and Respond to the Non-fiction Book *Exploring With Our Senses*

Before: Ask students what different textures they have felt with their hands and their feet in the Explore activities. Encourage them to list a number of different characteristics of texture.

During: Work as a whole group or in small groups based on students' reading level and needs, using a Shared Reading approach and the Lap Book.

Page 18: Read the text. Ask students if there are any words used to describe texture that are not on their class list. Add any new words.

Page 19: Read the text and ask students to imagine that they have an ice cube in their hands. Ask students to discuss how the ice cube would feel and what words they could use to describe it. Elicit that many words can be used to describe the texture of the ice cube (e.g., cold, wet, smooth).

Pages 20–21: Read through the Sort It Out with students. Model how to do the activity by choosing one example in addition to the apple to describe.

After: Have students work with a partner to write out words to describe some or all of the objects depending on their ability level.

- Refer students back to page 18 and ask them to examine each of the photos. Ask students:
  - What could you feel if you were the boy feeling the kittens?
  - What would the rock feel like? The gum? The cup of hot chocolate?

8. Make Different Observations

- Show students the Science poster **Which senses do you use?** Tell students that now that they have explored all five senses, they will be able to make different observations about the poster than the first time they looked at it. Ask them to identify a photo that shows something they could use their sense of touch to make different observations about (e.g., touching the cat to feel how furry it is, touching the water to feel how hot or cold it is, etc.). Ask questions about each example they give to encourage them to describe what each would feel like and to probe deeper into other areas such as temperature or wet and cold.

9. Reflect on Learning

- Have students record evidence of their learning on **PM 13: Look What I've Learned**. They could also record in their journal or with a video or an audio recording on a smart device or camera. Encourage them to note at least two things they learned about the sense of touch and something they still wonder about.
- Use **LM 23: This Is What I Can Do** as a self-assessment. Read the learning targets with students and have them respond on their own. Some students may need assistance.

OTHER LEARNING OPPORTUNITIES

Extend: Activity Bank

At any time, choose from the following options to replace or supplement the Core Learning Opportunities to meet students' needs and/or interests.

Literature Link
The Kissing Hand by Audrey Penn

10. Respond to Literature

- Read *The Kissing Hand* by Audrey Penn. Have students retell the story to you or another student. Discuss how our sense of touch can be related to our emotions.

11. Make Texture Collections

- Have students make their own collection of textures on poster paper based upon the word bank that you developed together in Explore 4.

12. Try a Morning Without Touch

- Have students do some of their morning activities wearing thick socks or mittens on their hands. Discuss with students what other senses they relied on and the difficulties they encountered. As a group, you could discuss Talk Time 8 in the fiction book *On the Trail.*

13. Explore Other "I Wonder ..." Statements

- Return to the "I wonder ..." statements not yet answered and any new wonderings that have come up. With students, plan and set up centres where they can explore these wonderings. Encourage them to make and test predictions.
- Working in small groups, students can rotate to all the centres or focus on one per group. They could share their findings in an oral, written, or electronic presentation.

UNIT 3

Unit Closer: Putting It All Together

Time
1–2 hours

Program Resources
PM 4: Finding Out
PM 9: I Found Out
LM 24: Popcorn
LM 25: Rate Your Learning
Fiction Book: *On the Trail*
Non-fiction Book: *Exploring With Our Senses*
Lap Book
Science poster: Which senses do you use?
Skills poster: Observing and Recording

Materials and Equipment
- microwave popcorn or popcorn kernels and a popcorn maker

Literacy Check
Can the student:
- comprehend and respond to a variety of grade-level texts?
- speak clearly about ideas and experiences in a logical sequence?

Looking Back

1. Consider the Learning Targets

- Display the learning targets that were introduced in the Unit Opener on a chart or screen. Explain that these are the big ideas about the senses.
- Read the learning targets aloud. Stop after each one, asking students to provide explanations and examples that illustrate the learning target.
- Ask students to think about how well they can do the things on the list. Use a Think Aloud strategy and a copy of **LM 25: Rate Your Learning** to model how students should rate themselves.
- Distribute copies of **LM 25** to complete as you read each of the learning targets. Some students may be able to read and complete it on their own.
- Return to the the Science poster **Which senses do you use?** Spend a few minutes reviewing the poster. Ask students which senses they are using when they pet a cat, smell a rose, or eat an orange.

2. Reread the Fiction Book *On the Trail*

Before: Ask students to talk about what they thought of the book *On the Trail*. What did they like about the book? What did they learn?
During: Distribute copies of *On the Trail*. In a Shared or Paired Reading, students can read through the book for enjoyment and talk about it.
After: Go over any discussion questions or activities from Talk Time on page 16 that have not been previously covered.

- Show students the Skills poster **Observing and Recording**. Review how to observe using the senses. Remind students that they need to be safe, and should never taste or touch anything unless an adult has said it is safe to do so.
- Take students on their own trail walk. As you walk, encourage them to point out things such a bird singing (sound) or asphalt being poured (smell), the feel of the wind on your skin (touch) or an airplane high in the sky (sight). The walk can last about 15 minutes and can be inside or outside. You can introduce this activity through Talk Time 4 in the non-fiction book *Exploring With Our Senses*.
- Once you return, discuss as a class what students observed with their senses during the walk. Which sense did they use the most? Jot down some of the key words used to describe their senses on a word wall.

3. Consider "I Wonder ... " Statements

- Ask students to think back on the things they have wondered about throughout the unit. Review students' copies of "I wonder ..." statements. Have them pick one important wondering that has been answered and tell a partner about it.
- Students can record their query and what they learned about it on **PM 9: I Found Out**.

- Ask students to think about other "I wonder …" statements that they might have now that they know more about the senses (e.g., How well do birds hear?). Record their questions, and, with students, plan an exploration that follows the inquiry steps. Set up the inquiry for students to experience in small groups at a centre. Provide copies of **PM 4: Finding Out** for students to complete as a group while following the steps.

4. Finish Reading the Non-fiction Book *Exploring With Our Senses*
Before: Ask students what they remember about the book. Prompt them to tell you that it is a non-fiction book.
During: Use the Lap Book to read with the whole group using a Think Aloud strategy to reinforce information from the non-fiction features of the book.
Pages 22–23: Use a Shared Reading approach or Read Aloud strategy to introduce and discuss the activity "Taste Test." Have students work with partners to do this activity. Model how to make a chart to record the following headings: Food, Blindfold/Nose Plugged, Blindfold/Nose Not Plugged, No Blindfold/Nose Not Plugged. Sight should not affect taste, but students may notice that the taste is less intense with their noses plugged. Guide them to make connections between taste and the sense of smell.
After: Choose discussion questions and activities from Talk Time on page 24 that students have not engaged in or responded to throughout the unit. Talk Time 2, 3, and 6 are good ways to summarize students' learning.

GOING FURTHER

5. Observe Popcorn with the Five Senses
Introduction
- Tell students that they will be using all five senses to make observations about popcorn, both popped and unpopped. (You can use microwave popcorn for this activity or a popcorn maker.)
- Discuss with students how it is important for scientists to make detailed observations. Encourage them to use as many words from this unit as possible to describe the popcorn. Again, show the Skills poster **Observing and Recording**. Remind students how to make scientific observations.

Science Check
Can the student:
- use appropriate vocabulary to describe all of the senses?

Preparation
- Have students use **LM 24: Popcorn** to record their observations of popcorn as they rotate through the following five centres:
  Touch: Set out some unpopped and popped kernels. Using their hands, students can feel the kernels and describe the texture of each. Encourage them to use the vocabulary that they have learned (e.g., slippery, smooth, sticky).
  Sight: Have students describe what the popcorn looks like before and after it is popped.
  Smell: Have students describe the smell of the popcorn before and after it is popped.

Sound: Have students shake the unpopped kernels in a plastic cup and record the sounds that they hear. Repeat with the popped kernels.
Taste: Tell students it is not healthy to eat the unpopped kernels, but allow them to lick an unpopped kernel. Have students describe what it tastes like. Allow them to eat some popped popcorn and describe its taste.

Sharing

- Have students compare their observations with a partner. Ask them if they used similar words to describe the popcorn.
- Have students make a poster to show some ways they use their senses every day. As an alternative, they could make a poster to show how one animal uses it's senses. Students who have completed a poster can be invited to share it with the class.

Evaluation

- Make a large copy of **LM 24** and as a class, fill it in with as many descriptive words as possible. Have students add any new words to their personal copy of **LM 24.**

UNIT 3

USING OUR SENSES

Table of Contents

Name:________________________________

Learning Targets

Put a check mark to show what you can do.

☐	I can explain what my five senses are and how I use each of my senses.
☐	I can sort objects and materials using my senses.
☐	I can explain how humans and animals use their senses to communicate and sense danger.
☐	I can describe my surroundings using all of my senses.
☐	I can explain how animals use their senses.
☐	I can describe how a human or an animal that has lost one of the five senses can live with this challenge.

Name:______________________________________

Braille Alphabet

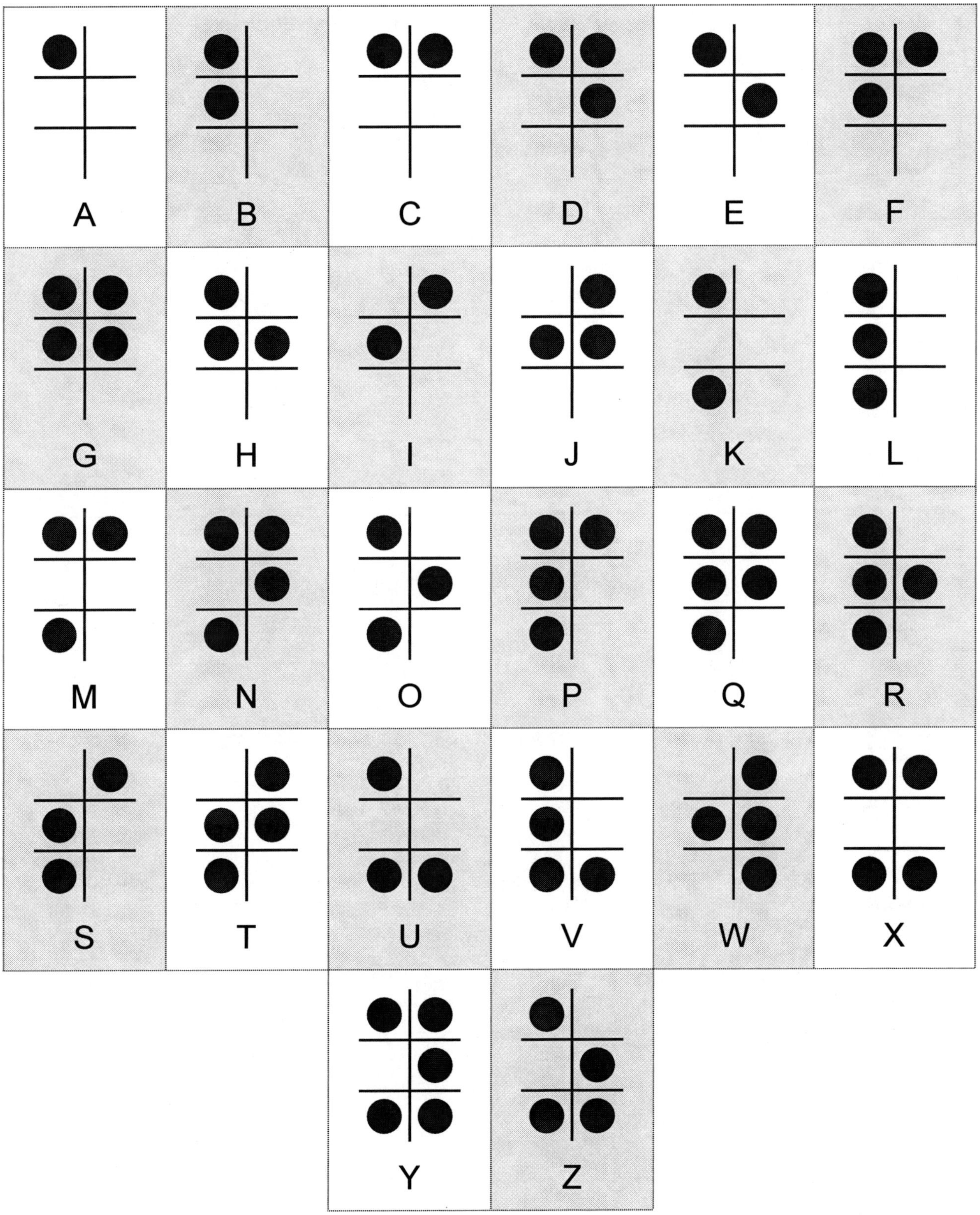

Name:____________________________________

This Is What I Can Do

Put a check mark to show what you can do.

☐	I can tell you that my eyes are used for sight.
☐	I can describe an object by characteristics such as colour and shape.
☐	I can sort objects and materials using my sense of sight.
☐	I can explain how my sense of sight helps to keep me safe.
☐	I can understand how people who have lost one sense can live with this challenge.
☐	I can explain how animals use their sense of sight to help them in their daily lives.

Put a  beside what you do best.

Put a blue  beside the one you need to practise.

LM 4 LINE MASTER

Name:____

Sound Scavenger Hunt

Quiet Sound	Loud Sound	Pretty Sound
Scary Sound	Nature Sound	People Sound
Machine Sound	Happy Sound	What Is That Sound?

Name:______________________________________

How Animals Use Their Hearing

My animal is:	
My animal has ears that are shaped like ...	
My animal lives ...	
I think my animal needs special ears because …	
I still wonder about ...	

Name:______________________________________

What Do Animal Ears Do?

Draw a line from each animal to how it is using its ears.

listen to music
find its way in the dark
listen for danger
listen for prey
listen to each other

Name:________________________________

Keeping My Ears Safe

When I listen to loud music, my ears feel ...

When I wear earplugs, my ears feel ...

Safety Rules for Keeping My Ears Safe

Name:____

American Sign Language Alphabet

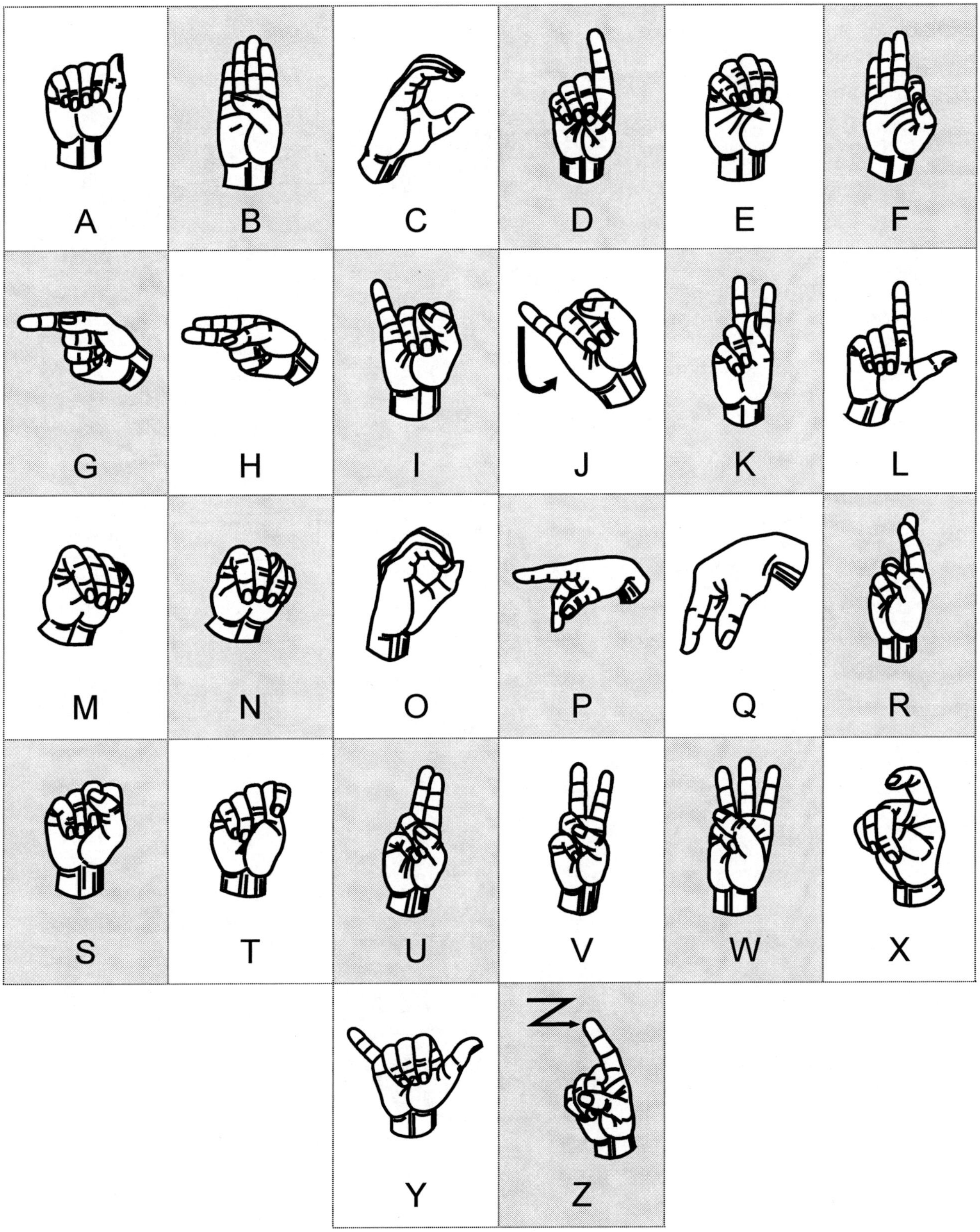

Name:______________________________________

Loud and Soft Sounds

Cut out the pictures. Sort them into three groups: objects that make loud noises, objects that make soft noises, and objects that make both.

Name:____

This Is What I Can Do

Put a check mark to show what you can do.

☐	I know that my ears are used for hearing.
☐	I can talk about which sounds are my favourite sounds and which sounds I do not like.
☐	I know which sounds are natural and which sounds are artificial.
☐	I can explain that humans and animals use their ears to listen for danger, to help them get around, and to communicate.
☐	I can explain how to protect my sense of hearing.
☐	I understand how devices can help people hear.

Put a ☺ beside what you do best.

Put a blue ? beside the one you need to practise.

Name:____________________________________

Mystery Containers

Circle the happy face if you liked the smell.
Circle the sad face if you did not like the smell.
Explain why you liked or did not like the smell.

Container	Like or Dislike	Why?
1	☺ ☹	
2	☺ ☹	
3	☺ ☹	
4	☺ ☹	
5	☺ ☹	
6	☺ ☹	
7	☺ ☹	
8	☺ ☹	

I like the smell in container ________ the best.

I like it because____.

I do not like the smell in container _________.

I do not like it because ____.

Name:____

How Do They Smell?

Name:________________________________

Different Smells

Circle the good smells with the colour green.
Circle the bad smells with the colour blue.
Circle the dangerous smells with the colour red.

Name:____________________________________

This Is What I Can Do

Put a check mark to show what you can do.

- [ ] I know that my nose is used for smelling.
- [ ] I can talk about which smell is my favourite smell and which smell I do not like.
- [ ] I can demonstrate how to smell safely using the wafting technique.
- [ ] I can explain how my nose can warn me of danger.
- [ ] I can explain how animals use their sense of smell.

Put a  beside what you do best.

Put a blue  beside the one you need to practise.

Name:____________________________________

Our Taste Likes and Dislikes

Taste	Classmates Who Liked This Taste
sweet	
sour	
bitter	
salty	

Our class liked ________________ taste the most.

Taste	Classmates Who Did Not Like This Taste
sweet	
sour	
bitter	
salty	

Our class did not like ________________ taste the most.

Name:______________________________

Jelly Bean Taste Test

Record your results.

When my eyes were closed and my nose was plugged, I thought:

Sample	Colour
1	
2	

When just my eyes were closed, I thought:

Sample	Colour
1	
2	

The correct colour of each jelly bean was:

Sample	Colour
1	
2	

Name:______________________________________

Tastes

Circle the items that taste sweet with the colour red.
Circle the items that taste sour with the colour green.
Circle the items that taste bitter with the colour blue.
Circle the items that taste salty with the colour yellow.

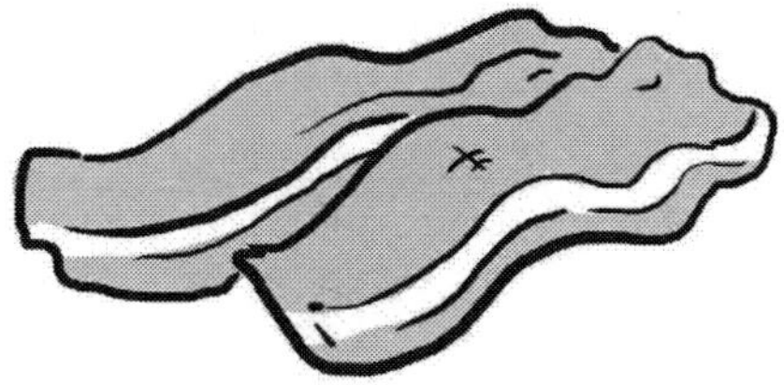

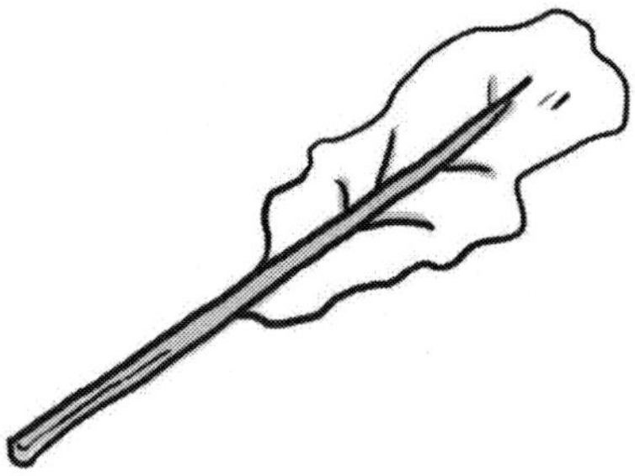
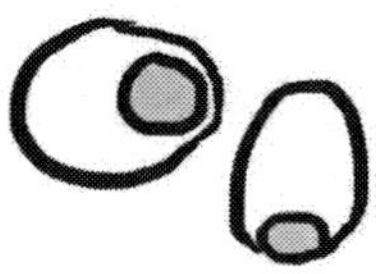

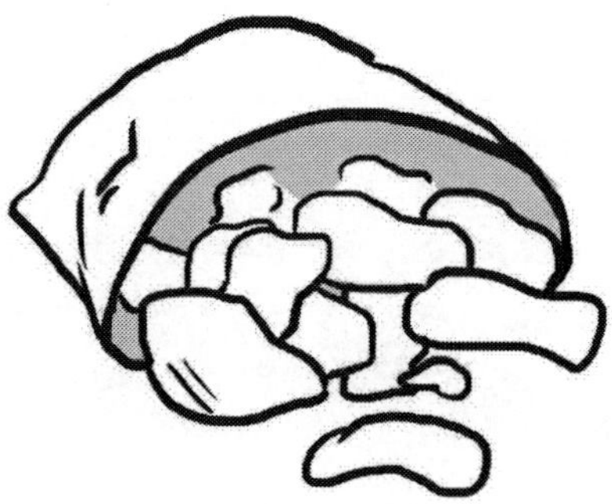
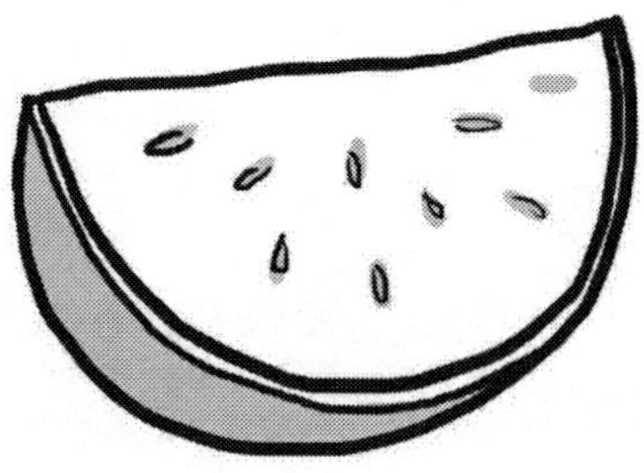

Name:________________________________

How Does My Lunch Taste?

Identify the taste of items in your lunch.
Test the item on your tongue. Circle the taste on the chart.

Food	Taste
	sweet sour bitter salty
	sweet sour bitter salty
	sweet sour bitter salty
	sweet sour bitter salty
	sweet sour bitter salty

Name:____________________________________

Good for Me or Bad for Me?

Circle the items that are safe for you to taste.

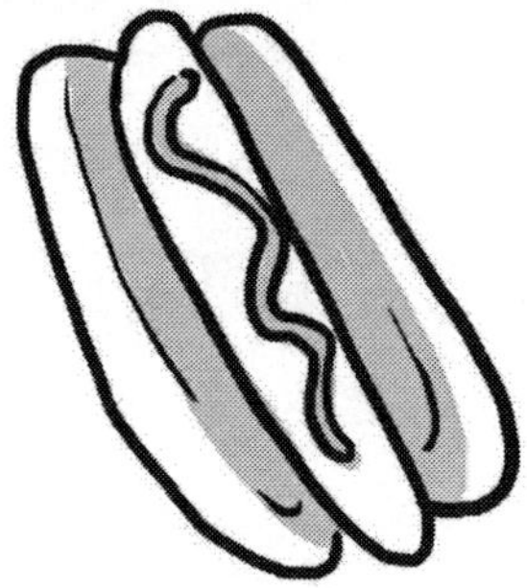

Name:____________________________________

This Is What I Can Do

Put a check mark to show what you can do.

☐	I know that my tongue is used for tasting.
☐	I can talk about my favourite things to taste and which things I do not like to taste.
☐	I can sort foods as sweet, salty, sour, or bitter.
☐	I can record observations about how different foods taste.
☐	I can explain why you have to be safe when tasting.

Put a  beside what you do best.

Put a blue  beside the one you need to practise.

Name:___________________________________

Mystery Bags

Bag Number	Texture Word	I think it is …	It is …

My favourite thing to feel is ______________________________.

I like this texture because ____.

My least favourite thing to feel is ___________________________.

I do not like this texture because ____.

Name:____

Foot Feel

Draw a small picture of textures that your feet can feel.

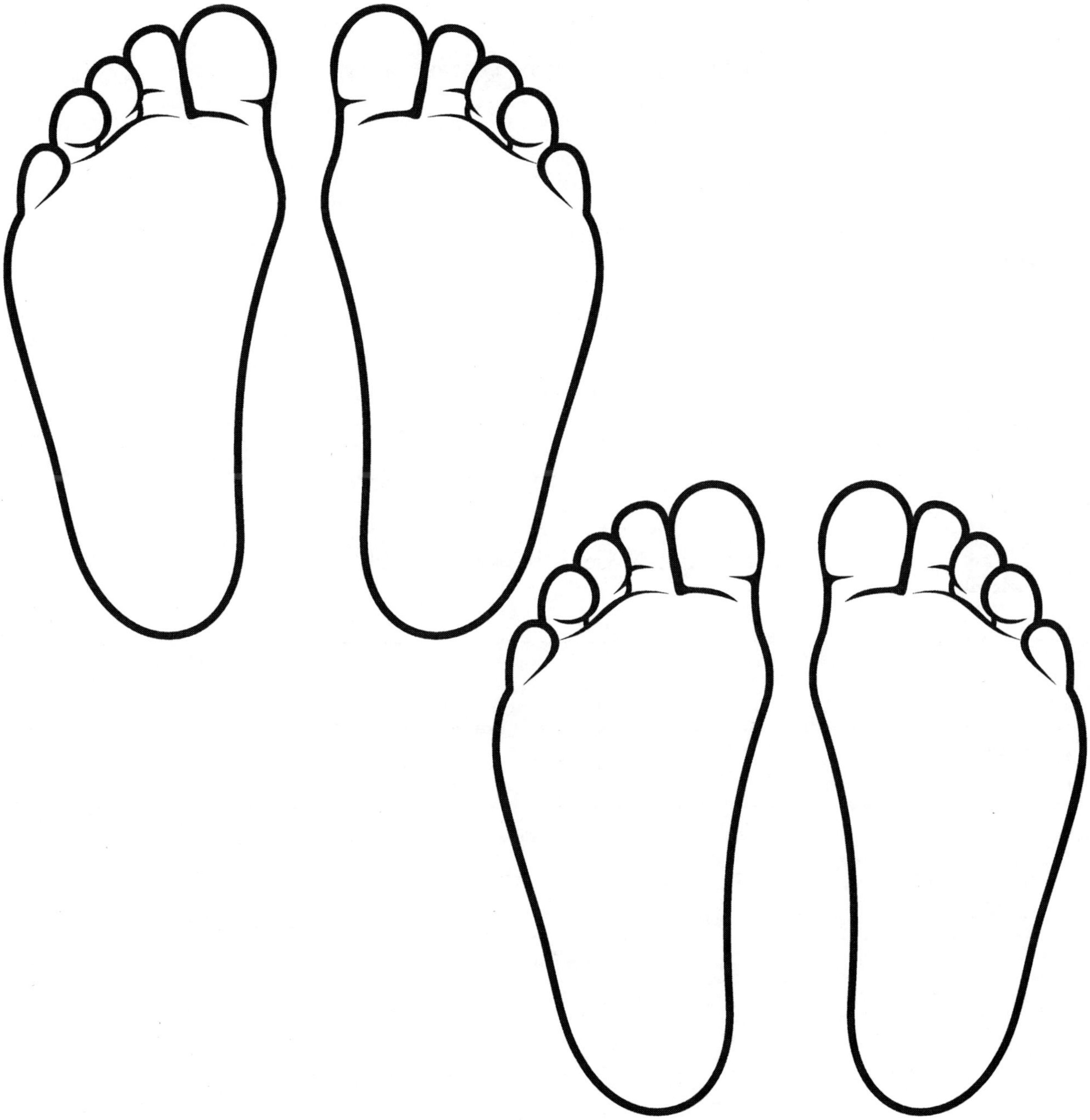

Draw a circle around the texture that feels the best on your foot.

Draw a square around the texture that you do not like to feel.

Name:____________________________________

This Is What I Can Do

Put a check mark to show what you can do.

☐	I can tell you that my skin gives me my sense of touch.
☐	I can describe textures using words.
☐	I can sort objects by their textures.
☐	I can explain how animals use their sense of touch.
☐	I can explain how my sense of touch helps to keep me safe.

Put a  beside what you do best.

Put a blue  beside the one you need to practise.

Name:______________________________________

Popcorn

Touch	Popcorn feels:
unpopped	
popped	

Sight	Popcorn looks:
unpopped	
popped	

Smell	Popcorn smells:
unpopped	
popped	

Sound	Popcorn sounds:
unpopped	
popped	

Taste	Popcorn tastes:
unpopped	
popped	

Name:____

Rate Your Learning

Circle the number that tells about you.

1 means I can do it very well.

2 means I can do it, but I need some practice.

3 means I need a lot more practice.

1	**2**	**3**	I can explain what my five senses are and how I use each of my senses.
1	**2**	**3**	I can sort objects and materials using my senses.
1	**2**	**3**	I can explain how humans and animals use their senses to communicate and to sense danger.
1	**2**	**3**	I can describe my surroundings using all of my senses.
1	**2**	**3**	I can explain how animals use their senses.
1	**2**	**3**	I can describe how a human or an animal that has lost one of the five senses can live with this challenge.

UNIT 4

DAILY AND SEASONAL CHANGES

Table of Contents

Unit Indicators Correlation Chart — Daily and Seasonal Changes*	
Indicator	**Assessment Opportunities**
By the end of grade 1, students will be able to:	
DS1.1 Compare and represent daily and seasonal changes of natural phenomena through observing, measuring, sequencing, and recording. [CP, SI]	
a. Pose questions about changes in natural phenomena (e.g., sunlight, temperature, humidity, and cloud cover) in the environment over the course of a day and a year.	Lesson 1: 1, 2 Lesson 4: 2
b. Identify the days of the week, months of the year, and seasons.	Lesson 1: 1, 3, 5
c. Observe daily and seasonal changes in the amount of heat and light from the sun, including the formation of shadows (e.g., length of day, temperature differences throughout the year, and changes in shadow length throughout a day and a year).	Lesson 1: 4, 6 Lesson 2: 3, 6, 7
d. Examine ways in which various cultures, including First Nations and Métis, represent daily and seasonal changes through oral traditions and artistic works.	Lesson 5: 3, 4, 5, 6 Lesson 6: 5
e. Use a variety of tools (e.g., rain gauge, thermometer, and wind vane) and techniques (e.g., chart, diagram, and table) to record changes in weather conditions (e.g., temperature, humidity, wind direction and strength, and amount and type of precipitation) that occur in daily and seasonal cycles.	Lesson 1: 3, 5 Lesson 2: 3, 4, 5, 6, 7
f. Document the visibility and position of objects (e.g., sun, moon, planets, and stars) in the sky at different times of the day and year.	Lesson 1: 4, 5, 6
g. Record observations of the shape and position of the moon throughout a month.	Lesson 6: 3, 6
h. Sequence or group objects, materials, and events according to one or more attributes related to daily and/or seasonal changes (e.g., group pictures by season, sequence activities according to time of day, group clothing items by season, and sequence stages of garden growth).	Lesson 3: 6
i. Create visual or physical representations of differences in natural phenomena at different times of the day and/or year.	Lesson 1: 3, 5 Lesson 3: 3, 4
j. Communicate observations about daily and seasonal changes using vocabulary such as days of the week, seasons of the year, today, tomorrow, tonight, morning, afternoon, evening, and night.	Lesson 1: 5, 6 Lesson 2: 6, 7, 8

Indicator	Assessment Opportunities
DS1.2 Inquire into the ways in which plants, animals, and humans adapt to daily and seasonal changes by changing their appearance, behaviour, and/or location. [CP, DM, SI]	
a. Pose questions about plant, animal, and human adaptation to daily and seasonal changes (e.g., Where do animals go during the night or the day? Why do some trees have no leaves in winter? Why do we wear jackets in winter?).	Lesson 3: 1, 2
b. Make predictions about plant, animal, and human adaptations to daily and seasonal changes based on observed patterns (e.g., some animals will migrate at particular times of the year, humans will wear mitts and scarves in winter, and some birds will disappear in winter).	Lesson 2: 1, 3, 4
c. Examine daily changes in the characteristics, behaviours, and location of plants, animals, and humans (e.g., some animals sleep at night, students go to school during the day, and some plants close their leaves at night).	Lesson 1: 1, 3
d. Examine seasonal changes in the characteristics, behaviours, and location of plants, animals, and humans (e.g., plants sprout in the spring, some trees lose their leaves in the fall, some rabbits change colour in the winter, some animals hibernate during the winter, and humans play different sports in the winter than in the summer).	Lesson 1: 1 Lesson 2: 7
e. Explore ways in which plant, animal, and human adaptations to daily and seasonal changes are represented through fiction and non-fiction writing and the arts (dance, drama, music, and visual art).	Lesson 3: 6 Lesson 4: 5
f. Construct representations of plant, animal, and human adaptations to daily and seasonal changes (e.g., humans wear different clothes, some plants lose their leaves in winter, some animals change colour, and some birds migrate).	Lesson 3: 5, 7, 8
g. Describe ways in which humans prepare to adapt to daily and seasonal changes (e.g., characteristics of clothing worn in different seasons, movement patterns of First Nations to follow animal migration, and features of buildings that keep people warm and dry).	Lesson 3: 5, 6
h. Pose new questions based on what was learned about plant, animal, and human adaptations to daily and seasonal changes.	Lesson 3: 7
i. Communicate questions, ideas, and intentions with classmates while conducting their explorations into daily and seasonal adaptations (e.g., share ideas about how animals survive at different times of the year).	Lesson 1: 3, 5, 6 Lesson 2: 7, 8 Lesson 3: 6

* Indicators are met in multiple lessons, but this correlation only identifies lessons in which the indictors are focused on.

Unit Planning Chart — Daily and Seasonal Changes

Lesson and Time*	Activities	Program Resources	Materials and Equipment*
Unit Opener: Getting Started 1–1.5 hours	**Introduce the Unit:** 1. Set Up an Ongoing Bulletin Board Display **Introduce the Books:** 2. Motivate Using the Fiction Book *Groundhog Day* 3. View the Non-fiction Book *Days and Seasons* **Introduce the Learning Targets:** 4. Post the Student-friendly Learning Targets	PM 1: I Wonder ... LM 1: Learning Targets Fiction Book: *Groundhog Day* Non-fiction Book: *Days and Seasons* Lap Book Science Poster: Seasons: Day and Night	
1: Observing Daily and Seasonal Changes 2–3 hours (plus 20–30 minutes per day for a week each month to make daily and seasonal observations)	**Engage:** 1. Activate and Build on Prior Knowledge 2. Elicit "I Wonder ..." Statements **Explore:** 3. Planning How to Observe and Record Daily and Seasonal Changes 4. Go On an Observation Walk **Explain:** 5. Use a Chart to Record Observations 6. Make Weekly and Monthly Comparisons 7. Reflect on Learning **Extend:** 8. Create Class Collages 9. Practise Vocabulary Words 10. Make Literature Connections	PM 1: I Wonder ... PM 13: Look What I've Learned LM 2: Daily Observation Record LM 3: Daily Observation Record — Letter to Parents LM 4: This Is What I Can Do Science Poster: Seasons: Day and Night Skills Poster: Observing and Recording Skills Poster: Finding Out	• chart paper • markers • crayons • pencils
2: Measuring Changes in Weather Conditions 3–4 hours	**Engage:** 1. Activate and Build on Prior Knowledge 2. Elicit "I Wonder ..." Statements **Explore:** 3. Make and Use a Simple Thermometer 4. Make a Rain Gauge 5. Make a Wind Vane **Explain:** 6. Add Measurements to Daily Observation Records 7. Make Weekly and Monthly Comparisons 8. Measure Weather 9. Reflect on Learning **Extend:** 10. Learn from a Weather Forecast 11. Make Ribbon Thermometers and Predict Temperatures 12. Explore Other "I Wonder ..." Statements	PM 1: I Wonder ... PM 7: Make a Bar Graph PM 13: Look What I've Learned LM 5: Make Weather Instruments LM 6: Measuring Temperature with a Thermometer LM 8: This Is What I Can Do Non-fiction Book: *Days and Seasons*	• clear plastic drinking bottle • clear plastic drinking straw • red food colouring • water (cool and hot) • rubbing alcohol • modelling clay or sticky tack • plastic bowls or tubs • ice cubes • red crayons • thermometer(s) • rain gauge • watering can • a plastic 2 L pop bottle with straight sides • 30 cm ruler • stones or coarse gravel • clear tape • wind vane or pictures of them • two paper plates • poster paper • straight pins • pencil with a new eraser • white glue • compass • marker • cameras or smart devices
3: Adapting to Days and Seasons 5–6 hours	**Engage:** 1. Activate and Build on Prior Knowledge 2. Elicit "I Wonder ..." Statements **Explore:** 3. Pretend It's Day and Night 4. Pretend It's Spring, Summer, Fall, and Winter 5. Create a Winter Web **Explain:** 6. Read and Respond to the Non-fiction Book *Days and Seasons* 7. Create Seasons in a Shoebox 8. Reflect on Learning **Extend:** 9. Respond to Talk Time 10. Make a Library Connection 11. Explore Other "I Wonder ..." Statements	PM 1: I Wonder ... PM 8: Make a Web PM 13: Look What I've Learned LM 9: Dramatization Scripts LM 10: Sort It Out LM 11: Picture Sort LM 12: This Is What I Can Do Non-fiction book: *Days and Seasons* Lap Book	• chart paper and coloured markers • highlighters • poster paper • scissors • magazines to cut up • glue sticks • 297 mm x 420 mm paper • coloured pencils, crayons • white mural paper • shoeboxes • modelling clay • pipe cleaners, construction paper, craft sticks, tissue paper, felt, and material scraps

Lesson and Time*	Activities	Program Resources	Materials and Equipment*
4: Exploring Light and Shadows 3–4 hours (plus 1 hour once a month to observe the sun and shadows)	**Engage:** 1. Activate and Build on Prior Knowledge 2. Elicit "I Wonder ..." Statements **Explore:** 3. Trace and Observe Shadow Changes **Explain:** 4. Track Shadow Records 5. Read and Respond to the Fiction Book *Groundhog Day* 6. Reflect on Learning **Extend:** 7. Compare Tube Shadows 8. Play Shadow Tag 9. View Shadow Shapes 10. Make a Shadow Theatre 11. Explore Other "I Wonder ..." Statements	PM 1: I Wonder ... PM 13: Look What I've Learned LM 12: Shadow Records LM 13: Changing Seasons LM 14: This Is What I Can Do Fiction Book: *Groundhog Day* Lap Book Skills Poster: Observing and Recording	• *Bear's Shadow* by Frank Asch or *Moonbear's Shadow* by Frank Asch • sidewalk chalk (or mural paper and washable markers or crayons) • digital cameras or smart devices • pictures of groundhogs
5: Cultural Perspectives 5–6 hours	**Engage:** 1. Activate and Build on Prior Knowledge 2. Elicit "I Wonder ..." Statements **Explore:** 3. Explore the Seasons Through Stories 4. View and Analyze Artwork **Explain:** 5. Retell a Story 6. Create a Story About the Seasons 7. Paint the Seasons 8. Reflect on Learning **Extend:** 9. Inuit Tapestries 10. Respond to Talk Time 11. Explore Other "I Wonder ..." Statements	PM 1: I Wonder ... PM 13: Look What I've Learned LM 15: Circle of the Seasons LM 16: This Is What I Can Do Traditional Knowledge Poster: Six Seasons	• thermometer • rain gauge • wind vane • First Nations and Métis stories about seasonal change • multimedia projector • cameras or smart devices • paints and brushes • large sheets of white paper for painting
6: Observing the Night Sky 4–5 hours	**Engage:** 1. Activate and Build on Prior Knowledge 2. Elicit "I Wonder ..." Statements **Explore:** 3. Explore the Changes of the Moon 4. Explore the Pictures That Stars Make 5. Explore Day and Night through Stories **Explain:** 6. Sequence Moon Phases 7. Retell a Story About Day and Night 8. Read and Respond to the Non-fiction Book *Days and Seasons* 9. Reflect on Learning **Extend:** 10. Make a Library Connection 11. Meet an Astronomer/Visit an Observatory	PM 1: I Wonder ... PM 13: Look What I've Learned LM 17: Observing the Moon LM 18: Observing the Moon — Letter to Parents LM 19: Help the Moon Find the Right Order LM 20: This Is What I Can Do Non-fiction Book: *Days and Seasons* Lap Book	• *Papa, Please Get the Moon for Me* by Eric Carle • multimedia projector • library books with pictures of stars in the night sky • crayons or markers and white paper (or white chalk/ white crayons and black paper) • cameras or smart devices
Unit Closer: Putting It All Together 3–4 hours	**Looking Back:** 1. Consider the Learning Targets 2. Reread the Fiction Book *Groundhog Day* 3. Consider "I Wonder ..." Statements 4. Reread the Non-fiction Book *Days and Seasons* 5. Make a Travel Poster **Going Further:** 6. Design a Plant or Animal for the Seasons	PM 4: Finding Out PM 9: I Found Out LM 21: Rate Your Learning LM 22: Design a Plant or Animal for the Seasons LM 23: Present Your Plant or Animal or the Seasons Fiction Book: *Groundhog Day* Non-fiction Book: *Days and Seasons* Lap Book	• modelling clay • art supplies such as pipe cleaners, buttons, toothpicks, craft sticks

* Time and materials lists are for Core Learning Opportunities only.

UNIT 4

Unit Opener: Getting Started

Time
1–1.5 hours

Program Resources
PM 1: I Wonder ...
LM 1: Learning Targets
Fiction Book: *Groundhog Day*
Non-fiction Book: *Days and Seasons*
Lap Book
Science Poster: Seasons: Day and Night

In this unit, students will identify natural objects that they can see in the sky and the changes in position of these objects at different times of the day and year. They will observe and record daily and seasonal changes in the amount of heat and light from the sun, length of the day, temperature throughout the year, and shadow length throughout a day and a year. They will learn how to use a rain gauge, thermometer, and wind vane to measure changes in weather conditions, and record their observations and measurements.

Through guided inquiry, students will investigate daily and seasonal changes, and develop skills in observing, measuring, grouping, sequencing, and recording changes in the environment from day to night and from season to season. They will make predictions, pose questions, communicate ideas, collaborate with other students, and explore visual and physical representations to demonstrate their understanding. They will also learn to use materials and tools safely.

***Traditional* Knowledge**

As well as developing an understanding of daily and seasonal changes in the environment, students will explore ways in which plants, animals, and people adapt to these changes. They will also learn how cultures such as First Nations and Métis share their understanding of daily and seasonal changes through their stories and works of art.

Introduce the Unit

1. Set Up an Ongoing Bulletin Board Display

- Display the Science poster **Seasons: Day and Night**. After students examine the illustrations on the poster, ask them:
  - What is the same about the photos? What is different? What might we be exploring based on the clues on the poster?
  - Record their suggestions on chart paper. This will assist you in activating students' prior knowledge before beginning the unit.
- Create a heading for the bulletin board that says Daily and Seasonal Changes. Read it to students.
- Post a large "I wonder ..." bubble like that on **PM 1: I Wonder ...** and invite students to generate "I wonder ..." statements about the unit. Record their ideas on a chart or paper strips. Use questions to guide them to formulate "I wonder ..." statements that reflect the big ideas of this unit:
  - I wonder how temperature and light change from day to night.
  - I wonder how temperature and light change with the different seasons.
  - I wonder if different cultures understand daily and seasonal changes in different ways.
  - I wonder how I can use tools to measure daily and seasonal changes in weather.
  - I wonder how the moon changes position and looks different in the sky over a month.
  - I wonder how plants, animals, and people survive daily and seasonal changes.

- Have students start a science journal for the unit and record an "I wonder ..." statement that they want to answer.
- Add vocabulary words, students' work, and photos of students involved in explorations of daily and seasonal changes as the unit progresses.

Introduce the Books

Notes
- This is a brief introduction to the books and the unit. Key concepts will be explored in more depth throughout the unit.
- This initial look at the book(s) can take place as a whole group, using the Lap Book, with small groups, at a centre, or during the literacy block of time.

2. Motivate Using the Fiction Book *Groundhog Day*

Before: Ask students to share their experiences of waiting for a certain day when something special will happen or they will do something special. What was it like to wait?
- Present the title of the book *Groundhog Day.* Show students the cover of the Lap Book. Ask them to predict what might happen in the story. Record their predictions on chart paper for reference during and after reading.

During: Distribute copies of the book or use the Lap Book. Use a Picture Walk to give students a preview. Stop at each two-page spread and ask:
- What do you see here?
- What do the pictures tell you about the characters?
- What do you think is happening? What might happen next?

After: Stop after page 9 in order not to reveal the ending. Assure students that they will have another opportunity to read the book.
- Invite students to examine what is the same or different on the spreads from pages 2–9. Ask students to suggest what this story might have to do with daily and seasonal changes.

3. View the Non-fiction Book *Days and Seasons*

- Show the cover of the Lap Book. Read the title aloud, and invite students to talk about the cover picture. Explain that both this book and *Groundhog Day* are part of the next science unit.
- Distribute copies of *Days and Seasons*. Start students on a Picture Walk through pages 2–9. Stop at each two-page spread and ask students what they might be learning from these pages.
- Provide a few minutes for students to sit in small groups and browse through the pages, talking briefly about what catches their attention on each spread. Invite students to identify any vocabulary words they notice within the book that they know are about the unit.
- Gather students together and ask them: What do you think you will learn from this book? What do you already know about what you see in the pictures? What is the main difference between this book and *Groundhog Day*? (*Groundhog Day* tells a story; *Days and Seasons* presents information through text and illustrations.) Introduce or review the terms *fiction* and *non-fiction*, and encourage students to apply the terms to other books they read in print and on-screen.

Introduce the Learning Targets

Notes
- The Learning Targets are developed from the science outcomes for this unit. If they seem overwhelming, leave them for now or choose key points to discuss.
- Lesson-specific learning targets are provided for each lesson.

4. Post the Student-friendly Learning Targets

- Make and post a chart of the learning targets from **LM 1: Learning Targets**. Read them with students. Tell students to go back to the learning targets to check off what they have learned.

1 Observing Daily and Seasonal Changes

Time
2–3 hours (plus 20–30 minutes per day for a week each month to make daily and seasonal observations)

Vocabulary
day
night
days of the week
months of the year
seasons
spring
summer
fall
winter
morning
afternoon
evening

Program Resources
PM 1: I Wonder ...
PM 13: Look What I've Learned
LM 2: Daily Observation Record
LM 3: Daily Observation Record — Letter to Parents
LM 4: This Is What I Can Do
Science Poster: Seasons: Day and Night
Skills Poster: Observing and Recording
Skills Poster: Finding Out

Materials and Equipment
- chart paper
- markers
- crayons
- pencils

GOAL

Students will plan how they will observe and record changes in their outdoor environment from day to day and from season to season. Then they will make and record their observations.

ASSESSMENT CHART

Science Indicators	Assessment Opportunities
DS1.1 a. Pose questions about changes in natural phenomena in the environment over the course of a day and a year.	Engage 1, 2
DS1.1 b. Identify days of the week, months of the year, and seasons.	Engage 1 Explore 3
DS1.1 c. Observe daily and seasonal changes in the amount of heat and light from the sun, including the formation of shadows.	Explore 4 Explain 6
DS1.1 e. Use tools and techniques to record changes in weather conditions that occur in daily and seasonal cycles.	Explore 3 Explain 5
DS1.1 f. Document the visibility and position of objects in the sky at different times of the day and year.	Explore 4 Explain 5, 6
DS1.1 i. Create visual or physical representations of differences in natural phenomena at different times of the day and/or year.	Explore 3 Explain 5
DS1.1 j. Communicate observations about daily and seasonal changes with appropriate vocabulary.	Explain 5, 6
DS1.2 c. Examine daily changes in the characteristics, behaviours, and location of plants, animals, and humans (e.g., some animals sleep at night, students go to school during the day, and some plants close their leaves at night).	Engage 1 Explain 3
DS1.2 d. Examine seasonal changes in the characteristics, behaviours, and location of plants, animals, and humans (e.g., plants sprout in the spring, some trees lose their leaves in the fall, some rabbits change colour in the winter, some animals hibernate during the winter, and humans play different sports in the winter than in the summer).	Engage 1
DS1.2 i. Communicate questions, ideas, and intentions with classmates while conducting their explorations into daily and seasonal adaptations.	Explore 3 Explain 5, 6
English Language Arts Indicators	**Assessment Opportunities**
CC1.1 e. Use inquiry to explore a question or topic of interest related to the topics and themes being studied.	Engage 1, 2 Explore 3, 4 Explain 5, 6
CC1.3 a. Use oral language to bring meaning to what is listened to, observed, felt, viewed, and read.	Engage 1, 2 Explore 3 Explain 5, 6

BACKGROUND INFORMATION

As students record their observations of daily and seasonal changes, it is important to record the day and month so they can identify if changes are happening from day to day or from season to season. Recording when the sun rises and sets provides data for students to conclude that the time from sunrise to sunset differs depending on the season. Recording weather will help students identify weather patterns from season to season. Recording drawings of what plants look like, what animals look like or are doing, and what people are wearing and/or doing will provide the information for identifying how plants, animals, and people adapt to seasonal changes.

A common misconception that students may have:

- The sun rises exactly in the east and sets exactly in the west every day. (Correction: The exact location of sunrise and sunset depends on where you are standing on Earth — closer to or farther away from the equator. In southern Canada, the sun rises in the southeast in winter, and in the summer, the sun rises in the northeast. In the winter, the sun sets in the southwest, and in the summer, the sun sets in the northwest.)

ASSESSMENT FOR LEARNING

Look for Evidence of Learning	Student-friendly Learning Targets
Can the student: • identify and understand vocabulary words for day and night, and the seasons? • identify clues in the environment that tell whether it is day or night, and what season it is? • follow the discussion and make appropriate and meaningful suggestions in planning how to record their observations of daily and seasonal changes?	(self-assessment) • I know and understand the words for day and night. • I know and understand the words for the seasons. • I can explain how I know that it is day or night.

DI DIFFERENTIATING INSTRUCTION

For EAL

Provide visual symbols for each of the vocabulary words on **LM 2: Daily Observation Record**. Create flashcards for each vocabulary word with a visual symbol for the meaning. Provide opportunities for students to practise identifying each vocabulary word.

For Enrichment

Challenge this group of students to record their own observations on enlarged copies of **LM 2: Daily Observation Record**. Invite them to share with the class the patterns they found. Compare their patterns to what you recorded with the rest of the class.

For Extra Support

When students are ready to begin recording their daily observations on their own record sheets, you may wish to chunk **LM 2: Daily Observation Record** and provide students with record sheets that show only one or two sets of entries per page. This will provide students with extra space for recording and help them focus their attention.

CURRICULUM CONNECTIONS

Students will have the opportunity to develop skills and concepts in the following area:

Mathematics

P1.1 f. Identify and describe a repeating pattern found in the environment (e.g., classroom, outdoors) using everyday language.
P1.1 g. Identify repeating events (e.g., days of the week, birthdays, seasons).

CORE LEARNING OPPORTUNITIES

Engage

Literacy Check
Can the student:
- identify and understand vocabulary words for day and night, and the seasons?

1. Activate and Build on Prior Knowledge

- Gather students and display the Science poster **Seasons: Day and Night**. Also display the chart paper on which you recorded students' suggestions about what they might be exploring in this unit in the Unit Opener 3. Model reading each entry to review their suggestions.
- Use the following questions to examine the pictures on the poster and to highlight the key concepts illustrated by the poster:
  - What is the same in each picture? What is different? (Each set of pictures shows a different season.)
  - Can you name each season? (spring, summer, fall, winter)
  - How do you know which season it is? What clues can you find in the pictures?
  - How do you know when it is day or night? What clues can you find in the pictures?
- As students identify each vocabulary word, record it on a flashcard for display on the Daily and Seasonal Changes bulletin board.
- Introduce the concept of collecting evidence and how important evidence, observations, and data are to drawing meaningful conclusions. Tell students that recording our clues will help us to put together evidence as scientists do.
- On chart paper, record the clues that tell it is day (The sun is shining. It is light.); it is night (The moon is in the sky. It is dark.); and which season it is. You might use the following format:

Tip
Depending on the time of year, you may wish to record the clues as key word entries instead of complete sentences. You might also illustrate each entry to help students connect the images with the words.

Spring	Summer	Fall	Winter
• The snow is melting. • There are puddles. • There are buds on the trees.	• The grass is green. • Green leaves are on the trees.	• The leaves are changing colour. • Leaves are falling to the ground.	• Snow is on the ground. • There are no leaves on the trees.

- Extend the discussion by asking students to share other clues that tell whether it is day or night, or what season it is. Ask students what they would like to investigate about what changes from day to night, and what changes from season to season. Record students' responses to each question on chart paper and post them so you can refer to their prior knowledge and questions throughout the unit.

Literacy Check
Can the student:
- read the "I wonder ..." statements in the class list and identify an "I wonder ..." statement for his or her personal list?
- copy an "I wonder ..." statement from the class list onto his or her personal list?

2. Elicit "I Wonder ..." Statements

- Model an "I wonder ..." form of inquiry with statements such as:
  - I wonder what changes from day to night.
  - I wonder what changes from season to season.
  - I wonder how day and night affect living things.
  - I wonder how changing seasons affect living things.

- Invite students to offer other "I wonder ..." statements. Record these on a chart or paper strips, and read them together. Provide students with copies of **PM 1: I Wonder ...** and ask them to record the statement(s) that especially interests them. Some students may require individual or small group assistance to identify statements and record them.

Explore

3. Planning How to Observe and Record Daily and Seasonal Changes

Step 1: Ask students: What can we *see* or *feel* that tell us it is day, night, or a particular season? Record their suggestions along the left side of the board or on a piece of chart paper. (e.g., amount of light, temperature, weather, what animals look like)

Step 2: For each of their suggestions, ask students: How might we keep a record of the changes we *see* or *feel*? Record their suggestions in the next column of the chart.

Step 3: Tell students that you are going to transfer their ideas to a chart that will keep their records organized so that they can make comparisons from day to day and season to season. Project or display **LM 2: Daily Observation Record**, and read it to students.

Step 4: Ask students: "We want to use what we see and feel in order to learn about the changes that happen from day to night and from season to season. How often should we record what we see and feel outside?" (For night observations, you will need to involve students' parents. Use **LM 3: Daily Observation Record — Letter to Parents/Guardians**. Invite them to help their children record the night entries on the record sheet each day and return the record sheet the next morning.)

- Focus students' attention on the Skills poster **Observing and Recording**. Read the text that goes with each picture and then ask students to identify the senses they will be using as they observe changes from day to day and season to season; the way in which they will be recording what they observe; and the graphic organizer they will be using to sort and compare.
- Focus students' attention on the Skills poster **Finding Out**. Read the text on the poster and ask students which skills they will be using. (Making a Plan, Observe and Wonder, Explore, Share).

Tip
You may wish to record observations three or four times a day for one week each month. This will provide the data that students will need to make comparisons and identify the changes that happen daily and from season to season.

Safety Check
Caution students to never look directly at the sun because it will hurt their eyes.

4. Go on an Observation Walk

- Review what students are looking for, and then take them outside for a 10–15 minute walk. Ask questions to guide students' observations:
  - How light is it? What can you see in the sky?
  - What landmark can we use to show where the sun is in the sky?
  - What is the weather like?
  - Are any changes happening to the plants we see?

Science Check
Can the student:
- make observations in response to guiding questions on the walk?
- use key vocabulary correctly to identify what he or she sees and feels?
- find appropriate evidence in the environment to answer questions?

Explain

✔ Literacy Check
Can the student:
- suggest appropriate vocabulary and responses to each section of the chart?
- record observations using words, symbols, and drawings as modelled by the teacher?
- identify and copy chosen words and symbols correctly?

5. Use a Chart to Record Observations

- Make poster-size copies of **LM 2: Daily Observation Record**. How independently students work to record their observations will depend on the time of year and your students' readiness.
- Involve students in completing the poster-size copy of **LM 2**. Provide individual students with opportunities to make entries in the appropriate columns under your guidance. This involvement will prepare them to complete their own observation records when they are ready.
- Model each step of the recording process on the class Daily Observation Record students complete their observation records on **LM 2**. (If you photocopy it on large paper, students will have more room to make their entries.) You may wish to develop the process of recording observations over a period of days, beginning with one or two entries on the first day and then adding one or two more entries each day until students can handle all of the recording.
- Keep the class Daily Observation Records so that they can be displayed for making comparisons at the end of each week and from month to month.
- Students should have a folder to store their copies of **LM 2**.

✔ Science Check
Can the student:
- follow and compare the records from one category over several record sheets?
- identify patterns from the displayed record sheets?
- distinguish between daily and seasonal changes?

6. Make Weekly and Monthly Comparisons

- At the end of each week, have students examine the Daily Observation Records. Ask students guiding questions such as:
  - What happens in the same order over and over again?
  - What happens to how the air feels over the day?
  - Why is it warmest during the day? When is it coldest? What pattern can we use to describe what happens to temperature over the day?
- Record students' observations and responses on chart paper so that you can review and add to them when you examine the observation records the following month. At that time, display all of the class Daily Observation Records. Ask students: What patterns did you see before that are still happening this month? Can you see any changes in temperature, daylight, what you see in the sky, the weather, what you see happening with people, animals, and plants?
- Through this process, students will discover daily and seasonal patterns based on direct observation and comparison of data.

✔ Science Check
Can the student:
- record what he or she has learned?
- show understanding of the key concepts?

7. Reflect on Learning

- Have students record evidence of their learning on **PM 13: Look What I've Learned**, in their journal, and/or with a video or audio recording on a smart device or camera. Encourage them to note one thing they learned and something they still wonder about. You may wish to ask each student to share orally what he or she learned and record what was learned in a sentence.
- Use **LM 4: This Is What I Can Do** as a self-assessment. Read the learning targets with students and have them respond on their own.

OTHER LEARNING OPPORTUNITIES

Extend: Activity Bank

At any time, choose from the following options to replace or supplement the Core Learning Opportunities to meet students' needs and/or interests.

8. Create Class Collages

- Label six pieces of poster paper with the following headings: Day, Night, Spring, Summer, Fall, Winter. Have students look in magazines for pictures that fit each heading. Have them cut out and glue the pictures they find onto the appropriate collage. Ensure that they can explain why each picture belongs under each heading. Provide an opportunity to view and discuss what students have chosen to represent day/night, and each season.

9. Practise Vocabulary Words

- Sprinkle a layer of sand or salt in cookie sheets and guide students to practise using their fingers to form the letters to print the vocabulary words they have learned (e.g., *day, night, days of the week, seasons, spring, summer, fall, winter*). As they form the letters, model how they can practise the sounds that each letter makes in the word.
- Provide students with modelling clay and model how they can roll pieces into long "snakes" and form the letters of key vocabulary words. Have students practise reading the words that they form.
- Use tempera paints and paintbrushes to practise printing and saying the vocabulary words from this lesson. Encourage students to use colours that suggest day, night, and each season. For example, students might use yellow to paint the word *day* and black to paint the word *night*.

10. Make Literature Connections

- Take your students to the library to look for fiction and non-fiction books about day and night and the seasons. Continue to reinforce the difference between fiction and non-fiction books. Use these books to create a class library for student reference and for reading aloud throughout this unit.

2 Measuring Changes in Weather Conditions

Time
3–4 hours

Vocabulary
thermometer
temperature
rain gauge
wind vane
wind direction

Program Resources
PM 1: I Wonder ...
PM 7: Make a Bar Graph
PM 13: Look What I've Learned
LM 5: Make Weather Instruments
LM 6: Measuring Temperature With a Thermometer
LM 8: This Is What I Can Do
Non-fiction Book: *Days and Seasons*

Materials and Equipment
- clear plastic drinking bottle
- clear plastic drinking straw
- red food colouring
- water (cool and hot)
- rubbing alcohol
- modelling clay
- plastic bowls or tubs
- ice cubes
- red crayons (one for each student)
- thermometer(s)
- rain gauge
- watering can
- a plastic 2 L pop bottle with straight sides
- 30-cm ruler
- scissors
- clear tape
- wind vane, or pictures of wind vanes
- two paper plates
- poster paper
- straight pins
- sharpened pencil with a new eraser
- white glue
- compass
- marker
- cameras or smart devices

GOAL

Students will make and use tools (e.g., thermometer, rain gauge, and wind vane) to measure changes in weather conditions. They will add this data to their records of daily and seasonal changes.

ASSESSMENT CHART

Science Indicators	Assessment Opportunities
DS1.1 c. Observe daily and seasonal changes in the amount of heat and light from the sun, including the formation of shadows.	Explore 3 Explain 6, 7
DS1.1 e. Use a variety of tools and techniques to record changes in weather conditions that occur in daily and seasonal cycles.	Explore 3, 4, 5 Explain 6, 7
DS1.1 j. Communicate observations about daily and seasonal changes using appropriate vocabulary.	Explain 6, 7, 8
DS1.2 d. Examine seasonal changes in the characteristics, behaviours, and location of plants, animals, and humans (e.g., plants sprout in the spring, some trees lose their leaves in the fall, some rabbits change colour in the winter, some animals hibernate during the winter, and humans play different sports in the winter than in the summer).	Explain 7
DS1.2 i. Communicate questions, ideas, and intentions with classmates while exploring daily and seasonal adaptations.	Explain 7, 8
English Language Arts Indicators	**Assessment Opportunities**
CR1.2 h. View and demonstrate understanding that visual texts are sources of information.	Engage 1 Explain 6, 7
CC1.1 a. Use words, symbols, and other forms, including appropriate technology, to express understanding of topics, themes, and issues.	Explain 6, 7, 8, 9
CC1.1 e. Use inquiry to explore a question or topic of interest related to the themes and topics being studied.	Engage 1, 2 Explore 3, 4, 5 Explain 8

BACKGROUND INFORMATION

A thermometer is usually made of a glass tube with coloured alcohol in it. Temperature is measured in degrees Celsius (metric) in Canada and most of the world. On this scale, the freezing point of water is 0 °C and the boiling point of water is 100 °C. The Fahrenheit scale (imperial) is used in the United States. On this scale, the freezing point of water is 32 °F and the boiling point of water is 212 °F. In order to get an accurate reading, students should look straight at the thermometer at eye level.

A rain gauge is a tool for measuring the amount of rain that falls in a certain period of time. Meteorologists use rainfall measurements along with data from other weather instruments to find patterns in the type of weather that follows certain weather conditions. They use this data to predict rainfall amounts, as well as other elements of weather.

A wind vane (sometimes called a weather vane) is a tool for measuring wind direction. Winds are named by the direction from which they are blowing. A north wind is blowing from the north. To read a wind vane, watch which direction the arrow points when the wind blows. The arrow will point in the direction from which the wind is blowing. If the arrow points west, the wind is blowing from the west. Because wind brings our weather, we know that if the wind is blowing from the east, the weather east of us is moving in.

ASSESSMENT FOR LEARNING

Look for Evidence of Learning	Student-friendly Learning Targets
Can the student: • read temperature, amount of precipitation, and wind direction using the constructed or provided tools? • demonstrate understanding of how a thermometer, rain gauge, and wind vane work? • use appropriate vocabulary to identify what he or she sees and feels when outside? • find appropriate evidence in the environment to answer questions for the daily observation record? • suggest appropriate vocabulary and responses to each section of the chart? • record observations and measurement data using words, symbols, and drawings as modelled by the teacher? • identify patterns using the Daily Observation Records? • distinguish between daily and seasonal changes?	(self-assessment) • I can follow directions to make tools for measuring temperature, rainfall, and wind direction. • I can use a thermometer, rain gauge, and wind vane to measure temperature, rainfall, and wind direction. • I can show and explain how a thermometer, rain gauge, and wind vane work. • I can use pictures, symbols, and words to record what we see and feel outdoors. • I can use measurements from a thermometer, rain gauge, and wind vane to record weather changes. • I can identify patterns and changes from day to night. • I can identify patterns and changes from season to season.

DI DIFFERENTIATING INSTRUCTION

For EAL

The terms *mass* and *measurement* may be new to some students. Pre-teaching these words may help with comprehension while reading the non-fiction book.

For Enrichment

Set up a Measuring Water centre. Put out several containers of different shapes and sizes for students to fill with water. Also provide some standard measurement instruments such as a bathroom or kitchen scale and measuring cups. Encourage students to explore and compare how much the containers will hold and what their mass is when filled with water.

For Extra Support

Break assignments into smaller, more manageable parts and provide structured directions for each part. Some students may need extra support with choosing which type of measurement tool to use.

CURRICULUM CONNECTIONS

Students will have the opportunity to develop skills and concepts in the following area:

Mathematics

SS1.1 Demonstrate an understanding of measurement as a process of comparing by identifying attributes that can be compared, ordering objects, and making statements of comparison.

CORE LEARNING OPPORTUNITIES

Engage

1. Activate and Build on Prior Knowledge

- Display the planning chart created in Lesson 1, Explore 3. Display a thermometer, rain gauge, and wind vane (or pictures of these measuring tools) and ask students to identify each one. If students do not recognize them, introduce them as tools for measuring what we see and feel when we go outside.
- Ask students:
  - What are we using to record what we see and feel when we go outside? (We are using words, symbols, and pictures.)
  - What changes can we *measure*?
  - Which of these tools or measuring devices can we use to tell how hot or cold it is outside? (The *thermometer* measures *temperature*, or how hot or cold it is outside.)
  - Record students' responses to each question on chart paper and post them so that you can return to their prior knowledge and questions throughout the unit.

✔ Literacy Check
Can the student:
- read the "I wonder ..." statements in the class list and identify an "I wonder ..." statement for his or her personal list?
- copy an "I wonder ..." statement from the class list onto his or her personal list?

2. Elicit "I Wonder ..." Statements

- Model an "I wonder ..." form of inquiry with statements such as: "I wonder how I can make tools to measure weather changes outside," "I wonder how I can use tools to measure weather changes outside."
- Invite students to offer other "I wonder ..." statements. Record these on a chart or paper strips, and then read them together. Provide students with copies of **PM 1: I Wonder ...** and ask them to record the "I wonder ..." statement(s) that especially interests them. Some students may require individual or small group assistance to identify statements and record them.

Explore

Note
Instructions for how to make a rain gauge can be found on **LM 5: Make Weather Instruments**. This is for teacher use.

Safety Check
Students should not handle rubbing alcohol or the thermometer containing rubbing alcohol.

3. Make and Use a Simple Thermometer

- Before beginning this activity, show students the Skills poster **Safety in Science Class**. Remind them to handle science tools carefully.
- Show students a thermometer and ask them to name it. Review with students that a thermometer is used to measure temperature. Ask students to share what they know about temperature. Use their suggestions to build their understanding of temperature as a measure of how hot or cold something is.
- Encourage students to consider how they might build a thermometer like the one you showed them.
- Tell students you will be making a thermometer and using it to measure the temperature of air and water.
- Distribute copies of **LM 6: Measuring Temperature With a Thermometer** to students. Note the level of the liquid in the straw when it is at room temperature. Have students use red crayons to mark the level of the liquid in the straw in the first thermometer on **LM 6**.

Safety Check
Make sure that the water is not hot enough to burn anyone and that you are the one who pours the hot water into the bowl or tub. Have paper towel to wipe up any spills.

- To show how the thermometer works, pour hot water from the tap into a plastic bowl or tub. Set the thermometer in the hot water and watch. As the temperature rises, so does the liquid in the straw. The liquid rises because the heat from the hot water causes the water-rubbing alcohol mixture to expand. Note the level of the liquid in the straw in the hot water. Have students use their red crayons to mark the level of the liquid in the second thermometer on **LM 6.**
- Then place ice cubes and water in a second plastic bowl or tub. Note the level of the liquid in the straw in the cold water. Have students use their red crayons to show the level of the liquid in the third thermometer on **LM 6.**
- Have a thermometer mounted outside the school. Show and explain to students how to read the outside temperature by the height of the liquid in the thermometer. Once inside, add the outside temperature to the class Daily Observation Record for the appropriate time of day.

Note
Instructions for how to make a rain gauge can be found on **LM 5: Make Weather Instruments.** This is for teacher use.

4. Make a Rain Gauge

- Explain to students that they are going to help make a rain gauge. Show students a commercial rain gauge and ask them if they have seen one before. Invite students to share their experiences with rain gauges and what they understand about how they work. Review with students that a rain gauge is used to measure how much rain falls.
- Encourage students to consider how they might build a rain gauge like the one you showed them. As you begin to make a class rain gauge, try to incorporate students' suggestions of materials to use.
- Provide an opportunity for students to see how the rain gauge works. Place the rain gauge outside on a flat surface and use a watering can to "rain" over the rain gauge. Make sure it rains enough that students will be able to see the water rising in the rain gauge. Show them how to use the ruler on the side to read how much rain fell.
- Place the rain gauge in an open area away from trees or buildings so that nothing interferes with the amount of rain that falls into the bottle(s).
- When it rains, guide students to use the ruler to identify how much rain has fallen and add this amount to the class Daily Observation Record.

Note
Instructions for how to make a wind vane can be found on **LM 5: Make Weather Instruments.** This is for teacher use.

5. Make a Wind Vane

- Tell students they are going to help make a wind vane. Show students an actual wind vane or pictures of wind vanes and ask them if they have seen one before. Invite students to share their experiences about how wind vanes work. Review with students that a wind vane is used to measure which direction the wind is coming from. Ask students if they have heard their parents say something like, "It's a north wind. That's why it feels cold." A north wind means that the wind is coming from the north. Make sure students know what direction north is.
- Encourage students to consider how they might build a wind vane like the one you showed them. As you begin making a wind vane, try to incorporate students' suggestions of materials to use. Involve students in the steps of making a class wind vane.

- Take the wind vane outside and set it on a flat surface. Use a compass to place it with the N on the north side. The wind vane will spin so that the arrow points into the wind. It always points in the direction the wind is coming from. When you take students outside for daily observations of weather conditions, guide them to add wind direction to their records. Also guide them to describe the wind as light, medium, or strong.

Explain

Literacy Check
Can the student:
- suggest appropriate vocabulary and responses to each section of the chart?
- record observations using words, symbols, and drawings as modelled by the teacher?
- record measurement data as modelled by the teacher?
- identify and copy chosen words and symbols correctly?

Science Check
Can the student:
- follow and compare the records from one category over several record sheets?
- identify patterns from the displayed record sheets?
- distinguish between daily and seasonal changes?

6. Add Measurements to Daily Observation Records

- As you work on daily observation records, guide students to add the measurement data using a thermometer, rain gauge, and wind vane. Help students understand that this will make their records more accurate and specific.

7. Make Weekly and Monthly Comparisons

- Add temperature, precipitation, and wind direction data to the weekly and monthly comparisons of daily observation records (as described in Lesson 1, Explain 6). As you guide students to identify patterns, include data gained from using tools to measure changes in weather conditions. Use questions such as the following to guide their examination and comparison:
  - What patterns do you see in the temperature? What happens to the temperature every day? What happens to the temperature of the air over the day? When is it warmest? When is it coldest? What pattern can we use to describe what happens to temperature over the day?
  - Is there a pattern in how much rain falls during a day, a week, or a month?
  - Is there a pattern in which direction the wind blows from at different times?
- Record students' observations and responses on chart paper so that you can review their observations later on in the unit.
- Over time, use this process to highlight daily and seasonal changes that might arise. Through this process, students will discover daily and seasonal patterns based on direct observation and comparison of data.

8. Measure Weather

- Read pages 22–23 of the non-fiction book *Days and Seasons* with students and provide the suggested materials to record the weather each day over two weeks. Repeat this process in different seasons so that students can identify the weather changes that occur with the seasons.

9. Reflect on Learning

- Have students record evidence of their learning on **PM 13: Look What I've Learned**, in their journal, and/or with a video or audio recording on a smart device or camera. Students can use words and/or pictures to show what they have learned. Encourage them to note one thing they learned and something they still wonder about. You may wish to ask each student to share orally what he or she learned and record what was learned in a sentence(s).

- Use **LM 8: This Is What I Can Do** as a self-assessment. Read the learning targets with students and have them respond on their own. Some students may need support.

OTHER LEARNING OPPORTUNITIES

Extend: Activity Bank

At any time, choose from the following options to replace or supplement the Core Learning Opportunities to meet students' needs and/or interests.

10. Learn from a Weather Forecast

- View a television weather forecast with students to identify the following: what weather conditions and changes the weather person talks about (e.g., wind speed and direction, amount and type of precipitation, temperature, humidity, cloud cover); what weather conditions and changes are measured; and how weather conditions and changes are measured. Investigate any weather conditions, measurements, or measuring tools that students are unfamiliar with.

11. Make Ribbon Thermometers and Predict Temperatures

- Distribute **LM 7: Thermometer** to students and have them cut out the thermometer and glue it onto a strip of heavy paper. Cut slits at the top and bottom of each thermometer. Prepare lengths of white ribbon that can be looped through these slits and fastened at the back of the heavy paper. Cut lengths of red ribbon about 1/3 the length of the white ribbon and glue them onto the white ribbons. Push the ends of white ribbon through the slits and fasten the ends in a loop at the back of the heavy paper. Students can move the loop of ribbon up and down to show temperature predictions. Use the ribbon thermometer when reading the fiction book, *Groundhog Day*. Students can move the ribbon to show the temperature as the seasons change.

12. Explore Other "I Wonder ..." Statements

- Return to the "I wonder ..." statements not yet answered, and new wonderings that have come up. With students, plan and set up centres where they can explore these wonderings. Encourage them to make and test predictions.
- Working in small groups, students can rotate to all the centres or focus on one per group. They could share their findings in an oral, written, or electronic presentation.

3 Adapting to Days and Seasons

Time
5–6 hours

Vocabulary
adapt

Program Resources
PM 1: I Wonder ...
PM 8: Make a Web
PM 13: Look What I've Learned
LM 9: Dramatization Scripts
LM 10: Sort It Out
LM 11: Picture Sort
LM 12: This Is What I Can Do
Non-fiction Book: *Days and Seasons*
Lap Book

Materials and Equipment
- chart paper and coloured markers
- highlighters
- poster paper
- scissors
- magazines to cut up
- glue sticks
- 297 mm x 420 mm paper
- coloured pencils, crayons
- white mural paper
- shoeboxes
- modelling clay
- pipe cleaners, construction paper, craft sticks, tissue paper, felt, and material scraps

GOAL

Students will develop an understanding of changes between day and night and between the seasons. They will also develop an understanding of how plants, animals, and people adapt to changes in the seasons.

ASSESSMENT CHART

Science Indicators	Assessment Opportunities
DS1.1 b. Identify the days of the week, months of the year, and seasons.	Engage 1 Explore 4
DS1.1 h. Sequence or group objects, materials, and events according to one or more attributes related to daily and/or seasonal changes.	Explore 5
DS1.1 i. Create visual or physical representations of differences in natural phenomena at different times of the day and/or year.	Explore 3, 4
DS1.2 a. Pose questions about plant, animal, and human adaptations to daily and seasonal changes.	Engage 1, 2
DS1.2 b. Make predictions about plant, animal, and human adaptations to daily and seasonal changes based on observation patterns.	Engage 1 Explore 3, 4
DS1.2 e. Explore ways in which plant, animal, and human adaptations to daily and seasonal changes are represented through writing and the arts.	Explore 3 Explain 6
DS1.2 f. Construct representations of plant, animal, and human adaptations to daily and seasonal changes.	Explore 5 Explain 7
DS1.2 g. Describe ways in which humans prepare to adapt to daily and seasonal changes.	Explore 5 Explain 6
DS1.2 h. Pose new questions based on what was learned about plant, animal, and human adaptations to daily and seasonal changes.	Explain 7
English Language Arts Indicators	**Assessment Opportunities**
CR1.3 g. Demonstrate attentiveness and comprehension as a listener through body language and facial expressions.	Engage 1, 2 Explore 3, 4, 5 Explain 6, 7, 8
CCC1.3 a. Use oral language to bring meaning to what is listened to, observed, felt, viewed, and read.	Engage 1, 2 Explore 3, 4, 5 Explain 6

BACKGROUND INFORMATION

Animals that are active at night are called nocturnal. Some animals, such as frogs, toads, and salamanders, are nocturnal to avoid the heat of the sun. Others animals, such as mice and flying squirrels, come out to feed, when they can take advantage of the dark to avoid predators. The red fox, coyote, and wolf hunt at night. Bats and owls have specially developed senses for hunting in the dark. Humans and other animals that lack highly developed senses to survive with little or no light, such as squirrels, grasshoppers, and groundhogs, are active during the day, and are called diurnal. Some animals are not strictly nocturnal or diurnal. Deer, cats, and rabbits, for example, are more active at dawn and dusk.

Some animals hibernate in the winter. In order to truly hibernate, the animal's body temperature drops and its breathing rate, metabolism, and heart rate slow down to save energy during the months when food is scarce. These animals eat large amounts of food in the summer and early fall and store this food energy in the form of fat. Their bodies use this fat for energy while they are hibernating. Animals that hibernate include bats, ground squirrels, groundhogs, chipmunks, frogs and snakes. Bears, raccoons, and skunks are not true hibernators. They go into a deep sleep, but they get up from time to time, especially when the temperature rises.

Some flowers, such as the poppy, dandelion, pansy, crocus, and tulip, close their petals at night. This may be an adaptation that keeps their pollen from becoming heavy and wet with dew. Insects can transfer dry pollen more easily and so there is a greater likelihood that these plants will reproduce. It is also possible that these flowers are conserving their energy and odour for the daytime when pollinating insects are more active. Evening primrose and honeysuckle bloom when the sun sets and are pollinated by nocturnal insects.

Adaptations happen over a very long time, usually hundreds of generations. Some students develop the misconception that adaptations to the environment happen spontaneously or that an animal decides to change.

***Traditional* Knowledge**

In winter, First Nations and Métis peoples use moose, deer, buffalo, elk, caribou, and bear hides to make warm outer clothing, blankets, rugs, and tipis. Using hides with the fur turned in toward the body provides insulation. First Nations and Métis peoples know when to trap and hunt animals to ensure maximum warmth. For example, the beaver is trapped in the winter because the fur is thicker at that time.

Men, women, and children worked hard during the summer and fall to hunt, gather, dry, and store food for the long winter. Before the buffalo were killed off, First Nations peoples on the prairies followed migrating buffalo herds.

ASSESSMENT FOR LEARNING

Look for Evidence of Learning	Student-friendly Learning Targets
Can the student: • use clues to identify day and night, and the seasons? • use clues to identify days of the week and months of the year? • dramatize the actions of plants, animals, and people during day and night? • dramatize how plants, animals, and people change from season to season? • identify how plants, animals, and people adapt to the seasons? • classify pictures that belong to each season? • draw a picture to illustrate something to do in each season? • represent ways in which plants, animals, and humans adapt to a chosen season?	(self-assessment) • I can tell when it is day and night. • I can use clues to tell when it is spring, summer, fall, and winter. • I know the days of the week. • I know the months of the year. • I can tell how plants, animals, and people change from day to night. • I can tell how plants, animals, and people change in different seasons.

DI DIFFERENTIATING INSTRUCTION

For EAL

To enhance students' understanding of the scripts for dramatization in Explore 3 and 4, gather pictures of key content words (e.g., red poppy, robin) so that you can show them as you read the script.

For Enrichment

Have students use non-fiction texts and online resources to research ways in which a chosen animal from Saskatchewan (or Canada) adapts to each season.

For Extra Support

Seat students close to you during the reading and discussion of the non-fiction text so that you can keep them on track and help them follow the text. Or, pair these students with students who are strong readers.

CORE LEARNING OPPORTUNITIES

Engage

1. Activate and Build on Prior Knowledge

- Use riddles to get students thinking about the characteristics and changes that apply to day and night and to the different seasons. Record the correct responses to each riddle on chart paper to develop students' word recognition. Examples of these riddles include:
  - When clouds do not cover the sky, you can see the sun. I am the time when you are active. What am I? (day)
  - I am the time when you sleep. It is dark. What am I? (night)
  - I bring puddles that you can splash in. When I arrive, the snow melts and it starts to get warmer. What season am I? (spring)
- Use riddles to help students learn/review the days of the week and the months of the year. Record the correct responses to each riddle on chart paper to develop students' word recognition. Examples of these riddles include:
  - I am the first day that you come to school during the week. My name begins with the first two letters in mother. What day of the week am I? (Monday)
  - I am the first month of summer holidays. Lots of people like to go camping when I arrive. My name begins with the first letter in jam. What month of the year am I? (July)
- Extend the discussion by asking questions such as the following:
  - What other clues tell you whether it is day or night? How can you tell it is day or night by what plants, animals, and people do?
  - What other clues tell you which season it is? How can you tell what season it is by what plants, animals, and people do?
  - Record students' responses to each question on chart paper and post them so that you can return to their prior knowledge and questions throughout the unit.

2. Elicit "I Wonder ..." Statements

- Model an "I wonder ..." form of inquiry with statements such as: "I wonder what other clues tell me it is spring, summer, fall, or winter," "I wonder how animals change with each season," "I wonder how plants change with each season."
- Invite students to offer other "I wonder ..." statements. Record these on a chart or paper strips, and then read them together. Provide students with copies of **PM 1: I Wonder ...** and ask them to record the "I wonder ..." statements that especially interest them. Some students may require individual or small group assistance to identify statements and record them.

Literacy Check
Is the student able to:
- read the "I wonder ..." statements in the class list and identify "I wonder ..." statements for their personal list?
- copy "I wonder ..." statements from the class list on their personal copy?

Explore

✔ Science Check
Can the student:
- dramatize the actions of plants, animals, and people during day and night?
- identify how plants, animals, and people adapt to day and night?

3. Pretend It's Day and Night

- Gather students together and tell them: "We are going to role-play what it is like to be plants, animals, and people when it is day and when it is night. Before we do that, let's predict what plants, animals, and people might do during the day and at night." Record students' predictions on the board or chart paper so that they can refer to their predictions following the dramatization.
- In an open space (e.g., classroom, gym), read the script on **LM 9: Dramatization Scripts** and ask students to listen and act out what they hear. (Feel free to adapt the script to incorporate students' predictions.) Read slowly and pause between ideas to give students time for their dramatizations.
- Following the dramatization, gather students to review their predictions and discuss their dramatizations. Ask them:
  - What did you predict about plants, animals, and people during the day and at night that you experienced in the dramatization?
  - What did the plants, animals, and people do during the day and at night in the dramatization that you did not predict?
  - Record key vocabulary words and names of plants and animals to develop word recognition.

Literature Links
What If You Had Animal Teeth? by Sandra Markle

Cold, Colder, Coldest: Animals That Adapt to Cold Weather by Michael Dahl

Animal Adaptations by Julie K. Lundgren

- Ask students: What new questions do you have about how plants, animals, and people change so they can survive from day to night? Record their questions on chart paper. With students, plan and set up centres so they can carry out explorations of these questions. Encourage them to make and check predictions. You may want to include a variety of fiction and non-fiction books that focus on plant and animal adaptations at these centres. Some possible titles include: *What If You Had Animal Teeth?* by Sandra Markle, *Cold, Colder, Coldest: Animals That Adapt to Cold Weather* by Michael Dahl, and *Animal Adaptations* by Julie K. Lundgren.

✔ Science Check
Can the student:
- dramatize the changes that occur with plants, animals, and people from season to season?
- identify how plants, animals, and people adapt to seasonal change?

4. Pretend It's Spring, Summer, Fall, and Winter

- Tell students they are going to act out what it is like to be plants, animals, and humans from season to season. Before they do that, they will predict what might change for plants from spring to summer, fall, and winter. Record students' predictions on the board or chart paper so they can refer to their predictions following the dramatization. Group their predictions by season as you record them. Repeat for animals and humans.
- In an open space (e.g., classroom, gym), read the script for the spring dramatization on **LM 9: Dramatization Scripts** and ask students to listen and dramatize what they hear in their own way. Read slowly. Pause between ideas and give students time to act out what they hear. (Feel free to adapt the script to reflect the changes that occur in your community and area and to incorporate students' predictions.)
- Following the dramatization, gather students to review their predictions and to share their experiences of the parts they dramatized. Record students' responses on the board or chart paper to reinforce the connection

that what we say can be written down. Ask students to join you in echo-reading the responses as you track the words with your hand. Repeat this procedure after you read the scripts for summer, fall, and winter on **LM 9**.

Science Check
Can the student:
- suggest ways in which plants, animals, and people get ready for winter?
- illustrate one way that plants, animals, or people get ready for winter?

5. Create a Winter Web

- Display the word *Winter* in the middle of the whiteboard or mural paper. Ask students to think of words that describe winter and record them in a circle or bubble around the word. Then draw a branch from this circle and label it *Plants*. Ask students: How do plants get ready for the long, cold winter? Record their suggestions. Follow the same process for *Animals* and *People*. (You could do this for any season.)
- Provide each student with a small square of paper and ask them to use crayons or markers to illustrate one way that plants, animals, or people get ready for winter. Have students add their drawings to the end of the appropriate branch on the web. You could provide students with **PM 8: Make a Web** to record the Winter Web.

Explain

Literacy Check
Is the student able to:
- contribute questions and ideas to the discussion?
- use the illustrations to enhance understanding?
- participate in reading the text?

6. Read and Respond to the Non-fiction Book *Days and Seasons*

Before: Over two or three sessions, use the following approach to guide students through the non-fiction book.

During: Show students the cover of *Days and Seasons*. Remind them of their Picture Walk through the book when the unit was introduced. Depending on students' abilities and the time of year, use the Lap Book to do a Shared Reading or distribute copies of the book and read in small groups. Use questions to guide students' discussion and interpretation of the illustrations and text on each spread.

Pages 2–3: There are four pictures on this spread. Ask students: What is the same about these pictures? What is different? Display four sheets of chart paper and record the name of a season at the top of each one.

- Read the text. Ask students: How do plants change over the year? How do people change the way they live during the year? Create headings for Plants, Animals, and Humans on each sheet of chart paper and record students' suggestions.
- Draw students' attention to the term *adapt* and ask them what the word means. Explain that when animals adapt, they change the way they look, what they do, and where they go to survive changes in nature. Ask students how animals change from season to season. Record their suggestions under the appropriate heading for the appropriate season.

Pages 4–5: Tell students that they will compare their suggestions about how plants change from season to season to the changes shown on the spread. Add any seasonal changes for plants that arise from the text that are not already recorded on the chart paper.

Pages 6–7: Ask students:

- What season do these photos show?
- What signs of spring are shown in each photo?
- How do plants change in spring? What do animals do in spring?
- How do people change the way they live in spring?

- Read the text. Make connections between the text and their suggestions on the Spring chart paper. Have them answer the question at the bottom of page 7, What else happens in the spring? Add any new ideas to the chart paper.
- **Pages 8–11:** Read the text. Follow the same process as outlined for spring changes above.
- Ask students to respond to the question on page 10, What else happens in the summer? Ask students to think about people, plants, and animals. Add their ideas to the appropriate section on the chart labelled Summer.

Pages 12–13: Read the text. Follow the same process as outlined for spring changes above. After reading, ask for students' suggestions to respond to the question on page 13, What else happens in the fall? Ask them to think about people, plants, and animals. Add their ideas to the appropriate section on the chart labelled Fall.

Pages 14–17: Read the text on pages 14–15. Follow the same process as outlined for spring changes above. Redirect students' attention to the question at the bottom of page 15, What do we wear in the winter? Add their ideas to the Humans section on the chart labelled Winter.

- Read the text on pages 16–17. After reading, ask students why the Arctic fox's fur might change from brown to white in winter. How does the colour change protect the Arctic fox? Explain to students that this colour change is one way that animals adapt. It is how the Arctic fox's body changes to help it survive in winter. The Arctic fox did not just decide to change the colour of its fur. A change like this takes a very long time to happen. It happens over many generations.
- Redirect students' attention to the question at the bottom of page 17, How else do animals adapt to the winter?

Pages 18–19: Read the text under each item of the Sort It Out. Then ask students to suggest answers to the first five questions.

After: Provide students with copies of **LM 10: Sort It Out** and direct them to cut out the pictures and the words *Spring, Summer, Fall,* and *Winter.* Instruct students to spread out all of their pictures and words on the floor. Ask students to find the word *Spring* and to group all the pictures of objects they see in spring. Repeat this procedure for Summer, Fall, and Winter. When all the pictures are grouped by season, ask students which objects they can see in more than one season.

- Read aloud the final question on page 18. Provide students with magazines they can cut up and ask them to search for pictures of objects they can see in spring, summer, winter, or fall. Provide each student with an enlarged copy of **LM 11: Picture Sort** so they can glue the pictures they find into the box for the appropriate season.

Science Check
Can the student:
- represent ways in which plants, animals, and people adapt to different seasons?

7. Create Seasons in a Shoebox

- You may set up this activity as an individual, paired, or small group project. Have students choose one of the four seasons: spring, summer, fall, or winter. Then have them create a diorama (a three-dimensional model) in a shoebox that depicts their chosen season and one change that takes place in either a plant, an animal, or a human in that particular season. Provide an assortment of materials for students to create their 3-D models (e.g., modelling clay, pipe cleaners, craft sticks, construction paper, tissue paper, felt, and scrap material.)

8. Reflect on Learning

- Have students record evidence of their learning on **PM 13: Look What I've Learned**, in their journal, and/or with a video or audio recording on a smart device or camera. If students are using the line master or their journal, they can use words and/or pictures to show what they have learned. Encourage them to note one thing they learned and something they still wonder about. You may wish to ask each student to share orally what he or she learned and record what was learned in a sentence(s).
- Use **LM 12: This Is What I Can Do** as a self-assessment. Read the learning targets with students. Then have them respond individually. Some students may need support.

OTHER LEARNING OPPORTUNITIES

Extend: Activity Bank

At any time, choose from the following options to replace or supplement the Core Learning Opportunities to meet students' needs and/or interests.

9. Respond to Talk Time

- Use Talk Time 1, 3, 4, 6–8 on page 24 of the non-fiction book *Days and Seasons* to extend discussion with students and to provide ideas for additional activities.

10. Make a Library Connection

- Provide an opportunity for students to have access to fiction and non-fiction picture books that show how plants, animals, and people adapt to daily and seasonal changes in the school or community library. Ask library staff to pull relevant books that can be used for this activity. Have students look in these books for examples of how plants, animals, and people change and do different things from day to night and from season to season. Provide a sharing time in which students can show and tell what they found in these books.

11. Explore Other "I Wonder ..." Statements

- Return to the "I wonder ..." statements not yet answered, and new wonderings that have come up. With students, plan and set up centres where they can explore these wonderings. Encourage them to make and test predictions.
- Working in small groups, students can rotate to all the centres or focus on one per group. They could share their findings in an oral, written, or electronic presentation.

4 Exploring Light and Shadows

Time
3–4 hours (plus 1 hour once a month to observe the sun and shadows)

Vocabulary
shadow

Program Resources
PM 1: I Wonder ...
PM 13: Look What I've Learned
LM 13: Shadow Records
LM 14: This Is What I Can Do
Fiction Book: *Groundhog Day*
Lap Book
Skills Poster: Observing and Recording

Materials and Equipment
- *Bear's Shadow* by Frank Asch or *Moonbear's Shadow* (the re-issue of the classic *Bear's Shadow* by Frank Asch) or a reading of *Bear's Shadow* (available on Youtube)
- sidewalk chalk or regular chalk (or mural paper and washable markers or crayons)
- digital cameras or smart devices
- digital or print pictures of groundhogs

GOAL

Students will explore how the length and shape of shadows changes throughout a day and a year.

ASSESSMENT CHART

Science Indicators	Assessment Opportunities
DS1.1 a. Pose questions about changes in natural phenomena in the environment over the course of a day and a year.	Engage 1
DS1.1 c. Observe daily and seasonal changes in the amount of heat and light from the sun, including the formation of shadows.	Explore 3 Explain 4
DS1.1 f. Document the visibility and position of objects in the sky at different times of the day and year.	Explore 3 Explain 4
DS1.2 d. Examine seasonal changes in the characteristics, behaviours, and location of plants, animals, and humans.	Explain 5
DS1.2 e. Explore ways in which plant, animal, and human adaptations to daily and seasonal changes are represented through writing and artwork.	Explain 5
DS1.2 f. Construct representations of plant, animals, and human adaptations to daily and seasonal changes.	Explain 5
DS 1.2 g. Describe ways in which humans prepare to adapt to daily and seasonal changes.	Explain 5
DS1.2 i. Communicate questions, ideas, and intentions with classmates while exploring daily and seasonal adaptations.	Explain 5
English Language Arts Indicators	**Assessment Opportunities**
CR1.2 g. Recognize feelings portrayed in visual and multimedia texts, including pictures, photographs, diagrams, pictographs, and icons.	Explore 1 Explain 5
CC1.1 a. Use words, symbols, and other forms, including appropriate technology, to express understanding of topics, themes, and issues.	Explore 3 Explain 4, 5, 6
CC1.1 e. Use inquiry to explore a question or topic of interest related to the themes and topics being studied.	Explore 3 Explain 4

BACKGROUND INFORMATION

Groundhog Day, on February 2, is a popular tradition. Legend has it that this is the day the groundhog comes out of his hole after a long winter's sleep. If the day is sunny and he sees his shadow, he goes back into his hole and there will be six more weeks of winter. If he doesn't see his shadow because the day is cloudy, he stays above ground and this is a sign that spring is on the way. This legend is a reminder of when nature had a more direct influence on people's lives and they watched for the awakening of animals as a sign of spring.

Groundhogs are also known as woodchucks or marmots. The average groundhog is 45–61 cm long, excluding its tail (18–25 cm), and weighs about 6 kg. The groundhog is a herbivore that eats greens, fruits, and vegetables. It eats all summer to build up reserves of fat. After the first frost, it goes into its underground burrow and sleeps until spring. While hibernating, the groundhog's heart rate slows and its body temperature decreases until it isn't much more than the temperature inside its burrow.

***Traditional* Knowledge**

First Nations children are taught hand shadow games. From these games, they learn how to identify the shapes of animals. Knowledge of animal shapes and silhouettes is important for hunters. Some Elders also tell stories with shadow animals. Aboriginal peoples view all life forms as interconnected, interdependent, and interrelated. Traditionally, they relied on their knowledge of animals for survival. Learning to identify the shapes of animals and birds is important for children.

ASSESSMENT FOR LEARNING

Look for Evidence of Learning	Student-friendly Learning Targets
Can the student: • identify changes in shadow formation during the day? • compare shadow records from different dates and identify changes in shadow formation during the year? • suggest why shadows change in length and in the direction they point? • contribute questions and ideas to discussion? • identify clues in illustrations that tell what season it is?	(self-assessment) • I can tell how shadows change from morning to night. • I can tell how shadows change during the year. • I know why shadows look different at different times of the day and the year. • I can use clues in pictures to tell what season it is.

DI DIFFERENTIATING INSTRUCTION

For EAL

The visual, interactive nature of the activities should help EAL students comprehend the key understandings about shadows. In addition to using illustrations and modelling, it is helpful to use facial expressions, gestures, and actions to dramatize meaning and to enhance understanding.

For Enrichment

Challenge students to find out why the sun appears to move in the sky during the day. Provide students with an opportunity to share what they learn. Encourage them to use visuals or models to show what they learned.

For Extra Support

For those students who are not yet ready to copy a model response that is written on a chart or board, you may wish to record a model response on a paper or mini-whiteboard that they can copy from at their desks.

CORE LEARNING OPPORTUNITIES

Engage

Literature Link
Bear's Shadow or *Moonbear's Shadow* by Frank Asch
(a reading is available on Youtube)

1. Activate and Build on Prior Knowledge

- Use a book such as *Bear's Shadow* or *Moonbear's Shadow* to introduce this lesson. Before reading, show students the cover and read the title. Ask students: What is a shadow? Where can you see Bear's shadow on the cover? If the book is not available, have students go outside on a sunny day to view and discuss what they know about their shadows.
- Tell students that they will be exploring how shadows are formed and how they change during a day and from season to season. Ask students:
  - What do you know about shadows?
  - What do shadows look like?
  - When do you see your shadow?
- Record students' responses to each question on chart paper and post them so that you can return to their prior knowledge and questions throughout the unit.

✔ Literacy Check
Can the student:
- read the "I wonder ..." statements in the class list and identify an "I wonder ..." statement for his or her personal list?
- copy an "I wonder ..." statement from the class list on his or her personal copy?

2. Elicit "I Wonder ..." Statements

- Model an "I wonder ..." form of inquiry with statements such as: "I wonder how shadows are formed," "I wonder when I can see my shadow."
- Invite students to offer other "I wonder ..." statements. Record these on a chart or paper strips, and then read them together. Provide students with copies of **PM 1: I Wonder ...** and ask them to record the "I wonder ..." statement(s) that especially interests them. Some students may require individual or small group assistance to identify statements and record them.

Explore

Safety Check
Ensure that students do not look directly at the sun.

3. Trace and Observe Shadow Changes

Note: This activity needs to be done on a sunny day so that students make the connection that the sun is the source of light. Although an overhead projector can work as a light source, it is important that students associate the length of shadows with the position of the sun in the sky.

- Explain to students that they make shadows when they block light from the sun. Take students outside on a sunny morning and model what they will be doing in pairs. Have a student stand on the sidewalk. Trace the student's feet with chalk. (It is important to trace the student's feet so that the student can stand in exactly the same position when the next shadow is traced later in the day.) Then show students how to trace the outline of the student's shadow with the chalk, label the tracing with a capital M for morning and print the name of the student in the foot outline. Also note where the sun is in the sky. Draw a symbol for the sun on the appropriate side of the shadow outline. Then place students in pairs and guide them to trace each other's feet and shadow outlines. Remind them to include the name of the student and to add M for morning.

- Bring students back outside before lunch when the sun is high in the sky. Repeat the same steps as you did in the morning, but this time have students mark an N to indicate noon.
- Bring students back outside in mid-afternoon. Repeat the shadow tracing procedure. Then ask students to examine the shadows they traced. Ask them:
  - Do your shadows point the same way all day? How do they change?
  - What happens to the length of your shadows during the day?
  - Why does the length of your shadow change from morning to afternoon?
- Take photographs of each student's set of shadow tracings. Print copies of each student's shadow tracings for use with Explain 4.
- Review the Skills poster **Observing and Recording**. Have students comment on how they made observations and then on how they recorded them.
- Follow the same procedure to trace students' shadows each month. Take photographs of each student's set of shadow tracings. Print copies of each student's shadow tracings each month. Suggestions for how to use these photographs are provided in Explain 5.

Science Check
Can the student:
- identify changes in shadow formation over the day?
- identify changes in shadow formation during the year?
- suggest why shadows change in length and in the direction they point?

Explain

4. Track Shadow Records

- Distribute copies of **LM 13: Shadow Records** to students. Model how to print the date, including the day of the week, on the first blank. Then have students glue the photographs of their shadow outlines in the appropriate spaces (Morning, Noon, Afternoon). Guide students to read the sentence starter: *My shadow looks different because.* Then ask students for suggestions for completing the sentence. Students will probably suggest that the sun moves in the sky. It is important to discuss that the sun is in a different position in the sky at different times of the day because Earth is moving and not the sun. Earth makes one complete spin on its axis every 24 hours. As Earth turns, it seems that the sun is moving across the sky, but it is really Earth that is moving.
- Have students complete a new copy of **LM 13** each time they trace their shadows. Store the line masters in folders. Make sure students understand that their shadow changes length and the direction it is pointing because the sun is in a different position in the sky.

Science Check
Can the student:
- identify and record the reason the shadow outlines look different?
- compare shadow records from different dates and identify differences?

Literacy Check
Can the student:
- contribute questions and ideas to the discussion?
- use the illustrations to enhance understanding?
- participate in reading the text?

Science Check
Can the student:
- point out clues that identify seasons in the illustrations?
- show how animals, plants, or humans change from one season to the next?

5. Read and Respond to the Fiction Book *Groundhog Day*

- Over two or three sessions, use the following approach to guide students through the fiction book:
- **Before:** Review the characters in the story and students' predictions about what might happen in the story from the Unit Opener. Show students photos of real groundhogs and talk about where groundhogs live. Distribute copies of *Groundhog Day* or use the Lap Book to do a Shared Reading.

During: Use the following questions to guide students' discussion and interpretation of the illustrations and text on each spread:

Pages 2–3:
- In what month of the year is Groundhog Day?
- In what season of the year is Groundhog Day?
- Why will Percy be a star?

Pages 4–11:
- What season is it?
- What clues in the pictures tell you what season it is?
- What clues tell you about the temperature?
- How has the thermometer changed from the previous picture?
- What does *hibernate* mean? What other animals are hibernating in the pictures? What do you notice about Percy's shadow?

Pages 12–13:
- What day is it?
- What does Percy have to do today?

Pages: 14–15:
- Percy saw his shadow. What did this mean?
- Why do you think Lila says, "Next year, *I'm* doing it"?

After: Discuss the Talk Time points on page 16, then have students illustrate one of the following: how people's clothes and activities change in the different seasons; how plants change from season to season; or how animals change from season to season.

6. Reflect on Learning

- Have students record evidence of their learning on **PM 13: Look What I've Learned**, in their journals, and/or by doing video or audio recording. Encourage them to note one thing they learned and something they still wonder about. You may wish to ask each student to share orally what he or she learned and record what was learned in a sentence(s). Students can use words and/or pictures to show what they have learned.
- Use **LM 14: This Is What I Can Do** as a self-assessment. Read the learning targets with students and have them respond on their own. Some students may need support.

OTHER LEARNING OPPORTUNITIES

Extend: Activity Bank

At any time, choose from the following options to replace or supplement the Core Learning Opportunities to meet students' needs and/or interests.

7. Compare Tube Shadows

- Instead of tracing students' shadows, you may wish to have students trace and label the shadow of a paper towel tube or a piece of doweling that is taped or glued (with a glue gun for stability) to a piece of board or mural paper. Compare the shadow lengths and shapes at different times of the day and year.

8. Play Shadow Tag

- Take students outside on a sunny afternoon to play shadow tag. The student who is "It" tags another student by stepping on his or her shadow. Variation: The student who is "It" tags another student when his or her shadow touches another student's shadow. Draw students' attention to the fact that their shadows move as they move.

9. View Shadow Shapes

- Gather an assortment of objects with different shapes. Use an overhead projector, light table, or flashlight as a light source. Ask students to look at each object and predict the shape of its shadow. Then have a student place the object between the light source and a white background to check their predictions.

10. Make a Shadow Theatre

- Use an overhead projector as a light source against a white background and demonstrate how you can use your hands to make a shadow animal. Provide opportunities for two to three students at a time to experiment with their hands to make different shadow animals, creatures, or objects and have the other students guess what they are making.

11. Explore Other "I Wonder ..." Statements

- Return to the "I wonder ..." statements not yet answered, and new wonderings that have come up. With students, plan and set up centres where they can explore these wonderings. Encourage them to make and test predictions.
- Working in small groups, students can rotate to all the centres or focus on one per group. They could share their findings in oral, written, or electronic presentations.

5 Cultural Perspectives

Time
5–6 hours

Program Resources
PM 1: I Wonder ...
PM 13: Look What I've Learned
LM 15: Circle of the Seasons
LM 16: This Is What I Can Do
Traditional Knowledge Poster: Six Seasons

Materials and Equipment
- thermometer
- rain gauge
- wind vane
- First Nations and Métis stories about seasonal change
- multimedia projector
- camera or smart devices for recording
- paints and brushes
- large sheets of white paper for painting

GOAL

Students will examine ways in which First Nations and Métis peoples understand seasonal changes and represent these understandings through stories. They will also examine ways in which seasons are portrayed in paintings by Chinese and Japanese artists.

ASSESSMENT CHART

Science Indicators	Assessment Opportunities
DS1.1 d. Examine ways in which various cultures, including First Nations and Métis, represent daily and seasonal changes through oral traditions and artistic works.	Explore 3, 4 Explain 5, 6
DS1.1 i. Create visual or physical representations of differences in natural phenomena at different times of the day and year.	Explain 7
English Language Arts Indicators	**Assessment Opportunities**
CR1.1 a. View, listen to, read, and respond to a variety of texts including First Nations and Métis resources that represent different viewpoints and perspectives on issues related to identity, community, and social responsibility.	Explore 3 Explain 5, 6
CR1.1 f. Show respect for own culture and the various cultures, lifestyles, and experiences represented in texts including First Nations and Métis cultures.	Engage 1, 2 Explore 3, 4 Explain 5, 7
CR1.2 a. Identify and locate the key information in pictures, charts, and other visual forms, including traditional and contemporary First Nations and Métis resources and performances.	Explore 3, 4

BACKGROUND INFORMATION

***Traditional* Knowledge**

Aboriginal peoples observe the natural world to watch for signs that the seasons are about to change. Natural phenomena, such as freeze-up and break-up of ice on waterways, are signs of changing seasons. The Nihithawak (Woodland Cree), Nēhinawak (Swampy Cree), and Denesųłiné (Dené) divide the year up into six seasons: spring, summer, fall, freeze-up, winter, and break-up. During freeze-up, the waterways cannot be used for travel because ice is forming on the surface of the water, but it is not thick enough to support the mass of a person. During break-up, people continue to use the food they preserved for winter. Break-up is a time to pack up trapping gear, get fishing nets ready, and prepare to move to another place.

Traditionally, as their environment changed from season to season, First Nations peoples made changes in the way they lived. They moved, according to the seasons, to various sites to gather resources to build up their food supply. (Note that much of the information below is presented in past tense, but there are people who follow these traditions today.)

In spring, some First Nations peoples hunted buffalo and birds as they migrated. Denesųłiné (Dené) hunted caribou, but did not travel south to hunt buffalo. (Moose are hunted in any season.) Because fish were spawning, people were careful about where they fished. They allowed fish to reproduce to ensure there were fish for the future. As plants began to grow and new leaves appeared on trees, they gathered roots, leaves, plants, and bark for food and medicine.

Summer was the time for fishing, hunting, and gathering plants, roots, herbs, berries, and nuts to dry and store for the winter. First Nations people also met and had trade fairs.

In the fall, people continued to hunt and gather food, much of which was smoked or dried to store for the winter. They hunted winter birds, rabbits, and beaver. They also hunted moose, elk, and deer. They used animal hides to make tipis, blankets, clothing, and moccasins for winter. The Nēhiyawak (Plains Cree) moved to areas where they would be sheltered from the cold winter winds and set up camps.

The winter is traditionally a time to tell stories. Stories are also told during teachable moments such as when hunting or when women are working together on a hide. First Nations and Métis peoples use oral tradition to preserve their history so it can be passed from generation to generation. They also use stories to teach the next generation how to live in a positive way.

ASSESSMENT FOR LEARNING

Look for Evidence of Learning	Student-friendly Learning Targets
Can the student: • identify seasonal clues and changes in stories? • view and contribute ideas about cultural artwork depicting the seasons? • identify similarities and differences in paintings depicting the seasons? • work with another student to plan a story about seasonal change? • represent the changing seasons accurately in a painting?	(self-assessment) • I can find clues in stories to tell me what season it is. • I can listen to stories and understand how plants, animals, and people change in different seasons. • I can look at artwork about the seasons and give my ideas about what I see. • I can work with a partner to plan a story about the changing seasons. • I can show the four seasons in a painting.

DI DIFFERENTIATING INSTRUCTION

For EAL
Use gestures and actions to add meaning when you are reading stories about the seasons. Try to bring the story to life through illustrations and use your expressions and movements to enhance understanding for EAL students.

For Enrichment
Challenge students to observe what happens around them and create a story to explain the changing seasons. Provide an opportunity for students to share their stories with other students.

For Extra Support
As you read and discuss First Nations and Métis stories about the changing seasons, involve students by asking direct questions that they will be able to answer to build their confidence.

CORE LEARNING OPPORTUNITIES

Engage

1. Activate and Build on Prior Knowledge

- Show students a thermometer, rain gauge, and wind vane, and name them. Review what each tool is used for. Explain that when they use these tools to measure changes in the weather, they are looking at daily and seasonal changes as a scientist does. A scientist observes, measures, and records changes. First Nations and Métis peoples observe weather changes and changes in plants and animals very carefully. They need to understand and predict these changes so they can survive in the different seasons. They find patterns in the changes, as other scientists do, and they tell stories to explain the patterns they observe.

***Traditional* Knowledge**

- Ask students: What do you know about stories that First Nations and Métis peoples tell regarding changes from day to day and from season to season? What stories have you heard? Record students' responses to each question on chart paper and post them so that you can return to their prior knowledge and questions throughout the unit.

Literacy Check
Can the student:
- read the "I wonder ..." statements in the class list and identify an "I wonder ..." statement for his or her personal list?
- copy an "I wonder ..." statement from the class list onto his or her personal list?

2. Elicit "I Wonder..." Statements

- Model an "I wonder ..." form of inquiry with statements such as: "I wonder what stories First Nations and Métis peoples tell about the sun," "I wonder what stories First Nations and Métis peoples tell about the changing seasons."
- Invite students to offer other "I wonder ..." statements. Record these on a chart or paper strips, and then read them together. Provide students with copies of **PM 1: I Wonder ...** and ask them to record the "I wonder ..." statement(s) that especially interests them. Some students may require individual or small group assistance to identify statements and record them.

Explore

***Traditional* Knowledge**

3. Explore the Seasons through Stories

- Display the Traditional Knowledge poster **Six Seasons** and ask the following questions to identify and discuss the components of the poster:
  - How does this poster connect to what we have been learning about? (It shows pictures of the four seasons. It also shows the words for the seasons.)
  - There are two other seasons shown around the outside: one is called Freeze Up and the other is called Break Up. Freeze Up is shown between fall and winter. What do you think Freeze Up is about? (This is the time when the ground and waterways are beginning to freeze. Ice begins to form on rivers, ponds, and lakes.)
  - Break Up is shown between Winter and Spring. What do you think Break Up is about? (This is the time when the ice on the lakes and rivers begins to melt and move. The ground begins to thaw after a long, cold winter.)
  - Look at the pictures of people engaged in activities. What are the people doing in each picture? (Break Up: This is the time when people make fish snares to catch fish that are spawning or laying eggs.

Spring: This is the season for planting. Summer: Summer is time for picking blueberries and other berries. Fall: It is time for hunting and preserving foods for winter. Fish and meat are smoked or dried. Freeze Up: The man is stringing snowshoes with strips of hide, and the boy is learning from watching. Winter: The woman is ice-fishing.)
- Why do you think the seasons are shown in a circle? (No season is more important than the others, and they flow into each other. The circle is also important to show how all of life is interconnected and equal. First Nations peoples represent the seasons in a circle because it represents the Circle of Life. One season leads to the next season in a cycle that repeats in the same way from year to year.)

Science Check
Can the student:
- identify seasonal clues and changes in the stories?
- participate meaningfully in after reading activities?

- Provide students with **LM 15: Circle of the Seasons**. Have students illustrate an activity that they do on their own, with their friends, or with their parents in each section of the circle.
- All First Nations language groups have stories associated with seasons. Invite Elders or Traditional Knowledge Keepers to share stories. (Follow the Protocol for Contacting Elders and Traditional Knowledge Keepers found in the the Program Overview.)
- Share First Nations and Métis stories about seasonal changes. Some examples are provided, but you or the librarian in your school may know of other books that could be used.

Literature Link
Changes by Penny Condon

Rainbow Crow by David Bouchard

Nanabush and the Geese by Linda Pelly

Byron Through the Seasons by LaLoche Children

The Legend of Lightning and Thunder by Paula Ikuutaq Rumbolt

4. View and Analyze Artwork

- Involve students in an online search for *Chinese seasons paintings* and *Japanese seasons paintings,* or paintings from the various cultures of students in your class. Project selected images for students to view and discuss. If you don't have access to a multimedia projector, print enlarged colour copies of selected images. Guide students to identify the seasons in each piece of artwork and then use the following questions to guide discussion:
  - What do you notice about how the seasons are represented?
  - What did the artists focus on in their paintings to represent each season?
  - What is the same in each set of four paintings? What is different?

Science Check
Can the student:
- view and contribute ideas about cultural artwork depicting the seasons?
- identify similarities and differences between sets of four paintings depicting the seasons?

Explain

5. Retell a Story

- Have students choose their favourite stories from the First Nations and Métis stories you read in **Explore 3**. Demonstrate how they can identify and gather objects to symbolize key events in the story and then use the objects to retell the events of the story in sequence. Or, draw pictures to represent key events in the story and then use the pictures to retell the events of the story in sequence.
- Provide time for students to gather objects or draw pictures to help them retell their chosen story. Then demonstrate how they should use their objects or pictures to practise retelling their chosen story. Provide an opportunity for students to retell their stories to their classmates or have them record their retellings using cameras or smart devices.

Literacy Check
Can the student:
- retell a story by relating the sequence of story events using objects or pictures as a guide?

***Traditional* Knowledge**

Science Check
Can the student:
- work with another student to plan a story about seasonal change?
- practise with his or her partner and then record their storytelling?

6. Create a Story About the Seasons
- This is a follow-up to Explore 3. Explain to students that First Nations and Métis peoples do not think of stories as fiction or make-believe. They view stories as true, real-life experiences that are passed down from generation to generation. The stories that students will be creating about seasonal changes in this activity will be make-believe. They are not based on real-life experiences and should be viewed differently from First Nations and Métis stories. Use Shared Writing to create a story about how one season changes to another season or about how plants, animals, or people adapt to each season. First, generate ideas for ways in which the coming of a new season or seasonal adaptations might be understood through the telling of a story. Choose an idea to develop as a class through Shared Writing.
- Display the Skills poster **Communicating and Teamwork**. Discuss how to work well together as a team, and the importance of making a plan and asking good questions. Have each student work with a partner to plan a story that tells about the coming of a new season or the ways in which plants, animals, and people change to adapt to a new season. Encourage them to sketch pictures or gather objects to represent the sequence of events in their story. When they have planned their story, have them practise telling their story. When they are ready, have them record their storytelling using cameras or smart devices.

Science Check
Can the student:
- represent the changing seasons accurately in a four-panel painting?

7. Paint the Seasons
- This is a follow-up to Explore 4. Provide students with large sheets of white paper suitable for painting. Model how students can fold their paper into four panels. Tell students they are going to illustrate the four seasons with paints. Review what stays mostly the same and what differs in the Chinese and Japanese paintings, or paintings from other cultures, that they examined. Brainstorm ways in which they might represent the changing seasons in their paintings. Then provide students with paints and brushes so that they can create their four-panel paintings.
- When students have finished their paintings, provide an opportunity for them to share their work with the class.

8. Reflect on Learning
- Have students record evidence of their learning on **PM 13: Look What I've Learned**, in their journal, and/or with a video or audio recording on a smart device or camera. They can use words and/or pictures to show what they have learned. Encourage them to note one thing they learned and something they still wonder about. You may wish to ask each student to share orally what he or she learned and record what was learned in a sentence or sentences.
- Use **LM 16: This Is What I Can Do** as a self-assessment. Read the learning targets with students and have them respond on their own. Some students may need assistance.

OTHER LEARNING OPPORTUNITIES

Extend: Activity Bank

At any time, choose from the following options to replace or supplement the Core Learning Opportunities and to meet students' needs and/or interests.

***Traditional* Knowledge**

Tip
Some Inuit Tapestries that would be appropriate for this activity include:
#371 Summer Afternoon
#393 Summer in Pangnirtung
#415 Spring Breakup
#436 Cleaning Sealskins
#450 Breaking Camp
#457 Sliding
#464 Winter Game
#465 Family Traveling
#469 Collecting Eggs

9. Inuit Tapestries

- Project Inuit tapestries about the seasons from the Pangnirtung Tapestry Studio at the Uqqurmiut Centre for Arts and Crafts in Pangnirtung, Nunavut. [http://www.uqqurmiut.com] Access images of the tapestries in the Index to Tapestries on the left side of the screen. The weavers tell the stories of their lives through the seasons in their tapestries. As the tapestries are viewed, identify the seasons and how people's lives change through the seasons.

10. Respond to Talk Time

- Complete Talk Time 9 on page 24 of the non-fiction book *Days and Seasons,* which asks students how they could divide up the year in ways other than the four seasons. First Nations students may raise the six seasons as depicted on the Traditional Knowledge poster **Six Seasons** or the dry season and rainy season in countries like Vietnam, as referenced in Talk Time 7. They might also raise ideas such as summer and the school year.

11. Explore Other "I Wonder ..." Statements

- Return to the "I wonder ..." statements not yet answered, and new wonderings that have come up. With students, plan and set up centres where they can explore these wonderings. Encourage them to make and test predictions.
- In small groups, students can rotate to all the centres or focus on one per group. They could share their findings in an oral, written, or electronic presentation.

6 Observing the Night Sky

Time
4–5 hours

Vocabulary
moon
stars

Program Resources
PM 1: I Wonder ...
PM 13: Look What I've Learned
LM 17: Observing the Moon
LM 18: Observing the Moon — Letter to Parents
LM 19: Help the Moon Find the Correct Order
LM 20: This Is What I Can Do
Non-fiction Book: *Days and Seasons*
Lap Book

Materials and Equipment
- *Papa, Please Get the Moon for Me* by Eric Carle
- multimedia projector
- library books with pictures of stars in the night sky
- crayons or markers and white paper (or white chalk/white crayons and black paper)
- cameras or smart devices

GOAL

Students will identify the pattern in the change of the moon's shape and learn that the moon can be seen in different positions in the night sky at different times.

ASSESSMENT CHART

Science Indicators	Assessment Opportunities
DS1.1 a. Pose questions about changes in natural phenomena in the environment over the course of a day and a year.	Engage 1, 2
DS1.1 d. Examine ways in which various cultures, including First Nations and Métis, represent daily and seasonal changes through oral traditions and artistic works.	Explore 5 Explain 7, 8
DS1.1 f. Document the visibility and position of objects in the sky at different times of the day and year.	Explore 3, 4 Explain 6
DS1.1. g. Record observations of the shape and position of the moon throughout a month.	Explore 3 Explain 6
English Language Arts Indicators	**Assessment Opportunities**
CR1.1 f. Show respect for own culture and the various cultures, lifestyles, and experiences represented in texts including First Nations and Métis cultures.	Explore 5 Explain 7
CR1.2 a. Identify and locate key information in pictures, charts, and other visual forms, including traditional and contemporary First Nations and Métis resources and performances.	Engage 1 Explore 5
CR1.3 d. Retell stories (including oral traditions shared by Elders and Knowledge Keepers) following sequence of events by answering who, what, when, where, why, and how questions.	Explain 7
CC1.2 e. Dramatize a story, such as a traditional First Nations, Métis, or Inuit story.	Explore 5

BACKGROUND INFORMATION

The moon does not emit light. It reflects light from the sun, and this makes part of the moon visible from Earth. When the moon is between Earth and the sun, the side that is lit by the sun is facing away from us and we do not see the moon. This is the new moon phase.

The moon appears to change shape over the course of a month as we view it from Earth. The changing shapes are called phases of the moon. This pattern begins with the phase of the new moon. Gradually, we can see more and more of the moon (waxing moon) as a crescent, then a quarter, and finally, a full moon. This takes about two weeks. Then the moon begins to decrease in size (waning moon) until we reach the new moon phase again. This takes about two weeks as well. For a diagram based on the current month, see http: www.moonconnection.com/moon_phases_calendar.phtml.

Common misconceptions that students may have:

- Phases of the moon are caused by a shadow from Earth or clouds.
- The moon goes around Earth in one day.
- The moon can only be seen at night.

***Traditional* Knowledge**

Traditionally, the Denesųłiné (Dené) of northern Saskatchewan use the stars and moon to travel at night. They keep track of the passing of time using the stars, especially when there is no sun in the winter months. Through careful observation of the phases of the moon, they derived a calendar for determining the cycle of the six seasons. They observe the world around them and recognize that the moon will have a certain appearance at certain times of the year. These changes in the moon let them know when to go to the hunting grounds and different camps.

ASSESSMENT FOR LEARNING

Look for Evidence of Learning	Student-friendly Learning Targets
Can the student: • keep a nightly record of the shape and location of the moon in the night sky? • use his or her drawings to identify how the moon's shape changes over a month? • identify what stories explain about day or night?	(self-assessment) • I can look at the moon in the night sky and draw a picture of its shape and where it is in the sky. • I can keep a record of how the moon looks and where it is in the night sky for a month. • I can tell how the moon's shape changes over a month. • I can tell what each story tells about day or night.

DI DIFFERENTIATING INSTRUCTION

For EAL

Bring stories to life through the use of illustrations and expressions and movements to enhance understanding for EAL students. For storytelling activities, place EAL students with students who are proficient English speakers.

For Enrichment

Challenge students to find out the names of the different phases of the moon and to find out why we see different amounts of the moon as it goes through its phases.

For Extra Support

For storytelling activities, work with students to help them identify pictures or objects to represent key events in the story. Practice retelling the story with them using the pictures/objects as reminders of what comes next in the story.

CURRICULUM CONNECTIONS

Students will have the opportunity to develop skills and concepts in the following areas:

Mathematics

P1.1 f. Identify and describe a repeating pattern found in the environment (e.g., classroom, outdoors) using everyday language.

Fine Arts

CP1.1 a. Use movements and movement patterns to respond to stimuli from diverse sources such as stories, poems, observations, visual images, music, sounds, or objects.

CORE LEARNING OPPORTUNITIES

Engage

Literature Link
Papa, Please Get the Moon for Me by Eric Carle

1. Activate and Build on Prior Knowledge

- Use *Papa, Please Get the Moon for Me* by Eric Carle to introduce this lesson. (If a copy of this picture book is not available, search for the title on Youtube and show students a reading of the story.)
- Before reading, show students the cover and read the title. Ask students:
  - Where can we see the moon? When can we see the moon?
  - What else can we see in the night sky besides the moon?
  - Who might be asking: Papa, please get the moon for me?
  - How might Papa get the moon?
- After reading, ask students:
  - Why did Papa have to wait to get the moon for his daughter?
  - What happened to the moon as his daughter was playing with it?
  - Why did the moon get smaller and smaller?
  - Was the moon gone forever? How do you know?
- As students share their explanations, you will gain a sense of their background knowledge about the moon.
- Show students pictures of the moon and stars in the night sky. Ask:
  - What else can you sometimes see in the night sky? (*Aurora borealis* or Northern Lights)

***Traditional* Knowledge**

- There are Aboriginal stories about the Aurora Borealis. The Nēhiyawak (Plains Cree) and Métis of the Plains never whistle at the Northern Lights. It is said that if you whistle, the spirits will come and take you away.
- Tell students they will be observing the moon and the stars in the night sky and recording how the moon changes shape and where it is in the sky.
- Record students' responses to each question on chart paper and post them so that you can return to their prior knowledge and questions throughout the unit.

Literacy Check
Can the student:
- read the "I wonder ..." statements in the class list and identify an "I wonder ..." statement for his or her personal list?
- copy an "I wonder ..." statement from the class list onto his or her personal list?

2. Elicit "I Wonder ..." Statements

- Model an "I wonder ..." form of inquiry with the following statements: "I wonder if I can see the moon in different places in the night sky on different nights," "I wonder if I can see a pattern in the way the moon changes shapes," and "I wonder if I can see pictures in the stars."
- Invite students to offer other "I wonder ..." statements. Record these on a chart or paper strips, and then read them together. Some students may require individual or small group assistance to identify statements and record them.

Explore

Tip
Time this observation project so that it begins at the new moon.

3. Explore the Changes of the Moon

- Explain to students that they have a new project that will take a whole month. Tell them that they are going to look for the moon two nights a week for the next month and draw a picture of its shape and where it is in the night sky. Ask them to recall how they showed where the sun was in the sky. (They chose a landmark such as a tree or a building so that they could

✔ Science Check
Can the student:
- demonstrate background knowledge about the moon and stars and how the moon changes its shape and location in the night sky?

show where the sun was in the sky compared to their chosen landmark. In this way, they could compare the drawings and see how the position of the sun changed in the sky.)

- Provide students with a booklet made up of two copies of **LM 17: Observing the Moon** and a copy of **LM 18: Observing the Moon — Letter to Parents**. You will have to ask for their help with this project.
- Have students start their observations at the full moon or new moon. At the end of each week, have students bring in their completed booklets. Have students examine their drawings and respond to the following questions:
  - How did the shape of the moon change over the week?
  - Did you see the moon in different places in the night sky?
  - How did the moon's place in the night sky change?
- At the end of the month, review the changes in the shape of the moon that took place over the course of the month.
- Reinforce the increasing and decreasing amount of the moon students observed by leading them through a movement activity in which they begin by making themselves as small as they can and then gradually expand so that more and more of them can be seen until they are fully visible. Then guide them to gradually becoming less and less visible until they are as small as they can be again.
- Encourage students who have access to smart devices to take photographs of the moon at the same time each night to add to the record of their drawings.

✔ Science Check
Can the student:
- identify and illustrate shapes or pictures in groupings of stars in the night sky?

4. Explore the Pictures That Stars Make

- Ask students: What can you see in the sky besides the moon at night? Did you ever lie on the ground and look at the stars? Invite them to share their experiences of star watching. Ask: Have you ever searched for shapes in the stars? Why do you think people like to imagine shapes in the stars? (It is like a connect-the-dots game.)
- Search for *night sky stars* or *stars at night* on the Web. Project the images of stars in the night sky for students to view. (If you do not have access to a multimedia projector, find images of stars in night skies in library resources.) Invite students to look for groups of stars that look like pictures or shapes to them. Model how you would like them to do this by finding a grouping of stars and suggesting what it looks like (e.g., an arrow or an animal). Ask students to take turns pointing out the grouping of stars they are looking at and naming the shape or picture they see.
- Provide students with paper and ask them to draw the shape or picture they see in the stars. You may wish to have them use chalk or white crayons on black paper to show the star grouping. Try to repeat this activity at different times of the year. Encourage students to recognize that the location of the stars change based on the seasons.
- Project the First Nations star chart found at the website of Wilderness Astronomy — Starchart: First ever overview of the "Canadian" constellations. [http://wildernessastronomy.com/resources/starchart-first-ever-overview-of-the-canadian-constellations/]. (If you do not have access to a multimedia projector, print copies of the star chart for

students to view.) Compare the shapes/pictures students found with what First Nations peoples named the star groupings.

***Traditional* Knowledge**

Literature Link

How the Loon Lost her Voice
by Anne Cameron

Rabbit and the Moon
by Douglas Wood

How Raven Freed the Moon
by Anne Cameron

The Story of Chakapas
Nihithawak, (Woodland Cree)
collected and transcribed
by G. Downes

5. Explore Day and Night through Stories

- Share First Nations and Métis stories about day and night. Some suggestions are provided. For each book, present the title and examine the cover illustration and ask students to predict what the story might be about. Record their predictions and confirm or adjust them as you read.
- Use the following suggestions to engage and involve your students in further readings of the stories:
  - Make stick or finger puppets for the characters in the story. As you reread/retell the story, students can use their puppets to dramatize the actions and events of the story.
  - Have students join in choral reading of repeated parts in the story. Teach students these parts before you begin reading or telling the story so they are ready to join in when you cue them.
  - Use classroom objects and rhythm instruments to create sound effects for a story.

Explain

Literacy Check
Can the student:
- make predictions about the stories based on the title and cover illustration?
- listen to and comprehend an oral story?
- identify what each story explains about day or night?
- participate meaningfully in discussion during reading activities?

Science Check
Can the student:
- connect his or her observations of the moon in the night sky to pictures of moon phases and arrange pictures of moon phases in the correct sequence?

6. Sequence Moon Phases

- This activity is a follow-up to Explore 3. Provide students with copies of **LM 19: Help the Moon Find the Correct Order**. Have them cut out the pictures and refer to their drawings on **LM 17: Observing the Moon** as they place the pictures in order. Then, have students glue the pictures in order onto a strip of poster paper to show the pattern of the moon phases.

7. Retell a Story About Day and Night

- Have students choose their favourite stories from the First Nations and Métis stories you read in Explore 5. Model how to retell the story events in sequence using objects or drawings to symbolize key events.
- Provide time for students to gather objects or draw pictures to help them retell their chosen story. Provide an opportunity for students to retell their stories to classmates or have them record their retellings using smart devices.

8. Read and Respond to the Non-Fiction Book *Days and Seasons*

Before: Show students the cover of the book and remind them of the earlier reading of it. Ask them what kind of book it is.
During: Using the Lap Book, read pages 20–21.
Page 20–21:
- Which picture shows daytime and which picture shows nighttime?
- What clues in the pictures tell you that it is day and night?
- What can prevent you from seeing the sun during the day?
- Why does the text say, "Sometimes you can see the moon and the stars?"
- Why does it usually get cooler at night?

After: Review monthly comparisons of observation data from Lessons 1 and 2. Ask students what they noticed about how days change from season to season. Compare what the text says with the patterns students have identified using their Daily Observation Records.

9. Reflect on Learning

- Have students record evidence of their learning on **PM 13: Look What I've Learned**, in their journal, and/or with a video or audio recording on a smart device or camera. If students are using the line master or their journal, they can use words and/or pictures to show what they have learned. Encourage them to note one thing they learned and something they still wonder about. You may wish to ask each student to share orally what he or she learned and record what was learned in a sentence(s).
- Use **LM 20: This Is What I Can Do** as a self-assessment. Read the learning targets with students and have them respond on their own. Some students may need assistance.

OTHER LEARNING OPPORTUNITIES

Extend: Activity Bank

At any time, choose from the following options to replace or supplement the Core Learning Opportunities to meet students' needs and/or interests.

10. Make a Library Connection

- Provide an opportunity for students to search for fiction and non-fiction picture books about the night sky, including the moon and stars, in the school or community library. Ask library staff for assistance in locating and pulling appropriate books. Provide time for students to look at and learn from the illustrations in these books.

11. Meet an Astronomer/Visit an Observatory

- Invite an astronomer to visit your classroom and share his or her interest in studying the night sky. If possible, arrange a visit to an observatory where students can use a telescope to view the night sky.

12. Explore Other "I Wonder ..." Statements

- Return to the "I wonder ..." statements not yet answered, and new wonderings that have come up. With students, plan and set up centres where they can explore these wonderings. Encourage them to make and test predictions.
- In small groups, students can rotate to all the centres or focus on one per group. They could share their findings in an oral, written, or electronic presentation.

UNIT 4 Unit Closer: Putting It All Together

Time
3–4 hours

Program Resources
PM 4: Finding Out
PM 9: I Found Out
LM 21: Rate Your Learning
LM 22: Design a Plant or Animal for the Seasons
LM 23: Present Your Plant or Animal for the Seasons
Fiction Book: *Groundhog Day*
Non-fiction Book: *Days and Seasons*
Lap Book

Materials and Equipment
- modelling clay or play dough
- art supplies such as pipe cleaners, buttons, toothpicks, craft sticks

Looking Back

1. Consider the Learning Targets

- Display the learning targets that were introduced in the Unit Opener on a chart or screen. Explain that these are the big ideas about daily and seasonal changes.
- Read the learning targets aloud. Stop after each one, to ask students to provide explanations and examples that illustrate the learning target.
- Ask students to think about how well they can do the things on the list. Use a Think Aloud strategy and a copy of **LM 21: Rate Your Learning** to model how students should rate themselves.
- Distribute copies of **LM 21** for students to complete as you read each of the learning targets. Some students may be able to read and complete it on their own.

2. Reread the Fiction Book *Groundhog Day*

Before: Using the Lap Book, show students the cover of the fiction book, *Groundhog Day*. Ask students to talk about what they thought of the book. What did they like about it? What did they learn from the book? Ask: What reasons would there be for the groundhog to see or not see his shadow? Is this is a good way to predict if there will be six more weeks of winter?
During: Distribute copies of *Groundhog Day*. Read the story as students follow the text in their own books and invite them to join in with the reading when they are able to.
After: Review the changes from season to season shown in the illustrations.

- At the end of the story, Lila says, "Next year, I'm doing it." Use Shared Writing to rewrite the story as students imagine it when Lila is the star the following year. Use this story to practise choral reading.
- Choose activities and discussion questions from Talk Time on page 16 that students have not engaged in or responded to throughout the unit.

3. Consider "I Wonder ..." Statements

- Ask students to think back to the things they have wondered about throughout the unit. Review students' copies of "I wonder ..." statements. Have them pick one important wondering that has been answered and tell a partner about it. Students can record their query and what they learned about it on **PM 9: I Found Out**
- Ask students to think about other "I wonder ..." statements that they would ask now (e.g., Does everyone in the world have the same seasons as in Saskatchewan/Canada? How do plants, animals, and people adapt to different seasons in different parts of the world?). Record their questions and review the Skills poster **Finding Out** and, with students, plan an exploration that follows the inquiry steps. Set up the inquiry for students to experience in small groups at a centre. Provide copies of **PM 4: Finding Out** for students to complete as a group.

4. Reread the Non-fiction Book *Days and Seasons*

- Distribute copies of *Days and Seasons*. Read the text as students follow along in their own books. Invite them to join in with the reading when they are able to.
- Choose any activities and discussion questions provided in Talk Time page 24 that have not yet been addressed for further exploration.

Going Further

5. Make a Travel Poster

- Explain to students that they will be making a travel poster. Provide each student with a large sheet of paper. Model how to divide it into four, separate quadrants.
- Have students label each quadrant with the names of the seasons.
- In each quadrant, have students draw and colour pictures of what people can do outside in each of the seasons in their community or area.

Science Check

Can the student:

- plan an imaginary plant or animal?
- identify what this imaginary plant or animal does during the day and night?
- identify how this imaginary plant or animal changes during all four seasons?
- plan this imaginary plant or animal with drawings?
- create a model of this imaginary plant or animal?
- explain what this imaginary plant or animal does during the day and night?
- explain how this imaginary plant or animal changes in all four seasons?
- respond to questions from other students?

6. Design a Plant or Animal for the Seasons

Introduction

- Tell students that this task will challenge them to use what they learned about daily and seasonal changes and how plants and animals change from season to season.

Preparation

- Present **LM 22: Design a Plant or Animal for the Seasons** to introduce the project.
- Generate, and record on chart paper, ideas for:
  - different imaginary plants and animals.
  - what these imaginary plants or animals might do during the day and at night (e.g., whether they are active during the day or night; whether they open or close at night).
  - ways in which these imaginary plants or animals might change in each season.
- Using Shared or Dictated Writing, make a criteria chart for each imaginary plant or animal. (Use **LM 22: Design a Plant or Animal for the Seasons**.)
- Provide modelling clay, pipe cleaners, buttons, toothpicks, craft sticks, and other materials so that students can create models of their imaginary plants or animals.

Presentation

- To prepare students for their presentation, review with them **LM 23: Present Your Plant or Animal for the Seasons**. Have students present their plants or animals. If needed, read aloud the points on the line master and/or the criteria chart.

Evaluation

- Have students take on the role of judges.
  - First, they should evaluate their own imaginary plant or animal and presentation, checking to see if their drawing and model met the criteria. Then, have students choose two things they like about their own presentation and one that needed improvement.
  - After each student's presentation, have the other students evaluate the student's model and presentation in the same way.

UNIT 4

DAILY AND SEASONAL CHANGES

Table of Contents

Name:_______________________________

Learning Targets

Put a check mark to show what you can do.

☐	I can name the days of the week, the months of the year, and the seasons of the year.
☐	I can talk about how different cultures view the night sky and seasonal changes.
☐	I know how temperature and light change from day to night.
☐	I know how temperature and light change from season to season.
☐	I can measure changes in the weather.
☐	I can show and tell how plants, animals, and people change from day to night.
☐	I can show and tell how plants, animals, and people change from season to season.

Name:____

Daily Observation Record

Month of the year: ________________________ Day of the week: ___________________________

	Morning	**Afternoon**	**Evening**
Daylight			
Light			
Temperature			
What we can see in the sky			
Weather			
People			
Animals			
Plants			

Name:___________________________________

Daily Observation Record — Letter to Parents

Dear Parents,

In Science class, we are learning about the changes that happen around us from day to night and from season to season. We are using the attached Daily Observation Record to record what we see and feel outside three times each day: morning, afternoon, and night. Please help your child record the night entries on the Observation Record using the same format as we used for the morning and afternoon records and return it each morning.

We will be using our daily records to identify patterns and changes from week to week and month to month. Through these comparisons, we will identify daily and seasonal changes based on our observations.

Thank you for helping your child develop the scientific skills of observing and recording.

Sincerely,

____

Name:______________________________

This Is What I Can Do

Put a check mark to show what you can do.

☐	I know and understand the words for day and night.
☐	I know and understand the words for the seasons.
☐	I can explain how I know that it is day or night.
☐	I can explain how I know that it is spring, summer, fall, or winter.
☐	I can use pictures, symbols, and words to record what we see and feel outdoors.
☐	I can identify patterns and changes from day to night.
☐	I can identify patterns and changes from season to season.

Put a  beside what you do best.

Put a blue  beside the one you need to practise.

Name:________________________________

Make Weather Instruments

These instructions are intended for the teacher who will be making the weather instruments as a class demonstration.

Safety Check
Ensure students do not handle the rubbing alcohol or the thermometer containing rubbing alcohol.

1. Make a Simple Thermometer

1. Fill the bottle about one-quarter full with equal parts of water and rubbing alcohol.

2. Add a few drops of food colouring to the water and rubbing alcohol mixture.

3. Put the drinking straw in the bottle so that the end is in the water-rubbing alcohol mixture, but it is not touching the bottom of the bottle.

4. Put modelling clay around the straw at the top of the bottle so that no air gets into the bottle and to hold the straw in place.

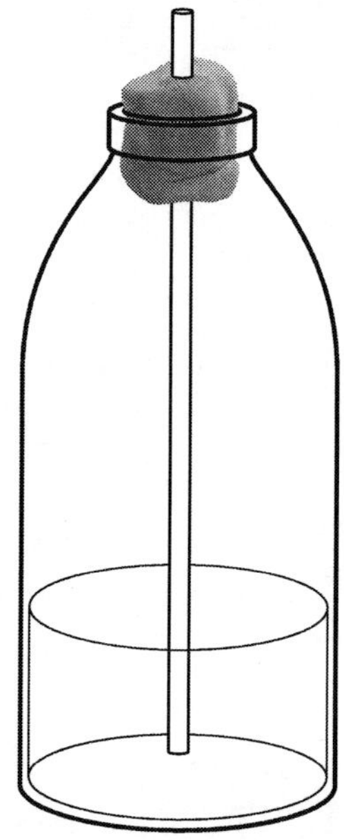

2. Make a Rain Gauge

1. Use scissors to cut a plastic pop bottle about 10 cm from the top. Save the top part.

2. Put stones or coarse gravel in the bottom of the bottle up to the point where the sides become straight. The stones or gravel will give the rain gauge weight and make it stable when placed outside.

3. Tape the ruler to the side of the bottle so the zero mark on the ruler is a centimetre or two above the stones.

4. Pour water into the bottle until the water level reaches the zero mark on the ruler.

5. Turn the top part of the bottle upside down and set it into the bottom part to act as a funnel.

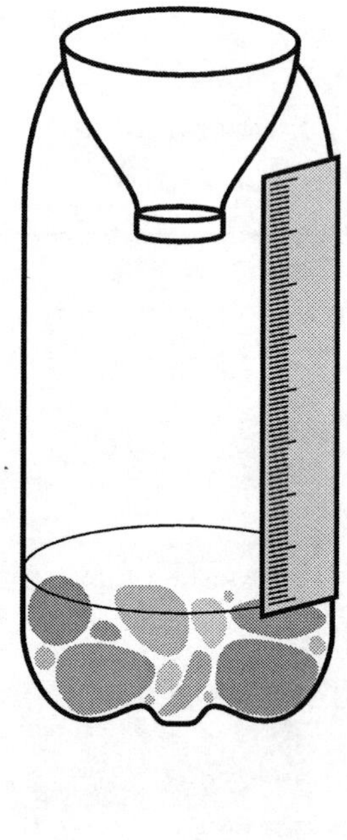

3. Make a Wind Vane

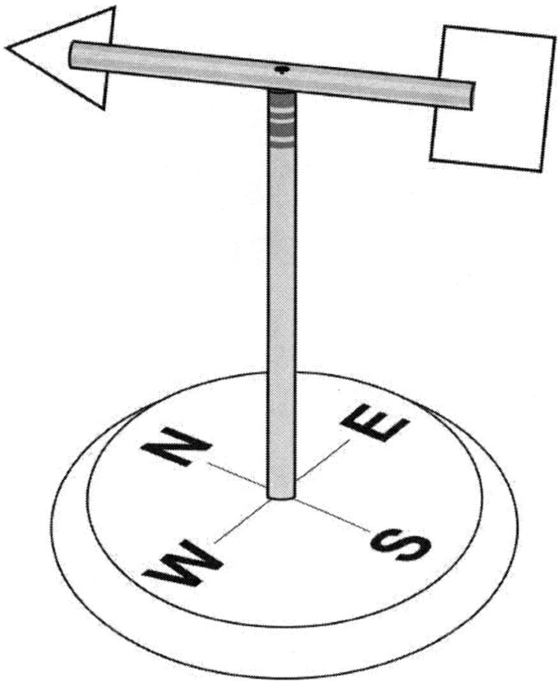

1. Turn a paper plate upside-down and use a marker to draw an X through the centre. At the ends of the lines, mark the directions (north, east, south, west).
2. Cut out a triangle and a square from poster paper. They should each be about 5 cm in width.
3. Use scissors to cut small slits at each end of a straw. Slide the arrow point into the slit at one end of the straw, and slide the arrow tail into the slit at the other end of the straw.
4. Push a straight pin through the centre of the straw and then into the eraser tip of the pencil. It is important to leave space between the eraser tip and the straw and between the straw and the head of the pin so that the arrow can spin.
5. Stick the sharpened end of the pencil through the centre of the paper plate and into a lump of modelling clay on the bottom of the paper plate.
6. Try blowing on the arrow. Does it spin easily? If not, make sure there is space between the eraser tip and the bottom of the straw. Also make sure there is space between the top of the straw and the head of the pin.
7. Place another paper plate under the plate. The lump of clay should be between the plates. Glue or staple the plate edges together. It's okay to flatten the clay a bit.

LM 6 LINE MASTER

Name:______________________________

Measuring Temperature With a Thermometer

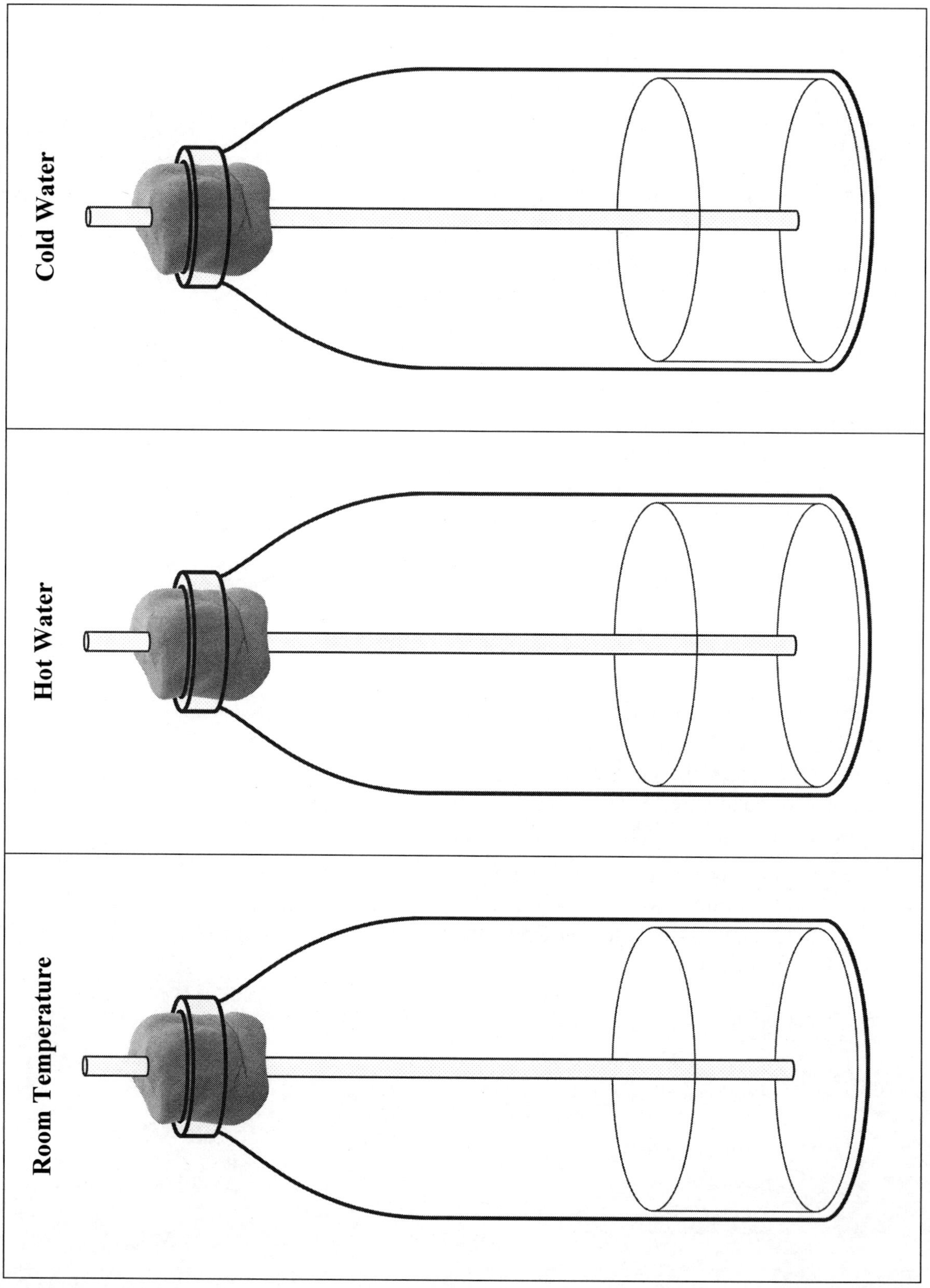

Name:________________________________

Thermometer

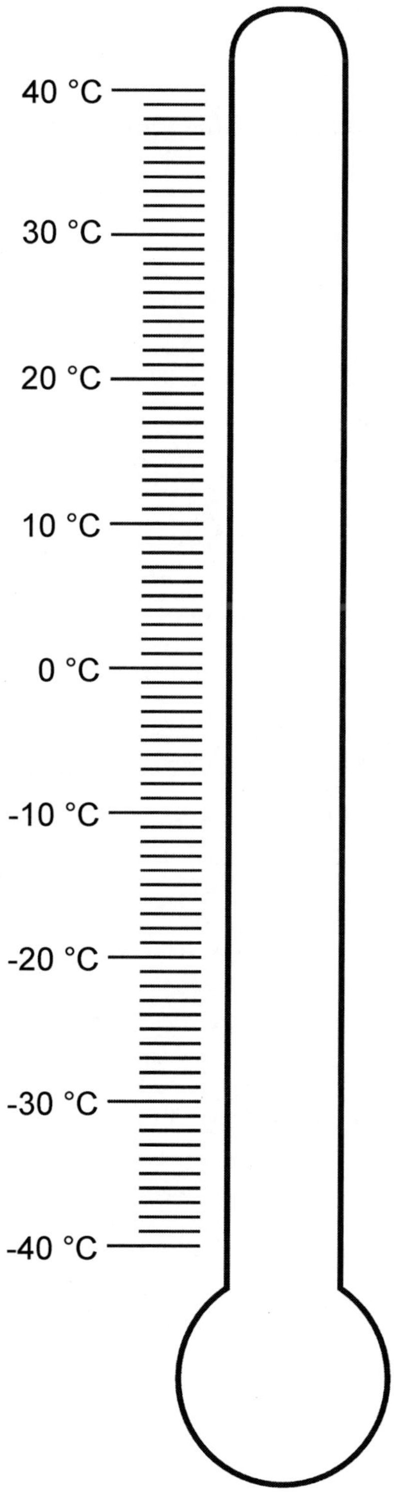

Name:______________________________

This Is What I Can Do

Put a check mark to show what you can do.

☐	I can use a thermometer to measure the temperature outside.
☐	I can use a rain gauge to measure how much rain falls.
☐	I can use a wind vane to find out the direction the wind is blowing from.
☐	I can use pictures, symbols, and words to record what we see and feel outdoors.
☐	I can use measurements from a thermometer, rain gauge, and wind vane to record weather changes.
☐	I can identify patterns and changes from day to night.
☐	I can identify patterns and changes from season to season.

Put a ☺ beside what you do best.

Put a blue ? beside the one you need to practise.

Name:______________________________

Dramatization Scripts

Read the scripts below to your students. This line master is not meant to be distributed to students.

Explore 3: Let's Pretend It's Day and Night

• **Imagine you are a red tulip**. The sun is shining. You stretch your green leaves toward the light. Your red petals are open. As day turns to night, you close your petals.
Other possible options include a robin, an owl, or a person.

Explore 4: Let's Pretend It's Spring, Summer, Fall, and Winter

Spring Dramatization:

• **Imagine it is spring.** The days get longer and the temperature outside gets warmer. The snow is melting and the water is making big puddles. People are wearing rubber boots when they walk in the puddles. Many children like to splash in the puddles. Green grass and dandelions start to show up in the ground. Buds show up on the branches of the trees. Spring is time for animal babies. The birds lay their eggs. They sit on their eggs until they hatch. Everywhere, animals are having their babies. There are baby elk and moose. There are baby foxes, coyotes, and skunks. All these babies drink their mother's milk. In ponds, frog eggs hatch. Little tadpoles stay in the water until they grow legs. People everywhere are happy to feel the warm sun on their skin. They walk and ride their bicycles. They play ball and soccer. Farmers are busy planting their crops in the fields. People get ready to plant their gardens. Saskatchewan comes to life in the spring!

Summer Dramatization:

• **Imagine it is summer.** The sun is shining brightly. It is going to be hot today. The bees are buzzing as they fly from flower to flower to drink the nectar. The plants are growing taller in the garden. All the leaves are fully open on the trees. The baby birds are out of the nest now and learning to fly. The baby rabbits and deer are growing, too. They nibble on sweet green grass. The baby skunks follow their mothers everywhere. The baby foxes and coyotes play in the sunshine. At the pond, the tadpoles have become frogs. They like to be in the mud eating lots of insects. Summer is when many people go to the beach and play in the water. They go camping and boating. The days are longest in summer so people spend a lot of time outdoors. The crops are growing and so are the gardens.

Fall Dramatization:

• **Imagine it is fall.** The days are shorter. The sun sets earlier. Nights are getting longer and colder. The temperature has dropped, and the flowers are gone. Their petals are brown. Leaves on the trees are changing colour. They are starting to fall from the trees. Soon they will cover the ground in a colourful carpet. You will help rake them up. It's time to dig out the root vegetables and store them in a cool place for winter. Farmers are busy harvesting their crops. Many birds are flying south to where it is warm in the winter. In Saskatchewan, fall is the hunting season. Lots of people in Saskatchewan go hunting for deer, moose, elk, bear, ducks, and geese. Fall brings the end of the growing season. People harvest their vegetables and crops. They are getting ready for winter.

Winter Dramatization:

• **Imagine it is winter.** The days are short. It is still dark when you leave for school. The nights are long. Snow covers the ground, and it is time to tell stories. It is time for snowsuits, boots, mitts, toques, and scarves. The branches on the trees are bare. All the animals have thicker coats to keep warm during the winter. It is hard for them to find food in the winter. Some people put out food for wild animals. Some people fill bird feeders with seeds. Some people put out carrots and green vegetables for rabbits. People in Saskatchewan like to spend time outside in the snow during the winter. They go sledding down hills. They go skiing, snowboarding, and snowmobiling. This is the time of year for ice hockey, figure skating, and curling. Sometimes, it is too cold to play outside. When this happens, people stay inside where it is nice and warm. In Saskatchewan, people's homes are built for winter. People have furnaces that blow warm air into all the rooms. Some people have fireplaces so they can sit by the fire. Winter can be dark and cold, but it can also be a lot of fun to build snowmen and snow forts, or just play in the snow.

Name:____

Sort It Out

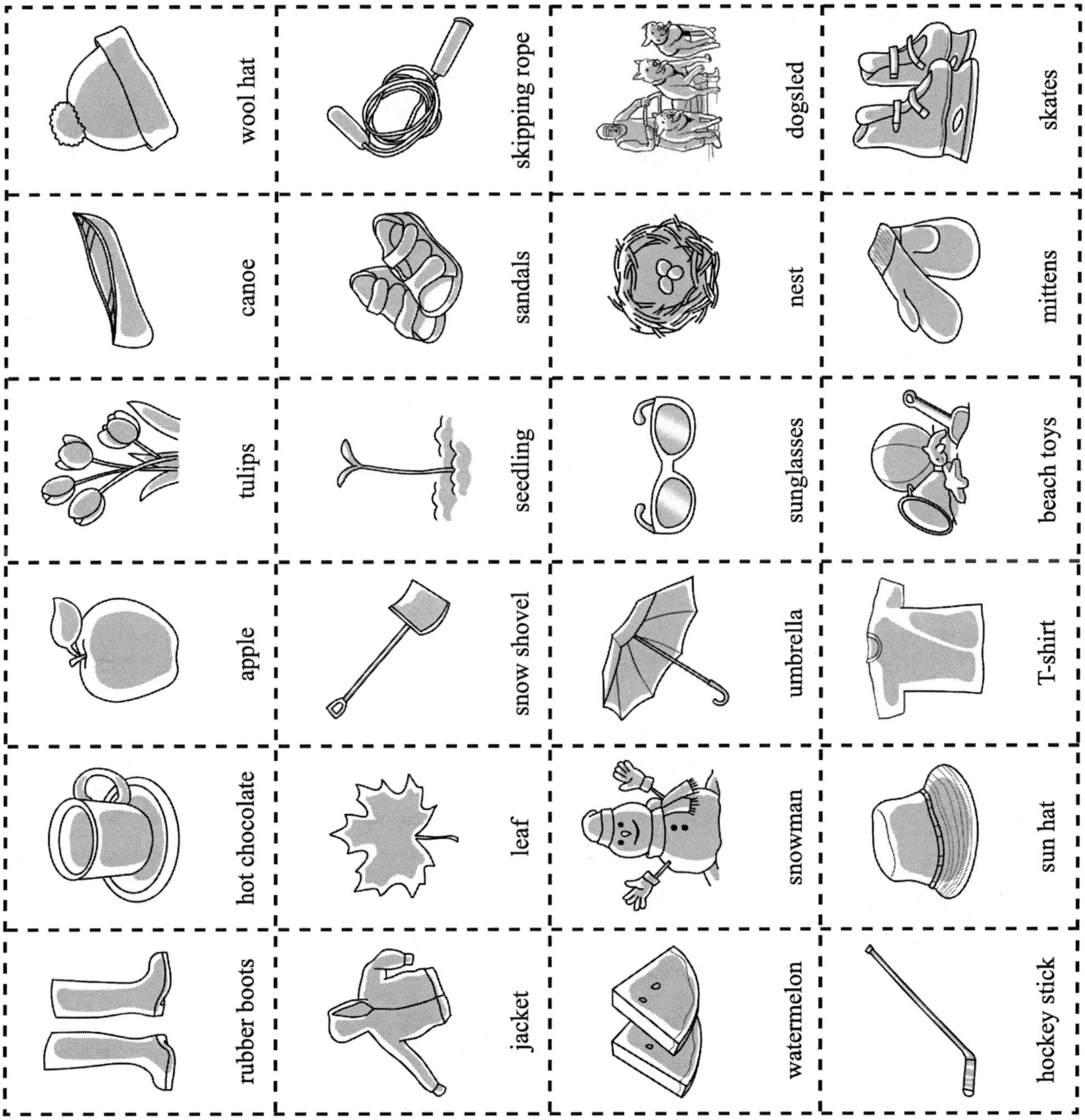

SPRING	SUMMEM	FALL	WETEN

Name:______________________________

Picture Sort

SPRING	SUMMER
FALL	WINTER

Name:____

This Is What I Can Do

Put a check mark to show what you can do.

	I can tell when it is day and night.
	I can use clues to tell when it is spring, summer, fall, and winter.
	I know the days of the week.
	I know the months of the year.
	I can tell how plants, animals, and people change from day to night.
	I can tell how plants, animals, and people change in different seasons.
	I can tell how plants, animals, and people get ready for winter.

Put a ☺ beside what you do best.

Put a blue ? beside the one you need to practise.

Name:______________________________

Shadow Records

I traced my shadow on ______________________________.

Morning	Noon	Afternoon

My shadows look different because ______________________________

______________________________.

Name:______________________________

This Is What I Can Do

Put a check mark to show what you can do.

☐	I can tell how shadows change from morning to night.
☐	I can tell how shadows change during the year.
☐	I know why shadows look different at different times of the day and the year.
☐	I can use clues in pictures to tell what season it is.
☐	I can find ways that animals, plants, and humans change from season to season.
☐	I can show how animals, plants, or humans change from season to season.

Put a ☺ beside what you do best.

Put a blue ? beside the one you need to practise.

Name:________________________________

Circle of the Seasons

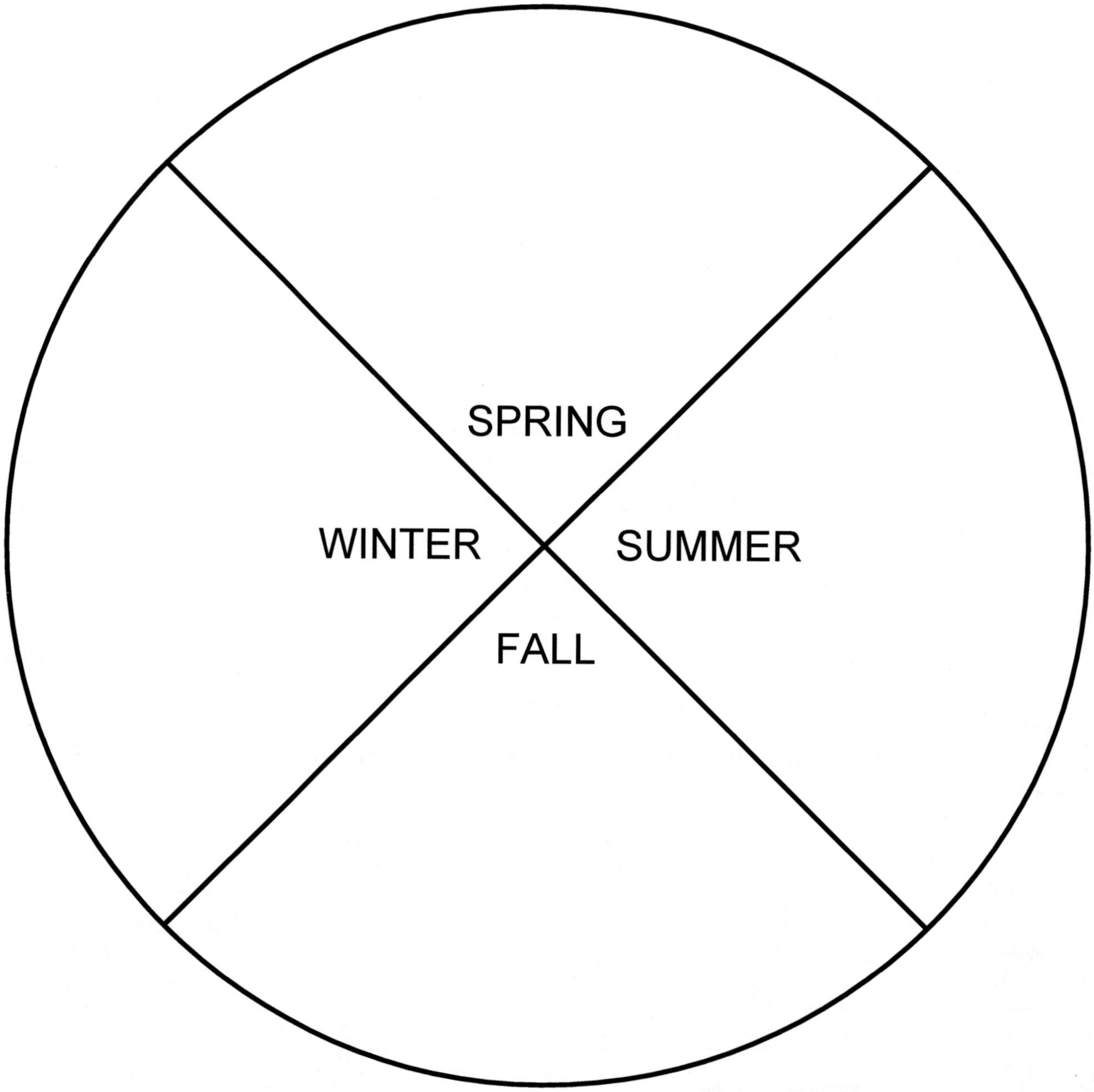

Name:______________________________________

This Is What I Can Do

Put a check mark to show what you can do.

☐	I can find clues in stories that tell what season it is.
☐	I can listen to stories and find ways that plants, animals, and people change in different seasons.
☐	I can look at pictures about the seasons and give my ideas about what I see.
☐	I can find what is the same and what is different when I look at paintings about the seasons.
☐	I can work with a partner to plan, practise, and present a story about the changing seasons.
☐	I can show four seasons in a painting.

Put a  beside what you do best.

Put a blue  beside the one you need to practise.

Name:____

Observing the Moon

Draw a picture of the shape of the moon on four different nights. Include a tree or a building in your picture. This will help you show where the moon is in the sky.

Night ____	Night ____
Night ____	Night ____

Name:_______________________________________

Observing the Moon — Letter to Parents

Dear Parents,

In Science class, we are learning about how the moon changes shape and position in the night sky. We are using the attached Observing the Moon Record to record our observations. Please help your child record these entries on the chart twice a week for four weeks. To show where the moon is in the night sky, have your child choose a landmark such as a tree or a building so he/she can show where the moon is compared to the chosen landmark.

At the end of each week during the month, please return the completed Observing the Moon Record to school with your child so that we can identify how the moon is changing shape and where it is in the night sky. The record will be sent home again with your child to continue the process of observing and recording the shape and position of the moon in the night sky.

Thank you for helping your child develop the scientific skills of observing and recording.

Sincerely,

____

Name:____

Help the Moon Find the Correct Order

Name:__________________________________

This Is What I Can Do

Put a check mark to show what you can do.

☐	I can look at the moon in the night sky and draw a picture of its shape and where it is in the sky.
☐	I can keep a record of how the moon looks and where it is in the night sky for a month.
☐	I can tell how the moon's shape changes over a month.
☐	I can put the stages of the moon in the correct order.
☐	I can find shapes or pictures in the stars in the night sky. I can draw the shapes or pictures I see.
☐	I can tell what each story says about day or night.
☐	I can plan, practise, and present a story about how my favourite star group came to be in the night sky.

Put a  beside what you do best.

Put a blue  beside the one you need to practise.

Name:________________________________

Rate Your Learning

Circle the number that tells about you.

1 means I can do it very well.

2 means I can do it, but I need some practice.

3 means I need a lot more practice.

1	**2**	**3**	I can name the days of the week, the months of the year, and the seasons of the year.
1	**2**	**3**	I can talk about how different cultures view the night sky and seasonal changes.
1	**2**	**3**	I know how temperature changes from day to night.
1	**2**	**3**	I know how temperature and light changes from season to season.
1	**2**	**3**	I can measure changes in the weather.
1	**2**	**3**	I can show and tell how plants, animals, and people change from day to night.
1	**2**	**3**	I can show and tell how plants, animals, and people change from season to season.

Name:________________________________

Design a Plant or Animal for the Seasons

This is your challenge: Design a new plant or animal that can survive in all seasons.

1. First, you need to plan your new plant or animal. Draw a picture of what it will look like.

2. Show what your plant or animal will do during the day and at night.

DAY	NIGHT

3. Show how your plant or animal will survive in each season.

SPRING	SUMMER
FALL	WINTER

4. Name your plant or animal: ______________________________

5. Make a model of your plant or animal. Use modelling clay, pipecleaners, buttons, toothpicks, craft sticks, and other materials.

Name:________________________________

Present Your Plant or Animal for the Seasons

1. Talk about your plant or animal.
   Talk about its name.
   Talk about what it does during the day.
   Talk about what it does at night.

2. Talk about how your plant or animal changes in each season.
   Talk about what it does to survive in spring, summer, fall, and winter.

3. Ask if anyone has a question to ask.
   Answer the questions.